GOLDBACH CONJECTURE

Other books in this series

Vol. 1 — Total Mean Curvature and Submanifolds of Finite Type — *Bang-yen Chen*

Vol. 2 — A Survey of Trace Forms of Algebraic Number Fields — *P E Conner & R Perlis*

Vol. 3 — Structures on Manifolds — *K Yano & M Kon*

GOLDBACH CONJECTURE

Edited by

Wang Yuan

The Institute of Mathematics
Academia Sinica, Beijing
The People's Republic of China

World Scientific

Published by
World Scientific Publishing Co Pte Ltd.
P O Box 128
Farrer Road
Singapore 9128

ISBN 9971-966-08-5
9971-966-09-3 pbk

Printed in Singapore by Singapore National Printers (Pte) Ltd.

PREFACE

The study of Goldbach conjecture has had very great achievements since 1920. In particular, I. M. Vinogradov proved in 1937 the three primes theorem and Chen Jing Run established the (1, 2) in 1966. Furthermore, we must point out that the investigation on Goldbach conjecture has given a tremendous impetus on the creation and development of many powerful number-theoretic methods which are very useful not only in number theory itself but also in many other fields of mathematics.

The three primes theorem and the (1, 2) have been collected in many books (see Refs. I). A monograph which often contains the latest results with possibly simplified proofs so that the reader can easily understand, is difficult to contain the main steps on the development of original ideas, however. The aim of the present collection is to select as far as we can the papers with origination and progress in techniques so that the reader can understand the major steps of the whole progress in the study of Goldbach conjecture. We hope it will be of benefit for further studies of this problem.

In order that the volume will not be too thick, some parts in a few papers are deleted, where the Editor's notes are given for exposition. All papers in Chinese, French, German and Russian have been translated into English.

I should like to express my gratitude to Professor Pan Cheng Biao and his students, and Professor Yu Kun Rui for their valuable assistance, and I must also thank Dr. K. K. Phua for his help in the publication of this collection.

October 1983 Wang Yuan

CONTENTS

INTRODUCTION

In a letter to Euler in 1742, Goldbach proposed two conjectures on the representations of integers as the sum of primes. These conjectures with some modifications may be stated as follows.

(A) Every even integer ≥ 6 is the sum of two odd primes.

(B) Every odd integer ≥ 9 can be represented as the sum of three odd primes.

Clearly, (B) can be derived from (A).

In his letter to Goldbach, Euler expressed his belief in these statements, though he could not prove it (see Dickson [1]).

It is shown that these two conjectures are correct by a lot of accumulated numerical calculations since Goldbach wrote his letter up-to-date, for example, Shen Mok Kong [1] has checked the conjecture (A) up to 33×10^6, and the further calculation up to 10^8 was made by Light, Forres, Hammond and Roe [1].

In his famous speech at the 2nd International Congress of Mathematics held in Paris in 1900, Hilbert [1] proposed 23 problems for the mathematicians in the 20th century, and the conjecture (A) is a part of his 8th problem. In 1912, the conjecture (A) is regarded as one of the four famous unsolved problems in the theory of prime numbers proposed by Landau [2] in his speech at the 5th International Congress held in Cambridge. Furthermore, in his speech at the mathematical society of Copenhagen in 1921, Hardy [1, 2] pronounced that the conjecture (A) is "probably as difficult as any of the unsolved problems in mathematics" and therefore Goldbach problem is not only one of the most famous and difficult problems in number theory, but also in the whole of mathematics.

There is no method to attack this problem and the research is confined only on checking the conjecture (A) by some numerical calculations or proposing some further conjectures on (A) since Goldbach wrote his letter up to 1920 (see Dickson [1], Hardy [1, 2]).

The first great achievements on the study of Goldbach problem were obtained in the 1920s. Using their "circle method," British mathematicians Hardy and Littlewood [2] proved in 1923 that every sufficiently large odd integer is the sum of three odd primes and almost all even integers are sums of two primes if the grand Riemann hypothesis is assumed to be true. Norwegian mathematician Brun [2, 3] established in 1919 by his "sieve method" that every large even number is the sum of two numbers each having at most nine prime factors. And in 1930, by using Brun's method with his own new idea, the "density" of integer sequence, Russian mathematician Schnirelman [1] first obtained a theorem in additive prime number theory, namely every integer ≥ 2 is the sum of at most c primes, hereafter we use $c, c_1, c_2, \ldots$ to denote absolute constants, but not the same constants at different occurrences. The study of Goldbach problem has a tremendous and deep development for the past sixty years. In particular, in 1937, using the circle method and his ingenious method on the estimation of exponential sum with prime variable, Russian mathematician I. M. Vinogradov [3] was able to remove the dependence on the grand Riemann hypothesis, thereby giving unconditional proofs of the above two conclusions of Hardy and Littlewood. And after a series of important improvements on Brun's method and his result, Chinese mathematician Chen Jing Run [2, 3] established in 1966 that every large even integer is the sum of a prime and a product of at most two primes.

We must mention that the breakthrough on the study of Goldbach conjecture is clearly inseparable from the great achievements on analytic number theory in the 19th century, in particular, the theory of Čebyšev, Dirichlet, Riemann, Hadamard, de la Vallée Poussin and von Mangoldt on the distribution of prime numbers which is the prerequisite of the present research.

Now we sketch the main ideas and progresses on the study of Goldbach conjecture as follow.

1. <u>Circle method</u>. The circle method has its genesis in a paper of Hardy and Ramanujan [1] in 1918 concerned with the partition function and the problem of representing numbers as the sums of squares. More generally, in a series of papers beginning in 1920 entitled "Some problems of 'partitio numerorum'," Hardy and Littlewood create and develop systematically a new analytic method, the circle method in additive number theory, where Goldbach problem is devoted in (III) and (V) of the series.

Let

$$\zeta(s) = \sum_{n=1}^{\infty} \frac{1}{n^s}, \qquad s = \sigma + it, \qquad \sigma > 1 .$$

When $\sigma \le 1$, $\zeta(s)$ may be defined by analytic continuation. $\zeta(s)$ is called the Riemann ζ-function. Riemann conjectured that all zeros $\zeta = \beta + it$ of $\zeta(s)$ on the half-plane $\sigma > 0$ lie on the line $\sigma = \frac{1}{2}$. This is an unsolved problem and it is denoted by (RH). The weaker conjecture that every ρ on $\sigma > 0$ has its real part $\le \theta$, where θ is a constant satisfying $\frac{1}{2} \le \theta < 1$, is called the quasi Riemann hypothesis which is denoted by (QRH). More generally, we may study the Dirichlet L-function

$$L(s, \chi) = \sum_{n=1}^{\infty} \frac{\chi(n)}{n^s}, \qquad s = \sigma + it, \qquad \sigma > 1,$$

where $\chi(n)$ is a character mod q. It is regular in s-plane if $\chi \ne \chi_0$, where χ_0 denotes the principal character. Otherwise it has an only pole at $s = 1$ and $L(s, \chi_0) = \prod_{p|q} (1 - \frac{1}{p^s}) \zeta(s)$, where p denotes a prime number. Similar to (RH) and (QRH), we may define (GRH) and (QGRH), namely all zeros of all the $L(s, \chi)$ on $\sigma > 0$ lie on $\sigma = \frac{1}{2}$, and every zero ρ of any $L(s, \chi)$ on $\sigma > 0$ satisfies $\beta \le \theta$, where θ is a constant as above. The two results of Hardy and Littlewood are based on the assumption of (QGRH) with θ satisfying $\frac{1}{2} \le \theta < \frac{3}{4}$.

Hereafter we use $p, p', p_1, p_2, \ldots$ to denote prime numbers. Let n be an integer >1. Let

$$(1) \qquad f(x) = \sum_{p>2} (\log p)\, x^p \quad ,$$

where $|x| = e^{-1/n}$. Then

$$f(x)^3 = \sum_{n=1}^{\infty} r_3(n)\, x^n \quad ,$$

where

$$(2) \qquad r_3(n) = \sum_{p_1+p_2+p_3=n} \log p_1 \log p_2 \log p_3$$

denotes a weight sum of the representations of n as the sums of three primes. We may define similarly $r_2(n)$, and thus the conjectures (A), (B) may be stated as follows:

$$r_2(n) > 0 \quad (2|n,\ n>4) \quad \text{and} \quad r_3(n) > 0 \quad (2\nmid n,\ n>7) .$$

By Cauchy's integral formula, we have

$$(3) \qquad r_3(n) = \frac{1}{2\pi i}\int_{\Gamma} f(x)^3\, x^{-n-1}\, dx \quad ,$$

where Γ is a circle with center o and radius $e^{-1/n}$. Since $f(x)$ is approximated closely by $f(e^{-1/n}\, e(\frac{h}{q}))$, where $e(y) = e^{2\pi i y}$ and $x(\varepsilon\Gamma)$ is a nearby point of $e^{-1/n}\, e(\frac{h}{q})$), the Γ is divided into the sum of small arcs ξ_{hq}, where the amplitude of x on ξ_{hq} lies between

$$\left(\frac{h}{q} - \frac{1}{q(q+q')}\right)2\pi \quad \text{and} \quad \left(\frac{h}{q} + \frac{1}{q(q+q'')}\right)2\pi \qquad (\text{mod } 1)$$

in which $\frac{h'}{q'}, \frac{h}{q}, \frac{h''}{q''}$ are three consecutive terms of the Farey series of order $N = [\sqrt{n}]$. Hence

$$(4) \qquad r_4(n) = \sum_{q=1}^{N} \sum_{h(q)}{}' \frac{1}{2\pi i}\int_{\xi_{hq}} f(x)^3\, x^{-n-1}\, dx \quad ,$$

where h runs over a reduced residue system mod q. When $x \in \xi_{hq}$, set

$$x = e(\frac{h}{q})e^{-Y}, \qquad Y = \eta + i\theta .$$

Then under the assumption of (QGRH) with $\frac{1}{2} \le \theta < \frac{3}{4}$, Hardy and Littlewood established that

$$(5) \qquad f(x) = \phi + \Phi ,$$

where

$$\phi = \frac{\mu(q)}{\phi(q)Y} \quad \text{and} \quad \Phi = o\left(n^{\theta + \frac{1}{4}} (\log n)^c \right) ,$$

in which $\mu(q)$ and $\phi(q)$ denote respectively the Möbius function and the Euler function. Substituting (5) into (4), we have

$$(6) \qquad r_3(n) \sim \frac{1}{2} \prod_{p \nmid n} (1 + \frac{1}{(p-1)^3}) \prod_{p|n} (1 - \frac{1}{(p-1)^2}) n^2 \quad (2 \nmid n) ,$$

and therefore the proposition (B) holds for $2 \nmid n$ and n is sufficiently large. More precisely, it is easily derived from (6) the asymptotic formula of $R_3(n)$, the number of representations of the odd number n as the sums of three primes, namely $R_3(n)$ is asymptotic to $r_3(n)(\log n)^{-3}$. But the circle method failed in treating $r_2(n)$, even the (GRH) is assumed to be true. The main difficulty is not in the principal term but in its error term. Hence if the term Φ in (5) is neglected, that is, ϕ is assumed to be used instead of f, then we have

$$(7) \qquad r_2(n) \sim 2 \prod_{p>2} (1 - \frac{1}{(p-1)^2}) \prod_{\substack{p|n \\ p>2}} \frac{p-1}{p-2} n^2 \quad (2|n) .$$

It follows from (7) that the number of representations $R_2(n)$ of the even number n as the sum of two primes is asymptotic to $r_2(n)(\log n)^{-2}$. This is the famous conjecture of Hardy and Littlewood [2] concerning the Goldbach conjecture (A).

Under the (GRH), Hardy and Littlewood proved that

$$(8) \qquad \sum_{\substack{m=2\\2|m}}^{n} \left(r_2(m) - 2 \prod_{p>2} \left(1 - \frac{1}{(p-1)^2}\right) \prod_{\substack{p|m\\p>2}} \frac{p-1}{p-2}\, m \right)^2 = o\left(n^{5/2+\varepsilon} \right),$$

hereafter we use ε to denote any preassigned positive number and the corresponding constant implied by the symbol o depends on ε only. Let $E(n)$ denote the number of even numbers less than n such that (A) is false. Then it yields from (8) immediately

$$(9) \qquad E(n) = o\left(n^{\frac{1}{2}+\varepsilon} \right),$$

and consequently, we have the conclusion that almost all even integers are the sums of two primes.

Later, Vinogradov introduced a number of notable refinements on the circle method, one of which is to replace $f(x)$ by the finite sum

$$(10) \qquad F(\alpha) = \sum_{2<p\le n} e(\alpha p) \quad .$$

The trivial orthogonality relation

$$(11) \qquad \int_0^1 e(\alpha k)d\alpha = \begin{cases} 1 , & \text{when } k = 0 , \\ 0 . & \text{otherwise} \end{cases}$$

gives

$$(12) \qquad R_3(n) = \sum_{p_1+p_2+p_3 = n} 1 = \int_0^1 F(\alpha)^3\, e(-\alpha n)d\alpha$$

which is used instead of (3).

Vinogradov's modification has its genesis in a paper on Waring's problem in 1928 (Cf. Vinogradov [1]).

Let $\tau = n^{-1}(\log n)^{c_1}$ and $Q = (\log n)^{c_2}$. When $q \le Q$, let

$$\mathcal{M}_{hq} = \left[\frac{h}{q} - \tau , \frac{h}{q} + \tau \right] , \qquad (h,q) = 1$$

which is called a "major arc". When n is sufficiently large, the major arcs are disjoint. The union of all $\mathcal{M}_{hq}$ is denoted by

$$\mathcal{M} = \bigcup_{1 < q \le Q} \ \bigcup_{h(q)}{}' \ \mathcal{M}_{hq} \quad ,$$

and its complement with respect to $[0,1]$ is called the "minor arcs" which is denoted by m. Hence we have

$$(13) \qquad R_3(n) = \int_{\mathcal{M}} F(\alpha)^3 \, e(-\alpha n) d\alpha + \int_{m} F(\alpha)^3 \, e(-\alpha n) d\alpha = I + J \quad \text{say,}$$

and thus the proof of (B) for large n is reduced to prove that I is the principal term of $R_3(n)$ and J gives only of lower order.

Remark. The distinction between major and minor arcs was first proposed by Hardy and Littlewood in their work on Waring problem.

The difficulty for the estimation of I can be removed by the following Siegel-Walfisz theorem.

Let $q \le Q$ and $(h,q) = 1$. Then

$$(14) \qquad \pi(x,q,h) = \sum_{\substack{p \le x \\ p \equiv h (\log q)}} 1 = \frac{1}{\phi(q)} \int_2^x \frac{dt}{\log t} + o\left(x e^{-c\sqrt{\log x}} \right),$$

where the constant implicit in o depends on c_2 only (Cf. Siegel [1], Walfisz [1].)

From (14), it gives

$$(15) \qquad F(\alpha) = \frac{\mu(q)}{\phi(q)} \sum_{m=2}^{n-1} \frac{e(\beta m)}{\log m} + o\left(n e^{-c\sqrt{\log n}} \right), \qquad \alpha = \frac{h}{q} + \beta \in \mathcal{M} \ .$$

Substituting (15) into the expression of I, we have

$$(16) \qquad I \sim \frac{1}{2} \prod_{p|n} \left(1 - \frac{1}{(p-1)^2}\right) \prod_{p \nmid n} \left(1 + \frac{1}{(p-1)^3}\right) \frac{n^2}{(\log n)^3} \quad , \qquad 2 \nmid n \ .$$

Hence the difficulty is concentrated to the estimation of $F(\alpha)$ when $\alpha \in m$. In 1937, using his creative and ingenious method on the estimation of exponential sum with prime variable, Vinogradov gave $F(\alpha)$ a non-trivial estimation, namely

$$(17) \qquad F(\alpha) \ll n(\log n)^{-c} \quad , \qquad \alpha \in m \quad ,$$

where c is a constant ≥ 3. Notice that for given c, we may take c_1, c_2 to be the constants depending on c. It follows by (17) that

$$(18) \qquad J \ll n(\log n)^{-c} \int_0^1 |F(\alpha)|^2 d\alpha \ll n^2 (\log n)^{-4} \quad .$$

Substituting (16) and (18) into (13), we have

$$R_3(n) \sim \frac{1}{2} \prod_{p|n} \left(1 - \frac{1}{(p-1)^2}\right) \prod_{p\nmid n} \left(1 + \frac{1}{(p-1)^3}\right) \frac{n^2}{(\log n)^3}, \quad 2\nmid n \quad ,$$

and thus we have proved that there exists a constant n_0 such that every odd integer $n (> n_0)$ is the sum of three odd primes. This theorem is called the "Vinogradov-Goldbach theorem" or "three primes theorem".

We should mention that the following two theorems had appeared before the proof of three primes theorem. (i) Every large odd number n can be represented as

$$(19) \qquad n = p_1 + p_2 + p_3 p_4$$

(Cf. Vinogradov [2], Estermann [2].) (ii) Every large number is the sum of two primes and a square (Cf. Estermann [3].)

If the Page theorem [1] is used instead of Siegel-Walfisz theorem on the evaluation of I, the n_0 in three primes theorem is calculable, and it was given by Borozdkin [1] that $n_0 = e^{e^{16.038}}$.

Using Vinogradov's method, several mathematicians have pointed out independently that almost all even integers are the sums of two primes. More precisely, they proved that for any given c,

$$(20) \qquad E(n) \ll n(\log n)^{-c} \quad ,$$

where the constant implicit in $\ll$ depends on c only. (See van der Corput [3], Estermann [4], Heilbronn [1], Hua [1], Tchudakov [1,2].)

In 1946, using the original method of Hardy and Littlewood such that Γ is divided into $\mathcal{M}$ and m, Russian mathematician Linnik

[3,4,5] gave $f(x)$ $(x \in m)$ a non-trivial estimation similar to (17), and therefore he gave a new proof for the three primes theorem. Linnik's estimation of $f(x)$ is based on his important density theorem for L-series which is used instead of the unproved (QGRH), namely

Let $\chi(n)$ be a primitive character mod q. Let $N(\beta,T)$ denote the number of zeros of $L(s,\chi)$ in the rectangle

$$\nu \le \sigma \le 1, \qquad |t| \le T,$$

where $T \ge q^{50}$, $\beta \ge 1$ and $\nu = \beta - \frac{1}{2}$. Then

(21) $$N(\beta,T) \ll q^{2\nu}\, T^{1-(\nu/1-\nu)} (\log T)^{10} + q^{30}$$

(Cf. also Tchudakov [3].)

Later, Vaughan [2] gave a simplified proof on the Linnik's estimation of $f(x)$ in 1975, and a further simple proof is given by Pan Cheng Biao [1] independently in 1977. In their proofs, only some elementary knowledge of L-function are used. Concerning the estimation of exponential sum $F(\alpha)$, Vaughan [5,6] gave also some modifications, and his idea is the use of identity

$$-\frac{L'}{L} = -\frac{L'}{L}(1-LG) - L'G = \left(-\frac{L'}{L} - F\right)(1-LG) - L'G + F - LFG$$

which is also pointed out by Pan Cheng Dong (see Pan Cheng Dong, Ding Xia Qi and Wang Yuan [1].)

By the application of further results on the density theorems of L-function, Vaughan [1] proved in 1972 that

(22) $$E(n) \ll n e^{-c\sqrt{\log n}} .$$

Later, (22) was improved by Montgomery and Vaughan [1] in 1975. They proved that there exists a constant δ such that

(23) $$E(n) \ll n^{1-\delta} .$$

Chen Jing Run and Pan Cheng Dong [1] pointed out that $\delta > 0.01$, and it was improved further by Chen Jing Run [5] to $\delta > 0.04$.

Besides, Linnik [6,7,8,9] was the first, who proved the following two important theorems by the use of circle method, namely (i) for any given positive integer $g > 1$, there exists $k_0 > 0$ such that for $k > k_0$, every large integer $\equiv kg \pmod 2$ can be represented by

$$(24) \qquad n = p_1 + p_2 + g^{x_1} + \dots + g^{x_k} ,$$

where $x_1, \dots, x_k$ are positive integers, and (ii) under the assumption of (RH), for any given integer $n > 1$, there exist p_1, p_2 such that

$$(25) \qquad |n - p_1 - p_2| \ll (\log n)^{3+\varepsilon} .$$

Concerning these two problems, A. I. Vinogradov [1], Gallagher [4], Kátai [1], Montgomery and Vaughan [1], Wang Yuan [7], Prachar [3], Pan Cheng Dong [5], Lu Min Gao [1], and Wang Yuan and Shan Zun [1] have made some valuable contributions, for example, Kátai proved that the right hand side of (25) can be replaced by $(\log n)^2$.

2. <u>Sieve method</u>. The historical origin of sieve method may be traced back to the "sieve of Eratosthenes" in 250 B.C. Eratosthenes noted that the prime numbers between $\sqrt{n}$ and n can be isolated by removing from the sequence $2, 3, \dots, n$ every number which is a multiple of a prime not exceeding $\sqrt{n}$. Let $\pi(x) (= \pi(x,1,1))$ denote the number of primes $\leq x$ and $\Pi = \prod_{p \leq \sqrt{n}} p$. Then

$$(26) \qquad 1 + \pi(n) - \pi(\sqrt{n}) = \sum_{a \leq n} \sum_{d | (a,\pi)} \mu(d)$$

$$= \sum_{d | \pi} \mu(d) \left[\frac{n}{d} \right] .$$

If we use $\frac{n}{d} + \theta$ $(-1 < \theta \leq 0)$ instead of $\left[\frac{n}{d}\right]$, then it will cause an error term

$$(27) \qquad O\left(2^{\pi(\sqrt{n})} \right)$$

in (26), and so the sieve of Eratosthenes with its large error term compared with n is almost useless.

It was a great achievement when Brun [3] in 1919 devised his new sieve method and applied it successfully to several difficult and important problems in number theory, in particular, the Goldbach problem. In 1947, Selberg [2] gave another sieve method which leads to more precise result than Brun's method in every known case, when it can be applied. Moreover, Selberg's upper bound method is surprisingly simple, and it has a certain air of finality. Indeed these methods represent the indispensable tools in number theory.

The essence of the methods of Brun and Selberg is to use some inequalities instead of

$$(28) \qquad \Delta(n) = \sum_{d|n} \mu(d) = \begin{cases} 1, & \text{when } n=1, \\ 0, & \text{otherwise,} \end{cases}$$

in order to decrease the error term in Eratosthenes sieve. Brun defined two sets of integers D_1 and D_2 such that

$$(29) \qquad \sum_{\substack{d|n \\ d\in D_1}} \mu(d) \le \Delta(n) \le \sum_{\substack{d|n \\ d\in D_2}} \mu(d) .$$

However, the construction of D_1 and D_2 is complicated and heavily combinatorial in character. Selberg noted that

$$(30) \qquad \Delta(n) \le \left(\sum_{d|n} \lambda_d \right)^2$$

holds for any set of real numbers λ_d's with $\lambda_1 = 1$. Choose suitable λ_d's. Then we obtain the Selberg's upper bound method. Selberg [2, 3,4] published only his upper bound method, and indicated its place in the construction of lower bound sieves, without ever publishing any detials. Selberg's idea was developed and accomplished by Wang Yuan [1,2], A. I. Vinogradov [2,3], Levin [1,2], and Jurkat and Richert [1].

Let $A = \{a_\nu\}$ be a finite set of integers. Let P denote a finite set of primes. Further let $F(A,P)$ be the number of elements in A which is unsifted by the sequence P. Take $a_\nu = \nu(n-\nu)$ $(1 \le \nu < n)$ and P the set of all primes $\le n^{1/(\ell+1)}$, where $2|n$ and ℓ is a natural number. Denote $F(A,P) = F(n, n^{1/(\ell+1)})$. Suppose that we can obtain a positive lower estimation for $F(n, n^{1/(\ell+1)})$ when n is large. Then it follows that every large even integer n is the sum of two numbers each being a product of at most ℓ prime factors, and we denote this proposition by (ℓ,ℓ). Similarly, we may define (ℓ,m) for $\ell \ne m$.

Brun was the first who proved the (9,9). Brun's method and his result were improved by several mathematicians, namely (7,7) (Rademacher [1], 1924), (6,6) (Estermann [1], 1932), and (5,7), (4,9), (3,15) and (2,366) (Ricci [1,2], 1937).

The power of the methods of Brun and Selberg will be vastly improved if some combinatorial relations are used. These combinatorial ideas are of two kinds. One is the use of combinatorial identities for iteration originated in a paper of Buchstab [1] in 1937, and the other is the introduction of weighted sieves in 1941, of which the pioneering work is due to Kuhn [1].

Let $F(A,q,q')$ denote the number of elements in A satisfying $a_\nu \equiv 0 \pmod q$ and $a_\nu \not\equiv 0 \pmod p$ $(p < q')$. Then

$$(31) \qquad F(A, p_s) = F(A, p_t) - \sum_{p_t \le p < t_s} F(A, p, p) \ .$$

This is called the Buchstab's identity. From a lower estimation of $F(A, p_t)$ and those upper estimations of $F(A,p,p)$, it yields a lower estimation of $F(A, p_s)$. Similarly, we may obtain an upper estimation of $F(A, p_s)$. To iterate by (31) successively, we may obtain better upper and lower estimations for $F(A,P)$. By the use of Selberg's method, the explicit expressions of upper and lower estimations for certain $F(A,P)$ were obtained by Jurkat and Richert [1] in 1965. Let $F(A,b,q,q')$ be the number of elements in A such that $a_\nu \not\equiv 0 \pmod p$ $(p < q)$ and a_ν satisfies at most b congruences of those $a_\nu \equiv 0 \pmod{p'}$ $(q \le p' < q')$. Then

$$(32) \qquad F(A, b, q, q') \ge F(A, q) - \frac{1}{b+1} \sum_{q \le p < q'} F(A, p, q,) \ .$$

Choose suitable q, q' and b. Then a positive lower estimation of $F(A, b, q, q')$ often leads to a better result on Goldbach problem. Buchstab proved (5,5) [2] in 1938 and (4,4) [3] in 1940, where, (4,4) was also announced by Tartakovskiĭ [1,2], and Kuhn [3] established (a,b) $(a+b \le 6)$ in 1954.

By the combination of the methods of Brun, Selberg, Buchstab and Kuhn, Wang Yuan was able to prove (3,4) [1] in 1956, and (3,3), (a,b) $(a+b \le 5)$ [3] and (2,3) [4,5] in 1957, where (3,3) was also obtained by A. I. Vinogradov [2,3] in 1956 independently. (2,3) was announced by Selberg [3] but no proof had ever appeared. Later, Levin [2,3] and Barban [4,5] in 1963 gave other proofs of (2,3). In their proofs, the numerical calculation is simple but the use of deep analytic method is required.

If we take $A = \{n-p,\ p < n\}$ and P the set of all primes $\le n^{1/(\ell+1)}$, then a positive lower estimation for $F(A,P)$ leads to $(1,\ell)$. This set A was first introduced in 1932 by Estermann [1] who proved (1,6) by Brun's method under the assumption of (GRH). Wang Yuan [2] and A. I. Vinogradov [2,3] improved the (1,6) to (1,4) in 1956 under the same hypothesis, and Wang Yuan [3,6] gave further improvement (1,3) in 1957.

In order to remove the unproved hypothesis in the above results, it needs new idea and method. In the sieve so far considered, the sequence A is sifted, for each $p \in P$, by the residue class o mod p. But in some applications, it should sift, for each $p \in P$, the sequence A by the residue classes

$$h_{p,1}, \ldots, h_{p,k(p)} \pmod{p} \ .$$

The methods of Brun and Selberg can be applied effectively to this case unless $k(p)$ is, on the average, exceedingly small compared with p. Otherwise they are ineffective. In 1941, Linnik [1] devised an ingenious method, the so called large sieve. It yields a non-trivial upper estimation for the number of unsifted elements of A not exceeding n when k(p) is, on the average, comparatively large. Hungarian mathematician Rényi [1,2] improved Linnik's methods in various respects, and he proved successfully (1,c) in 1948. Further important improvements on the large sieve were obtained by Roth [1] and Bombieri [1] in 1965. In Rényi's paper, a mean value theorem for $\pi(x,k,h)$ is proved by means of large sieve that may be used instead of (QGRH) in the proof of (1,c), namely

$$(33)\qquad \sum_{k \le x^{\delta}} \max_{(k,k)=1} \left| \pi(x,k,h) - \frac{\operatorname{li} x}{\phi(k)} \right| = O\left(\frac{x}{(\log x)^{c_1}} \right) .$$

Notice that $\pi(x,k,h)$ should be replaced by a weight sum in his original paper. If (33) holds with $\delta = \frac{1}{2} - \varepsilon$, it may be used instead of (GRH) in the proofs of the results due to Estermann, A. I. Vinogradov and Wang Yuan (Cf. Wang Yuan [6].)

In 1961, Barban [1] proved (33) with $\delta = \frac{1}{6} - \varepsilon$ and (1,9). In 1962, Pan Cheng Dong [2] established independently (33) with $\delta = \frac{1}{3} - \varepsilon$, and derived (1,5). In 1962, Wang Yuan [6] pointed out that (1,4) can be derived from $\delta = \frac{1}{3} - \varepsilon$. Pan Cheng Dong [3] in 1962 and Barban [3] in 1963 proved independently that (33) holds for $\delta = \frac{3}{8} - \varepsilon$, and derived (1,4) without the use of heavy calculations. In 1965, Buchstab [7,8] establihsed (1,3) by the use of $\delta = \frac{3}{8} - \varepsilon$ with heavy calculations. Bombieri [1] and A. I. Vinogradov [4] proved independently (33) with $\delta = \frac{1}{2} - \varepsilon$, and so it follows easily (1,3). (33) with $\delta = \frac{1}{2} - \varepsilon$ is called the Bombieri-Vinogradov's mean value theorem. More precisely, Bombieri established the following important formula

$$(34)\qquad \sum_{k \le x^{\frac{1}{2}}/(\log x)^{c_2}} \max_{(h,k)=1} \left| \pi(x,k,h) - \frac{\operatorname{li} x}{\pi(k)} \right| = O\left(\frac{x}{(\log x)^{c_1}} \right)$$

where c_1 is any given constant and c_2 is a constant depending on c_1. Although Bombieri's formula is only slightly stronger than

(33) with $\delta = \frac{1}{2} - \varepsilon$, it has many important applications in number theory. For example, (34) can be used instead of (GRH) in the Hooley's proof of the following famous theorem. Let $N(n)$ be the number of representations of $n = p + u^2 + v^2$. Then

$$N(n) \sim \frac{\pi n}{\log n} \prod_{p \geq 3} \left(1 + \frac{\chi(p)}{p(p-1)}\right) \prod_{\substack{p \equiv 1 \pmod 4 \\ p | n}} \frac{(p-1)^2}{p^2 - p + 1}$$

(35) $$\cdot \prod_{\substack{p \equiv 3 \pmod 4 \\ p | n}} \frac{p^2 - 1}{p^2 - p - 1} ,$$

where $\chi(n)$ is the non-principal character mod 4.

<u>Remark</u>. Using their circle method, Hardy and Littlewood [2] conjectured (35), but they failed to prove it even under the assumption of (GRH). In 1957, it was Hooley [1] who first gave an elegant proof of (35) under the assumption of (GRH), and then Linnik [10,11] proved (35) unconditionally by his complicated dispersion method in 1960. Another advantage of Bombieri's paper is his proof of (35) which is creative and simple. The further simplified proof of (35) is given by Gallagher [1,2].

In 1966, Chen Jing Run [2,3] gave an important improvement on weighted sieve, and so he proved (1,2) which is called the Chen's theorem, that is, every large even integer is the sum of a prime and a product of at most 2 primes. Let

(36) $$M = N - \Omega + o(n^{9/10}) ,$$

where

$$N = F(n, n^{1/10}) - \frac{1}{2} \sum_{n^{1/10} \leq p < n^{1/3}} F(n, p, n^{1/10})$$

and

$$\Omega = \frac{1}{2} \sum_{\substack{p < n \\ (p_{1,2})}} \sum_{\substack{n - p = p_1 p_2 p_3 \\ p_3 \leq n/p_1 p_2}} 1$$

in which $2|n$, $A=\{n-p, p<n\}$ and $(p_{1,2})$ denotes the condition $n^{1/10} \le p_1 < n^{1/3} \le p_2 \le (\frac{n}{p_1})^{\frac{1}{2}}$. Then a positive lower estimation for M when n is large implies (1,2). In fact, $M>0$ means that there exists a prime p such that $n-p$ has at most 1 prime factor in the interval $[n^{1/10}, n^{1/3}]$ and 1 prime factor $> n^{1/3}$, or $n-p$ has only prime factors $> n^{1/3}$, and so the assertion follows. N in the right hand side of (36) is given by Kuhn's inequality (32) with suitable choice of parameters (see Wang Yuan [6]), and it may be estimated by the methods of Brun, Selberg and Buchstab combined with the Bombieri-Vinogradov's formula. Chen Jing Run's ingenious idea is the introduction of Ω, and gave it a non-trivial estimation. All the later simplified proofs on Chen's theorem are concentrated on the simplification of the estimation of Ω, in particular, Pan Cheng Dong, Ding Xia Qi and Wang Yuan [1] pointed out that the estimation of Ω can be derived immediately by the following mean value theorem similar to (34).

Let $2 \le y \le x$ and $\pi(y,a,q,h) = \sum_{\substack{ap \le y \\ ap \equiv h (\mathrm{mod}\, q)}} 1$. Then

(37) $$\sum_{q \le x^{\frac{1}{2}}/(\log x)^{c_2}} \max_{y \le x} \max_{(h,q)=1} \left| \sum_{c_3 < a \le c_4} f(a) \left[\pi(y,a,q,h) - \frac{\mathrm{li}\,\frac{y}{a}}{\phi(q)}\right] \right| = o\left(\frac{x}{(\log x)^{c_1}}\right)$$

holds uniformly on c_3, c_4 satisfying $(\log y)^{2c_2} < c_3 \le c_4 < y^{1-\varepsilon}$, where $|f(a)| \le 1$, $c_2 = c_1 + 7$ and the constant implicit in o depends on ε and c_1.

Furthermore, Pan Cheng and Ding Xia Qi [1,2] established a mean value theorem which includes (34) and (37).

3. <u>Density</u>. Let A denote a set of distinct non-negative

integers with its element denoted by a. Let $A(n) = \sum_{1 \le a \le n} 1$. Further let $\alpha = \inf_{n \ge 1} \frac{A(n)}{n}$ which is called the Schnirelman density of A. Clearly $0 \le \alpha \le 1$, and $\alpha = 1$ means that A contains all natural numbers. Similarly we may define B, b, B(n), β and C, c, C(n), γ. The sequence of all distinct numbers with the form of $a + b (a \in A, b \in B)$ will be denoted by $C = A + B$. We define $2A = A + A$ and $sA = A + (s-1)A$ by induction. Schnirelman [1,2] established two simple but important theorems, namely (i) if $0 \in A$ and $1 \in B$, then $\gamma \ge \alpha + \beta - \alpha\beta$, and (ii) if $0 \in A$, $1 \in B$ and $\alpha + \beta \ge 1$, then $\gamma = 1$, that is C contains all natural numbers. It follows from (i) that if $\alpha > 0$, then there exists an integer s_0 such that the density of $s_0 A$ is $\ge \frac{1}{2}$, and consequently, $2s_0 A$ contains all natural numbers by (ii), that is, (iii) if $0 \in A$ and $\alpha > 0$, then every positive integer can be represented as the sum of $2s_0$ elements of A. Let A^* be a set of non-negative integers in which the element is allowed to be repeated. Let A be the set of all distinct elements in A^* and r(a) denote the number of repetitions of a in A^*. Then by Schwarz inequality, we have

$$\left(\sum_{1 \le a \le n} r(a)\right)^2 \le \sum_{1 \le a \le n} r(a)^2 \sum_{1 \le a \le n} 1$$

$$= A(n) \sum_{1 \le a \le n} r(a)^2 ,$$

and therefore

$$\text{(iv)} \qquad \alpha \ge \left(\sum_{1 \le a \le n} r(a)\right)^2 \Big/ n \sum_{1 \le a \le n} r(a)^2 .$$

The concept of Schnirelman's density is certainly simple but it is very useful. Let r(a) denote the number of representations of $a = p_1 + p_2$. Then Brun's method yields

$$r(a) \le \frac{ca}{(\log n)^2} \sum_{k|a} \frac{\mu(k)^2}{k} .$$

Take A^* be the set contained 0,1 and the numbers of the form $a = p_1 + p_2$. Then it follows by (iv) that A has positive density.

Hence we have by (iii) the famous Schnirelman-Goldbach theorem, namely there exists a constant c such that every integer greater than 1 is the sum of at most c primes.

Let s be the smallest integer such that every large integer is the sum of at most s primes. Then Schnirelman's original method implies that $s \leq 800{,}000$. Since some results on Schnirelman's density and Brun's method are further improved, in particular, Khintchine [1] proved in 1932 that $\gamma \geq \min(1, 2\alpha)$ if $A = B$, Mann [1] established in 1942 the famous $\alpha + \beta$ conjecture, that is, $\gamma \geq \min(1, \alpha + \beta)$, and Selberg devised his new sieve method, the estimation of s is improved also, namely $s \leq 2{,}208$ (Romanov, 1935 [1]), $s \leq 71$ (Heilbronn, Landau and Scherk, 1936 [1]), $s \leq 67$ (Ricci, 1936 [1,2]) and so on. The best record $s \leq 6$ is due to Vaughan [3]. However the precision of this result is still inferior to $s \leq 4$ implied by the three primes theorem. By Schnirelman's method, we may estimate also the smallest integer s such that every integer > 1 is the sum of at most s primes.

Although the three primes theorem and the (1,2) are inferior to (1,1) only by one step, it seems impossible to solve the conjecture (A) (or 1,1)) by some modifications of the present methods, even we cannot give a conditional proof by the assumption of (GRH) and the formula (33) with $\delta = 1-\varepsilon$, that is,

$$\sum_{k \leq x^{1-\varepsilon}} \max_{(h,k)=1} \left| \pi(x,k,h) - \frac{\operatorname{li} x}{\phi(k)} \right| = O\left(\frac{x}{(\log x)^c} \right)$$

which is usually called the Halberstam conjecture. Hence there are many who believe that Hardy's address that the conjecture (A) is "probably as difficult as any of the unsolved problems in mathematics" is still valid now as it was then. Hence it is convinced that a completely new idea is needed in the further study on Goldbach conjecture (A).

I. REPRESENTATION OF AN ODD NUMBER AS THE SUM OF THREE PRIMES

SOME PROBLEMS OF 'PARTITIO NUMERORUM'; III: ON THE EXPRESSION OF A NUMBER AS A SUM OF PRIMES.

By

G. H. HARDY and J. E. LITTLEWOOD.
New College, Oxford. Trinity College, Cambridge.

1. Introduction.

1. 1. It was asserted by GOLDBACH, in a letter to EULER dated 7 June, 1742, that *every even number 2m is the sum of two odd primes*, and this proposition has generally been described as 'Goldbach's Theorem'. There is no reasonable doubt that the theorem is correct, and that the number of representations is large when m is large; but all attempts to obtain a proof have been completely unsuccessful. Indeed it has never been shown that every number (or every *large* number, any number, that is to say, from a certain point onwards) is the sum of 10 primes, or of 1 000 000; and the problem was quite recently classified as among those 'beim gegenwärtigen Stande der Wissenschaft unangreifbar'.[1]

In this memoir we attack the problem with the aid of our new transcendental method in 'additiver Zahlentheorie'.[2] We do not solve it: we do not

[1] E. LANDAU, 'Gelöste und ungelöste Probleme aus der Theorie der Primzahlverteilung und der Riemannschen Zetafunktion', *Proceedings of the fifth International Congress of Mathematicians*, Cambridge, 1912, vol. 1, pp. 93—108 (p. 105). This address was reprinted in the *Jahresbericht der Deutschen Math.-Vereinigung*, vol. 21 (1912), pp. 208—228.

[2] We give here a complete list of memoirs concerned with the various applications of this method.

G. H. HARDY.

1. 'Asymptotic formulae in combinatory analysis', *Comptes rendus du quatrième Congrès des mathematiciens Scandinaves à Stockholm*, 1916, pp. 45—53.

2. 'On the expression of a number as the sum of any number of squares, and in particular of five or seven', *Proceedings of the National Academy of Sciences*, vol. 4 (1918), pp. 189—193.

1922, 3 (with J. E. Littlewood) *Acta Mathematica*, 44, 1–70.

even prove that any number is the sum of 1 000 000 primes. In order to prove anything, we have to assume the truth of an unproved hypothesis, and, even on this hypothesis, we are unable to prove Goldbach's Theorem itself. We show, however, that the problem is not 'unangreifbar', and bring it into contact with the recognized methods of the Analytic Theory of Numbers.

3. 'Some famous problems of the Theory of Numbers, and in particular Waring's Problem' (Oxford, Clarendon Press, 1920, pp. 1—34).

4. 'On the representation of a number as the sum of any number of squares, and in particular of five', *Transactions of the American Mathematical Society,* vol. 21 (1920), pp. 255—284.

5. 'Note on Ramanujan's trigonometrical sum $c_q(n)$', *Proceedings of the Cambridge Philosophical Society,* vol. 20 (1921), pp. 263—271.

G. H. Hardy and J. E. Littlewood.

1. 'A new solution of Waring's Problem', *Quarterly Journal of pure and applied mathematics,* vol. 48 (1919), pp. 272—293.

2. 'Note on Messrs. Shah and Wilson's paper entitled: On an empirical formula connected with Goldbach's Theorem', *Proceedings of the Cambridge Philosophical Society,* vol. 19 (1919), pp. 245—254.

3. 'Some problems of 'Partitio numerorum'; I: A new solution of Waring's Problem', *Nachrichten von der K. Gesellschaft der Wissenschaften zu Göttingen* (1920), pp. 33—54.

4. 'Some problems of 'Partitio numerorum'; II: Proof that any large number is the sum of at most 21 biquadrates', *Mathematische Zeitschrift,* vol. 9 (1921), pp. 14—27.

G. H. Hardy and S. Ramanujan.

1. 'Une formule asymptotique pour le nombre des partitions de *n*', *Comptes rendus de l'Académie des Sciences,* 2 Jan. 1917.

2. 'Asymptotic formulae in combinatory analysis', *Proceedings of the London Mathematical Society,* ser. 2, vol. 17 (1918), pp. 75—115.

3. 'On the coefficients in the expansions of certain modular functions', *Proceedings of the Royal Society of London* (A), vol. 95 (1918), pp. 144—155.

E. Landau.

1. 'Zur Hardy-Littlewood'schen Lösung des Waringschen Problems', *Nachrichten von der K. Gesellschaft der Wissenschaften zu Göttingen* (1921), pp. 88—92.

L. J. Mordell.

1. 'On the representations of numbers as the sum of an odd number of squares', *Transactions of the Cambridge Philosophical Society,* vol. 22 (1919), pp. 361—372.

A. Ostrowski.

1. 'Bemerkungen zur Hardy-Littlewood'schen Lösung des Waringschen Problems', *Mathematische Zeitschrift,* vol. 9 (1921), pp. 28—34.

S. Ramanujan.

1. 'On certain trigonometrical sums and their applications in the theory of numbers', *Transactions of the Cambridge Philosophical Society,* vol. 22 (1918), pp. 259—276.

N. M. Shah and B. M. Wilson.

1. 'On an empirical formula connected with Goldbach's Theorem', *Proceedings of the Cambridge Philosophical Society,* vol. 19 (1919), pp. 238—244.

Our main result may be stated as follows: *if a certain hypothesis* (a natural generalisation of Riemann's hypothesis concerning the zeros of his Zeta-function) *is true, then every large odd number n is the sum of three odd primes; and the number of representations is given asymptotically by*

(1. 11)
$$\bar{N}_3(n) \sim C_3 \frac{n^2}{(\log n)^3} \prod_{\mathfrak{p}} \left(\frac{(\mathfrak{p}-1)(\mathfrak{p}-2)}{\mathfrak{p}^2-3\mathfrak{p}+3}\right),$$

where $\mathfrak{p}$ runs through all odd prime divisors of n, and

(1. 12)
$$C_3 = \Pi\left(1+\frac{1}{(\varpi-1)^3}\right),$$

the product extending over all odd primes ϖ.

Hypothesis R.

1. 2. We proceed to explain more closely the nature of our hypothesis. Suppose that q is a positive integer, and that

$$h = \varphi(q)$$

is the number of numbers less than q and prime to q. We denote by

$$\chi(n) = \chi_k(n) \qquad (k = 1, 2, \ldots, h)$$

one of the h Dirichlet's 'characters' to modulus q[1]: χ_1 is the 'principal' character.

By $\bar{\chi}$ we denote the complex number conjugate to χ: $\bar{\chi}$ is a character.

By $L(s, \chi)$ we denote the function defined for $\sigma > 1$ by

$$L(s) = L(\sigma + it) = L(s, \chi) = L(s, \chi_k) = \sum_{n=1}^{\infty} \frac{\chi(n)}{n^s}.$$

Unless the contrary is stated the modulus is q. We write

$$\bar{L}(s) = L(s, \bar{\chi}).$$

By

$$\varrho = \beta + i\gamma$$

[1] Our notation, so far as the theory of L-functions is concerned, is that of Landau's *Handbuch der Lehre von der Verteilung der Primzahlen*, vol. 1, book 2, pp. 391 *et seq.*, except that we use q for his k, k for his $\varkappa$, and ϖ for a typical prime instead of p. As regards the 'Farey dissection', we adhere to the notation of our papers *3* and *4*.

We do not profess to give a complete summary of the relevant parts of the theory of the L-functions; but our references to Landau should be sufficient to enable a reader to find for himself everything that is wanted.

we denote a typical zero of $L(s)$, those for which $\gamma = 0$, $\beta \leqq 0$ being excluded. We call these the *non-trivial* zeros. We write $N(T)$ for the number of ϱ's of $L(s)$ for which $0 \leqq \gamma \leqq T$.

The natural extension of Riemann's hypothesis is

HYPOTHESIS R. Every ϱ has its real part less than or equal to* $\frac{1}{2}$.[1]

We shall not have to use the full force of this hypothesis. What we shall in fact assume is

HYPOTHESIS R. There is a number $\Theta < \frac{3}{4}$ such that

$$\beta \leqq \Theta$$

for every ϱ of every $L(s)$.

The assumption of this hypothesis is fundamental in all our work; *all the results of the memoir, so far as they are novel, depend upon it*[2]; and we shall not repeat it in stating the conditions of our theorems.

We suppose that Θ has its smallest possible value. In any case $\Theta \geqq \frac{1}{2}$. For, if ϱ is a complex zero of $L(s)$, $\bar{\varrho}$ is one of $\bar{L}(s)$. Hence $1 - \bar{\varrho}$ is one of $L(1-s)$, and so, by the functional equation[3], one of $L(s)$.

Further notation and terminology.

1. 3. We use the following notation throughout the memoir.

A is a positive absolute constant wherever it occurs, but not the same constant at different occurrences. B is a positive constant depending on the single parameter r. O's refer to the limit process $n \to \infty$, the constants which they involve being of the type B, and o's are uniform in all parameters *except* r.

ϖ is a prime. $\mathfrak{p}$ (which will only occur in connection with n) is an odd prime divisor of n. p is an integer. If $q = 1$, $p = 0$; otherwise

$$0 < p < q, \quad (p, q) = 1.$$

(m, n) is the greatest common factor of m and n. By m n we mean that n is divisible by m; by m n the contrary.

$\Lambda(n)$, $\mu(n)$ have the meanings customary in the Theory of Numbers. Thus $\Lambda(n)$ is $\log \varpi$ if $n = \varpi^m$ and zero otherwise: $\mu(n)$ is $(-1)^k$ if n is a product of

[1] The hypothesis must be stated in this way because

(a) it has not been proved that no $L(s)$ has real zeros between $\frac{1}{2}$ and 1,

(b) the L-functions associated with *imprimitive* (uneigentlich) characters have zeros on the line $\sigma = 0$.

[2] Naturally many of the results stated incidentally do not depend upon the hypothesis.

[3] Landau, p. 489. All references to 'Landau' are to his *Handbuch*, unless the contrary is stated.

k different prime factors, and zero otherwise. The fundamental function with which we are concerned is

(1. 31) $$f(x) = \sum_{\varpi} \log \varpi \, x^{\varpi}.$$

To simplify our formulae we write

$$e(x) = e^{2\pi i x}, \quad e_q(x) = e\left(\frac{x}{q}\right).$$

Also

(1. 32) $$c_q(n) = \sum_{p} e_q(n p).$$

If χ_k is primitive,

(1. 33) $$\tau_k = \tau(\chi_k) = \sum_{p} e_q(p)\, \chi_k(p) = \sum_{m=1}^{q} e_q(m)\, \chi_k(m).$$[1]

This sum has the absolute value[2] $\sqrt{q}$.

The Farey dissection.

1. 4. We denote by Γ the circle

(1. 41) $$|x| = e^{-H} = e^{-\frac{1}{n}}.$$

We divide Γ into arcs $\xi_{p,q}$ which we call *Farey arcs*, in the following manner. We form the Farey's series of order

(1. 42) $$N = [\sqrt{n}],$$

the first and last terms being $\frac{0}{1}$ and $\frac{1}{1}$. We suppose that $\frac{p}{q}$ is a term of the series, and $\frac{p'}{q'}$ and $\frac{p''}{q''}$ the adjacent terms to the left and right, and denote by $j_{p,q}$ $(q > 1)$ the intervals

$$\frac{p}{q} - \frac{1}{q(q+q')}, \quad \frac{p}{q} + \frac{1}{q(q+q'')};$$

by $j_{0,1}$ and $j_{1,1}$ the intervals $\left(0, \frac{1}{N+1}\right)$ and $\left(1 - \frac{1}{N+1}, 1\right)$. These intervals just

[1] $\chi_k(m) = 0$ if $(m, q) > 1$.

[2] Landau, p. 497.

fill up the interval (0, 1), and the length of each of the parts into which $j_{p,q}$ is divided by $\frac{p}{q}$ is less than $\frac{1}{qN}$ and not less than $\frac{1}{2qN}$. If now the intervals $j_{p,q}$ are considered as intervals of variation of $\frac{\theta}{2\pi}$, where $\theta = \arg x$, and the two extreme intervals joined into one, we obtain the desired dissection of Γ into arcs $\xi_{p,q}$.[1]

When we are studying the arc $\xi_{p,q}$, we write

(1. 43) $$x = e^{\frac{2p\pi i}{q}} X = e_q(p) X = e_q(p) e^{-Y},$$

(1. 44) $$Y = \eta + i\theta.$$

The whole of our work turns on the behaviour of $f(x)$ as $|x| \to 1$, $\eta \to 0$, and we shall suppose throughout that $0 < \eta \leqq \frac{1}{2}$. When x varies on $\xi_{p,q}$, X varies on a congruent arc $\zeta_{p,q}$, and

$$\theta = -\left(\arg x - \frac{2p\pi}{q}\right)$$

varies (in the inverse direction) over an interval $-\theta'_{p,q} \leqq \theta \leqq \theta_{p,q}$. Plainly $\theta_{p,q}$ and $\theta'_{p,q}$ are less than $\frac{2\pi}{qN}$ and not less than $\frac{\pi}{qN}$, so that

$$\bar{\theta}_{p,q} = \operatorname{Max}(\theta_{p,q}, \theta'_{p,q}) < \frac{A}{qN}.$$

In all cases $Y^{-s} = (\eta + i\theta)^{-s}$ has its principal value

$$\exp(-s \log(\eta + i\theta)),$$

wherein (since η is positive)

$$-\frac{1}{2}\pi < \Im \log(\eta + i\theta) < \frac{1}{2}\pi.$$

By $N_r(n)$ we denote the number of representations of n by a sum of r primes, attention being paid to order, and repetitions of the same prime being allowed, so that

(1. 45) $$\sum_{n=2}^{\infty} N_r(n) x^n = \left(\sum_{\varpi} x^{\varpi}\right)^r.$$

[1] The distinction between major and minor arcs, fundamental in our work on Waring's Problem, does not arise here.

By $\nu_r(n)$ we denote the sum

(1. 46) $$\nu_r(n) = \sum_{\varpi_1+\varpi_2+\cdots+\varpi_r=n} \log\varpi_1 \log\varpi_2 \ldots \log\varpi_r,$$

so that

(1. 47) $$\sum_{n=2}^{\infty} \nu_r(n)\, x^n = (f(x))^r.$$

Finally S_r is the *singular series*

(1. 48) $$S_r = \sum_{q=1}^{\infty} \left(\frac{\mu(q)}{\varphi(q)}\right)^r c_q(-n).$$

2. Preliminary lemmas.

2. 1. *Lemma 1. If* $\eta = \Re(Y) > 0$ *then*

(2. 11) $$f(x) = f_1(x) + f_2(x),$$

where

(2. 12) $$f_1(x) = \sum_{(q,n)>1} \Lambda(n) x^n - \sum_{\varpi} \log\varpi (x^{\varpi^2} + x^{\varpi^3} + \cdots),$$

(2. 13) $$f_2(x) = \frac{1}{2\pi i}\int_{2-i\infty}^{2+i\infty} Y^{-s}\,\Gamma(s)\,Z(s)\,ds,$$

Y^{-s} *has its principal value,*

(2. 14) $$Z(s) = \sum_{k=1}^{h} C_k \frac{L'_k(s)}{L_k(s)},$$

C_k *depends only on* p, q *and* χ_k,

(2. 15) $$C_1 = -\frac{\mu(q)}{h}$$

and

(2. 16) $$|C_k| \leqq \frac{\sqrt{q}}{h}$$

We have

$$f_2(x) = f(x) - f_1(x) = \sum_{(q,n)=1} \Lambda(n)\, x^n$$

$$= \sum_{1 \leqq j \leqq q,\, (q,j)=1} e_q(pj) \sum_{l=0}^{\infty} \Lambda(lq+j)\, e^{-(lq+j)Y}$$

$$= \sum_j e_q(pj) \sum_l \Lambda(lq+j) \frac{1}{2\pi i} \int_{2-i\infty}^{2+i\infty} Y^{-s}\, \Gamma(s)\, (lq+j)^{-s}\, ds,$$

$$= \frac{1}{2\pi i} \int_{2-i\infty}^{2+i\infty} Y^{-s}\, \Gamma(s)\, Z(s)\, ds,$$

where

$$Z(s) = \sum_j e_q(pj) \sum_l \frac{\Lambda(lq+j)}{(lq+j)^s}.$$

Since $(q, j) = 1$, we have[1]

$$\sum_l \frac{\Lambda(lq+j)}{(lq+j)^s} = -\frac{1}{h} \sum_{k=1}^{h} \chi_k(j) \frac{L'_k(s)}{L_k(s)};$$

and so

$$Z(s) = \sum_{k=1}^{h} C_k \frac{L'_k(s)}{L_k(s)},$$

where

$$C_k = -\frac{1}{h} \sum_{j=1}^{q} e_q(pj)\, \bar{\chi}_k(j).$$

Since $\bar{\chi}_k(j) = 0$ if $(q, j) > 1$, the condition $(q, j) = 1$ may be omitted or retained at our discretion.

Thus[2]

$$C_1 = -\frac{1}{h} \sum_{1 \leqq j \leqq q,\, (q,j)=1} e_q(pj)$$

$$= -\frac{1}{h} \sum_{1 \leqq m \leqq q,\, (q,m)=1} e_q(m) = -\frac{\mu(q)}{h}.$$

[1] Landau, p. 421.
[2] Landau, pp. 572—573.

Again, if $k > 1$ we have[1]

$$C_k = -\frac{1}{h}\sum_{j=1}^{q} e_q(pj)\,\bar{\chi}_k(j) = -\frac{\chi_k(p)}{h}\sum_{m=1}^{q} e_q(m)\,\bar{\chi}_k(m).$$

If χ_k is a primitive character,

$$\sum_{m=1}^{q} e_q(m)\,\bar{\chi}_k(m) = \tau(q, \bar{\chi}_k),$$

$$|\tau(q, \bar{\chi}_k)| = \sqrt{q},\text{[2]}$$

$$|C_k| = \frac{\sqrt{q}}{h}.$$

If χ is imprimitive, it belongs to $Q = \frac{q}{d}$, where $d > 1$. Then $\bar{\chi}_k(m)$ has the period Q, and

$$\sum_{m=1}^{q} e_q(m)\,\chi_k(m) = \sum_{n=1}^{Q} e_q(n)\,\bar{\chi}_k(n)\sum_{l=0}^{d-1} e_q(lQ).$$

The inner sum is zero. Hence $C_k = 0$, and the proof of the lemma is completed.[3]

2. 2. *Lemma 2. We have*

(2. 21)
$$|f_1(x)| < A(\log(q+1))^A \eta^{-\frac{1}{2}}.$$

We have

$$f_1(x) = \sum_{(q,n)>1} \Lambda(n)x^n - \sum_{\varpi} \log\varpi\,(x^{\varpi^2} + x^{\varpi^3} + \cdots) = f_{1,1}(x) - f_{1,2}(x).$$

But

$$|f_{1,1}(x)| \leqq \sum_{\varpi \mid q} \log\varpi \sum_{r=1}^{\infty} |x|^{\varpi^r}$$

$$< A\log(q+1)\log q\sum_{r=1}^{\infty}|x|^{2^r} < A(\log(q+1))^2\sum_{r=1}^{\infty} e^{-\eta 2^r}$$

$$< A(\log(q+1))^A \log\frac{1}{\eta} < A(\log(q+1))^A\eta^{-\frac{1}{2}}.$$

[1] Landau, p. 485. The result is stated there only for a primitive character, but the proof is valid also for an imprimitive character when $(p, q) = 1$.

[2] Landau, pp. 485, 489, 492.

[3] See the additional note at the end.

Also

$$\sum_{r \geqq 2, \varpi^r \leqq \xi} \log \varpi < A \sqrt{\xi},$$

and so

$$|f_{1,2}(x)| \leqq \sum_{r \geqq 2, \varpi} \log \varpi |x|^{\varpi^r} < A(1 - |x|) \sum_n \sqrt{n} |x|^n$$

$$< A(1 - |x|)^{-\frac{1}{2}} < A\eta^{-\frac{1}{2}}.$$

From these two results the lemma follows.

2. 3. *Lemma 3. We have*

(2. 31) $$\frac{L'(s)}{L(s)} = -\frac{\mathfrak{b}}{s-1} + \frac{\mathfrak{d} - \mathfrak{b}}{s} + b - \frac{1}{2}\psi\left(\frac{s+\mathfrak{a}}{2}\right) + \sum_{\varrho}\left(\frac{1}{s-\varrho} + \frac{1}{\varrho}\right),$$

where

$$\psi(z) = \frac{\Gamma'(z)}{\Gamma(z)},$$

the $\mathfrak{a}$'s, $\mathfrak{b}$'s, $\mathfrak{d}$'s *and* b's *are constants depending upon* q *and* χ, $\mathfrak{a}$ *is* 0 *or* 1,

(2. 32) $$\mathfrak{b}_1 = 1, \qquad \mathfrak{b}_k = 0 \qquad (k > 1),$$

and

(2. 33) $$0 \leqq \mathfrak{d} < A \log (q + 1).$$

All these results are classical except the last.[1]

The precise definition of $\mathfrak{d}$ is rather complicated and does not concern us. We need only observe that $\mathfrak{d}$ does not exceed the number of different primes that divide q,[2] and so satisfies (2. 33).

2. 41. *Lemma 4. If* $0 < \eta \leqq \frac{1}{2}$, *then*

(2. 411) $$f(x) = \frac{\mu(q)}{hY} + \sum_{k=1}^{h} C_k G_k + P,$$

where

(2. 412) $$G_k = \sum_{\varrho_k} \Gamma(\varrho) Y^{-\varrho},$$

[1] Landau, pp. 509, 510, 519.

[2] Landau, p. 511 (footnote).

(2. 413) $$|P| < A\sqrt{q}\,(\log(q+1))^A \left(\frac{1}{h}\sum_{k=1}^{h}|b_k| + \eta^{-\frac{1}{2}} + |Y|^{\frac{1}{4}}\delta^{-\frac{1}{2}}\right),$$

(2. 414) $$\delta = \arc\tan\frac{\eta}{|\theta|}.$$

We have, from (2. 13) and (2. 14),

(2. 415) $$f_2(x) = \frac{1}{2\pi i}\int_{2-i\infty}^{2+i\infty} Y^{-s}\Gamma(s)\,Z(s)\,ds$$

$$= \sum_{k=1}^{h}\frac{C_k}{2\pi i}\int_{2-i\infty}^{2+i\infty} Y^{-s}\Gamma(s)\frac{L'_k(s)}{L_k(s)}\,ds = \sum_{k=1}^{h} C_k f_{2,k}(x),$$

say. But[1]

(2.416) $$\frac{1}{2\pi i}\int_{2-i\infty}^{2+i\infty} Y^{-s}\Gamma(s)\frac{L'(s)}{L(s)}\,ds = -\frac{\mathfrak{b}}{Y} + R + \sum_{\varrho}\Gamma(\varrho)\,Y^{-\varrho} + \frac{1}{2\pi i}\int_{-\frac{1}{4}-i\infty}^{-\frac{1}{4}+i\infty} Y^{-s}\Gamma(s)\frac{L'(s)}{L(s)}\,ds,$$

where

$$R = \left\{Y^{-s}\Gamma(s)\frac{L'(s)}{L(s)}\right\}_0,$$

$\{f(s)\}_0$ denoting generally the residue of $f(s)$ for $s=0$.

Now[2]

$$\frac{L'(s)}{L(s)} = \log\frac{\pi}{Q} + \sum_{\nu=1}^{\mathfrak{c}}\frac{\varepsilon_\nu \log\varpi_\nu}{\varpi_\nu^s - \varepsilon_\nu} + \sum_{\nu=1}^{\mathfrak{c}}\frac{\bar{\varepsilon}_\nu \log\varpi_\nu}{\varpi_\nu^{1-s} - \bar{\varepsilon}_\nu}$$

$$-\frac{1}{2}\psi\left(\frac{s+\mathfrak{a}}{2}\right) - \frac{1}{2}\psi\left(\frac{1-s+\mathfrak{a}}{2}\right) - \frac{\bar{L}'(1-s)}{\bar{L}(1-s)},$$

where Q is the divisor of q to which χ belongs, $\mathfrak{c}$ is the number of primes which divide q but not Q, $\varpi_1, \varpi_2, \ldots$ are the primes in question, and ε_ν is a root of unity. Hence, if $\sigma = -\frac{1}{4}$, we have

[1] This application of Cauchy's Theorem may be justified on the lines of the classical proof of the 'explicit formulae' for $\psi(x)$ and $\pi(x)$: see Landau, pp. 333—368. In this case the proof is much easier, since $Y^{-s}\Gamma(s)$ tends to zero, when $|t|\to\infty$, like an exponential $e^{-a|t|}$. Compare pp. 134—135 of our memoir 'Contributions to the theory of the Riemann Zeta-function and the theory of the distribution of primes', *Acta Mathematica*, vol. 41 (1917), pp. 119—196.

[2] Landau, p. 517.

(2. 417)
$$\left|\frac{L'(s)}{L(s)}\right| < A\log q + A\,c\log q + A\log(|t|+2) + A$$
$$< A\,(\log(q+1))^A \log(|t|+2).$$

Again, if $s = -\frac{1}{4} + it$, $Y = \eta + i\theta$, we have

$$|Y^{-s}| = |Y|^{\frac{1}{4}} \exp\left(t \arctan\frac{\theta}{\eta}\right),$$

$$|Y^{-s}\Gamma(s)| < A\,|Y|^{\frac{1}{4}}(|t|+2)^{-\frac{3}{4}} \exp\left(-\left(\frac{1}{2}\pi - \arctan\frac{|\theta|}{\eta}\right)|t|\right),$$

$$< A\,|Y|^{\frac{1}{4}} \frac{|t|^{-\frac{1}{2}}}{\log(|t|+2)} e^{-\delta|t|};$$

and so

(2. 418)
$$\left|\frac{1}{2\pi i}\int_{-\frac{1}{4}-i\infty}^{-\frac{1}{4}+i\infty} Y^{-s}\Gamma(s)\frac{L'(s)}{L(s)}\,ds\right| < A\,(\log(q+1))^A\,|Y|^{\frac{1}{4}}\int_0^\infty t^{-\frac{1}{2}} e^{-\delta t}\,dt$$
$$< A\,(\log(q+1))^A\,|Y|^{\frac{1}{4}}\delta^{-\frac{1}{2}}.$$

2. 42. We now consider R. Since

$$\sum\left(\frac{1}{s-\varrho} + \frac{1}{\varrho}\right) = 0 \qquad (s = 0),$$

we have

$$R = \{(\mathfrak{b} + b)\,\Gamma(s)\}_0 + \left\{\frac{\mathfrak{d} - \mathfrak{b}}{s} Y^{-s}\Gamma(s)\right\}_0 - \frac{1}{2}\left\{Y^{-s}\Gamma(s)\psi\left(\frac{s+\mathfrak{a}}{2}\right)\right\}_0$$
$$= A_1(\mathfrak{b} + b) - (\mathfrak{d} - \mathfrak{b})(A_2 + A_3\log Y) + C_1(\mathfrak{a}) + C_2(\mathfrak{a})\log Y,$$

where each of the C's has one of two absolute constant values, according to the value of $\mathfrak{a}$. Since

$$0 \leq \mathfrak{b} \leq 1, \quad 0 \leq \mathfrak{d} < A\log(q+1), \quad |\log Y| < A\log\frac{1}{\eta} < A\eta^{-\frac{1}{2}},$$

we have

(2. 421)
$$|R| < A\,|b| + A\log(q+1)\,\eta^{-\frac{1}{2}}.$$

From (2. 415), (2. 416), (2. 418), (2. 421) and (2. 15) we deduce

$$f_{2,k}(x) = -\frac{\mathfrak{b}}{Y} + G_k + P_k,$$

$$|P_k| < A\,(\log(q+1))^A \left(|b| + \eta^{-\frac{1}{2}} + |Y|^{\frac{1}{4}}\delta^{-\frac{1}{2}}\right),$$

(2. 422)
$$f_2(x) = +\frac{\mu(q)}{hY} + \sum_k C_k G_k + P,$$

(2. 423)
$$|P| < A\sqrt{q}\,(\log(q+1))^A \left(\frac{1}{h}\sum_k |b_k| + \eta^{-\frac{1}{2}} + |Y|^{\frac{1}{4}}\delta^{-\frac{1}{2}}\right).$$

Combining (2. 422) and (2. 423) with (2. 11) and (2. 21), we obtain the result of Lemma 4.

2. 5. *Lemma 5. If $q > 1$ and χ_k is a primitive (and therefore non-principal*[1]*) character, then*

(2. 51)
$$L(s) = \frac{a e^{bs}}{\Gamma\left(\frac{s+\mathfrak{a}}{2}\right)} \prod_{\varrho} \left(\left(1 - \frac{s}{\varrho}\right) e^{\frac{s}{\varrho}}\right),$$

where

$$a = a(q, \chi) = a_k,$$

(2. 521)
$$|L(1)| = \pi q^{-\frac{1}{2}} |L(0)| \qquad (\mathfrak{a} = 1),$$

(2. 522)
$$|L(1)| = 2 q^{-\frac{1}{2}} |L'(0)| \qquad (\mathfrak{a} = 0).$$

Further

(2. 53)
$$1 - \Theta \leq \Re(\varrho) \leq \Theta,$$

and

(2. 54)
$$\left|\frac{L'(1)}{L(1)}\right| < A\,(\log(q+1))^A.$$

This lemma is merely a collection of results which will be used in the proof of Lemmas 6 and 7. They are of very unequal depth. The formula (2. 51) is classical.[2] The two next are immediate deductions from the functional equation for $L(s)$.[3] The inequalities (2. 53) follow from the functional equation and the

[1] Landau, p. 480.

[2] Landau, p. 507.

[3] Landau, pp. 496, 497.

absence (for primitive χ) of factors $1-\varepsilon_\nu \varpi_\nu^{-s}$ from L. Finally (2. 54) is due to GRONWALL.[1]

2. 61. *Lemma 6. If $M(T)$ is the number of zeros ϱ of $L(s)$ for which*

$$0 \leqq T \leqq |\gamma| \leqq T+1,$$

then

$$M(T) < A(\log(q+1))^A \log(T+2). \tag{2. 611}$$

The ϱ's of an imprimitive $L(s)$ are those of a certain primitive $L(s)$ corresponding to modulus Q, where $Q|q$, together with the zeros (other than $s=0$) of certain functions

$$E_\nu = 1-\varepsilon_\nu \varpi_\nu^{-s},$$

where

$$|\varepsilon_\nu| = 1,\ \varpi_\nu | q.$$

[1] T. H. GRONWALL, 'Sur les séries de Dirichlet correspondant à des caractères complexes', *Rendiconti del Circolo Matematico di Palermo*, vol. 35 (1913), pp. 145—159. Gronwall proves that

$$\frac{1}{|L(1)|} < A \log q (\log\log q)^{\frac{3}{8}}$$

for every *complex* χ, and states that the same is true for *real* χ if hypothesis R (or a much less stringent hypothesis) is satisfied. LANDAU ('Über die Klassenzahl imaginär-quadratischer Zahlkörper', *Göttinger Nachrichten*, 1918, pp. 285—295 (p. 286, f. n. 2)) has, however, observed that, in the case of a real χ, Gronwall's argument leads only to the slightly less precise inequality

$$\frac{1}{|L(1)|} < A \log q \sqrt{\log\log q}.$$

Landau also gives a proof (due to HECKE) that

$$\frac{1}{|L(1)|} < A \log q$$

for the special character $\left(\frac{-q}{n}\right)$ associated with the fundamental discriminant $-q$.

The first results in this direction are due to Landau himself ('Über das Nichtverschwinden der Dirichletschen Reihen, welche komplexen Charakteren entsprechen', *Math. Annalen*, vol. 70 (1911), pp. 69—78). Landau there proves that

$$\frac{1}{|L(1)|} < A (\log q)^6$$

for complex χ.

It is easily proved (see p. 75 of Landau's last quoted memoir) that

$$|L'(1)| < A(\log q)^2,$$

so that any of these results gives us more than all that we require.

The number of ϖ_ν's is less than $A \log(q+1)$, and each E_ν has a set of zeros, on $\sigma = 0$, at equal distances

$$\frac{2\pi}{\log \varpi_\nu} > \frac{2\pi}{\log(q+1)}.$$

The contribution of these zeros to $M(T)$ is therefore less than $A(\log(q+1))^2$; and we need consider only a primitive (and therefore, if $q > 1$, non-principal) $L(s)$.

We observe:

(a) that $\mathfrak{a}$ is the same for $L(s)$ and $\bar{L}(s)$;

(b) that $L(s)$ and $\bar{L}(s)$ are conjugate for real s, so that the b corresponding to $\bar{L}(s)$ is $\bar{b}$, the conjugate of the b of $L(s)$;

(c) that the typical ϱ of $\bar{L}(s)$ may be taken to be either $\bar{\varrho}$ or (in virtue of the functional equation) $1 - \varrho$, so that

$$S = \sum\left(\frac{1}{\varrho} + \frac{1}{1-\varrho}\right) = \sum\left(\frac{1}{\varrho} + \frac{1}{\bar{\varrho}}\right)$$

is real.

Bearing these remarks in mind, suppose first that $\mathfrak{a} = 1$. We have then, from (2. 51) and (2. 521),

$$\frac{\pi^2}{q} = \left|\frac{L(1)\bar{L}(1)}{L(0)\bar{L}(0)}\right| = A\left|e^b \prod\left(\left(1-\frac{1}{\varrho}\right)e^{\frac{1}{\varrho}}\right) e^{\bar{b}} \prod\left(\left(1-\frac{1}{1-\varrho}\right)e^{\frac{1}{1-\varrho}}\right)\right|$$

$$= A\, e^{2\Re(b)+S},$$

since

$$\left(1-\frac{1}{\varrho}\right)\left(1-\frac{1}{1-\varrho}\right) = 1.$$

Thus

$$|2\Re(b) + S| < A \log(q+1). \tag{2. 612}$$

On the other hand, if $\mathfrak{a} = 0$, we have, from (2. 51) and (2. 522),

$$\frac{4}{q} = \left|\frac{L(1)\bar{L}(1)}{L'(0)\bar{L}'(0)}\right| = A\left|e^b \prod\left(\left(1-\frac{1}{\varrho}\right)e^{-\frac{1}{\varrho}}\right) e^{\bar{b}} \prod\left(\left(1-\frac{1}{1-\varrho}\right)e^{\frac{1}{1-\varrho}}\right)\right|,$$

and (2. 612) follows as before.

2. 62. Again, by (2. 31)

$$\frac{L'(1)}{L(1)} = \mathfrak{b} + b - \frac{1}{2}\psi\left(\frac{1+\mathfrak{a}}{2}\right) + \sum\left(\frac{1}{1-\varrho} + \frac{1}{\varrho}\right). \tag{2. 621}$$

for every non-principal character (whether primitive or not). In particular, when χ is primitive, we have, by (2. 621), (2. 54), and (2. 33),

$$(2.\ 622)\qquad |\Re(b)+S| = \left|\Re\frac{L'(1)}{L(1)} - \mathfrak{b} + \frac{1}{2}\psi\left(\frac{1+\mathfrak{a}}{2}\right)\right| < A\,(\log(q+1))^A.$$

Combining (2. 612) and (2. 622) we see that

$$(2.\ 623)\qquad S < A\,(\log(q+1))^A$$

and

$$(2.\ 624)\qquad |\Re(b)| < A\,(\log(q+1))^A.$$

2. 63. If now $q > 1$, and χ is primitive (so that $\mathfrak{b} = 0$), and $s = 2 + iT$, we have, by (2. 31), (2. 33), and (2. 624),

$$0 < \sum\left(\frac{2-\beta}{(2-\beta)^2+(T-\gamma)^2} + \frac{\beta}{\beta^2+\gamma^2}\right) = \Re\sum\left(\frac{1}{s-\varrho}+\frac{1}{\varrho}\right)$$

$$= \Re\frac{L'(s)}{L(s)} - \Re\left(\frac{\mathfrak{b}}{s}\right) - \Re(b) + \frac{1}{2}\Re\left(\psi\left(\frac{s+\mathfrak{a}}{2}\right)\right)$$

$$\leqq \left|\frac{L'(s)}{L(s)}\right| + \left|\frac{\mathfrak{b}}{s}\right| + |\Re(b)| + \left|\psi\left(\frac{s+\mathfrak{a}}{2}\right)\right|$$

$$< A + A\log(q+1) + A\,(\log(q+1))^A + A\log(|T|+2)$$

$$< A\,(\log(q+1))^A \log(|T|+2),$$

$$\sum_{|T-\gamma|\leqq 1} \frac{2-\beta}{(2-\beta)^2+(T-\gamma)^2} < A\,(\log(q+1))^A \log(|T|+2).$$

Every term on the left hand side is greater than A, and the number of terms is not less than $M(T)$. Hence we obtain the result of the lemma. We have excluded the case $q = 1$, when the result is of course classical.[1]

2. 71. *Lemma 7. We have*

$$(2.\ 711)\qquad |b| < A q\,(\log(q+1))^A.$$

Suppose first that χ is non-principal. Then, by (2. 621) and (2. 54),

$$(2.\ 712)\qquad |b| < A\,(\log(q+1))^A + \left|\sum\left(\frac{1}{1-\varrho}+\frac{1}{\varrho}\right)\right|.$$

[1] Landau, p. 337.

We write

$$\sum = \sum_1 + \sum_2, \tag{2. 713}$$

where $\sum_1$ is extended over the zeros for which $1 - \Theta \leqq \Re(\varrho) \leqq \Theta$ and $\sum_2$ over those for which $\Re(\varrho) = 0$. Now $\sum_1 = S'$, where S' is the S corresponding to a primitive $L(s)$ for modulus Q, where $Q \mid q$. Hence, by (2. 623),

$$\left|\sum_1\right| < A\,(\log (Q+1))^A < A\,(\log (q+1))^A. \tag{2. 714}$$

Again, the ϱ's of $\sum_2$ are the zeros (other than $s = 0$) of

$$\prod_\nu \left(1 - \frac{\varepsilon_\nu}{\varpi_\nu^s}\right),$$

the ϖ_ν's being divisors of q and ε_ν an m-th root of unity, where $m = \varphi(Q) < q$[1]; so that the number of ϖ_ν's is less than $A \log q$ and

$$\varepsilon_\nu = e^{2\pi i \omega_\nu},$$

where either $\omega_\nu = 0$ or

$$\frac{1}{q} \leqq |\omega_\nu| \leqq \frac{1}{2}.$$

Let us denote by ϱ_ν a zero (other than $s = 0$) of $1 - \varepsilon_\nu \varpi_\nu^{-s}$, by ϱ'_ν a ϱ_ν for which $|\varrho_\nu| \leqq 1$, and by ϱ''_ν a ϱ_ν for which $|\varrho_\nu| > 1$. Then

$$\left|\sum_2 \left(\frac{1}{1-\varrho} + \frac{1}{\varrho}\right)\right| \leqq \sum_\nu \left(\sum_{\varrho'_\nu} + \sum_{\varrho''_\nu}\right)\left|\frac{1}{1-\varrho} + \frac{1}{\varrho}\right|. \tag{2. 715}$$

Any ϱ_ν is of the form

$$\varrho_\nu = \frac{2\pi i (m + \omega_\nu)}{\log \varpi_\nu},$$

where m is an integer. Hence the number of zeros ϱ'_ν is less than $A \log \varpi_\nu$ or than $A \log (q+1)$; and the absolute value of the corresponding term in our sum is less than

$$\frac{A}{|\varrho|} < \frac{A \log \varpi_\nu}{|\omega_\nu|} < A q \log (q+1); \tag{2. 716}$$

[1] For (Landau, p. 482) $\varepsilon_\nu = X(\varpi_\nu)$, where X is a character to modulus Q.

so that

$$\left|\sum_{\varrho'_\nu}\right| < A q\,(\log(q+1))^2. \tag{2. 717}$$

Also

$$\left|\sum_{\varrho''_\nu}\right| \leq \sum_{\varrho''_\nu}\left|\frac{1}{\varrho(1-\varrho)}\right| < \sum_{\varrho''_\nu}\frac{1}{|\varrho|^2} \tag{2. 718}$$

$$< A\,(\log \varpi_\nu)^2 \sum_{m=1}^{\infty}\frac{1}{m^2} < A\,(\log(q+1))^2.$$

From (2. 715), (2. 717) and (2. 718) we deduce

$$\left|\sum\nolimits_2\right| < A q\,(\log(q+1))^A; \tag{2. 719}$$

and from (2. 713), (2. 714) and (2. 719) the result of the lemma.

2. 72. We have assumed that χ is not a principal character: For the principal character (mod. q) we have[1]

$$L_1(s) = \prod_{\varpi\,|\,q}\left(1-\frac{1}{\varpi^s}\right)\zeta(s).$$

Since $\mathfrak{a} = 0$, $\mathfrak{b} = 1$, we have

$$\sum_{\varpi\,|\,q}\frac{\log\varpi}{\varpi^s-1} + \frac{\zeta'(s)}{\zeta(s)} = \frac{L'_1(s)}{L_1(s)}$$

$$= \frac{\mathfrak{b}-1}{s} - \frac{1}{s-1} + b - \frac{1}{2}\psi\left(\frac{1}{2}s\right) + \sum\left(\frac{1}{s-\varrho}+\frac{1}{\varrho}\right),^{2}$$

$$\sum_{\varpi\,|\,q}\frac{\log\varpi}{\varpi-1} + \lim_{s\to 1}\left(\frac{\zeta'(s)}{\zeta(s)}+\frac{1}{s-1}\right) = \mathfrak{b}-1+b-\frac{1}{2}\psi\left(\frac{1}{2}\right) + \sum\left(\frac{1}{1-\varrho}+\frac{1}{\varrho}\right),$$

$$|b| < A\log(q+1) + \left|\sum\left(\frac{1}{1-\varrho}+\frac{1}{\varrho}\right)\right|.$$

This corresponds to (2. 712), and from this point the proof proceeds as before.

[1] Landau, p. 423.

[2] $\sum$ refers to the complex zeros of $L_1(s)$, not merely to those of $\zeta(s)$.

2. 81. *Lemma 8. If* $0 < \eta \leqq \frac{1}{2}$ *then*

(2. 811)
$$f(x) = \frac{\mu(q)}{hY} + \sum_{k=1}^{h} C_k G_k + P,$$

where

(2. 812)
$$G_k = \sum_{\varrho_k} \Gamma(\varrho)\, Y^{-\varrho},$$

(2. 813)
$$|P| < A\sqrt{q}\,(\log(q+1))^A \left(q + \eta^{-\frac{1}{2}} + |Y|^{\frac{1}{4}} \delta^{-\frac{1}{2}}\right),$$

(2. 814)
$$\delta = \operatorname{arc\,tan} \frac{\eta}{|\theta|}.$$

This is an immediate corollary of Lemmas 4 and 7.

2. 82. *Lemma 9. If* $0 < \eta \leqq \frac{1}{2}$ *then*

(2. 821)
$$f(x) = \varphi + \Phi,$$

where

(2. 822)
$$\varphi = \frac{\mu(q)}{hY},$$

(2. 823)
$$|\Phi| < A\sqrt{q}\,(\log(q+1))^A \left(q + \eta^{-\frac{1}{2}} + |Y|^{-\Theta} \delta^{-\Theta-\frac{1}{2}} \log\left(\frac{1}{\delta} + 2\right)\right),$$

(2. 824)
$$\delta = \operatorname{arc\,tan} \frac{\eta}{|\theta|}.$$

We have

(2. 825)
$$|G_k| \leqq \sum\nolimits_1 |\Gamma(\varrho)\, Y^{-\varrho}| + \sum\nolimits_2 |\Gamma(\varrho)\, Y^{-\varrho}|,$$

where $\sum_1$ extends over ϱ_k's for which $|\gamma| \geqq 1$, $\sum_2$ over those for which $|\gamma| < 1$. In $\sum_1$ we have

$$|\Gamma(\varrho)\, Y^{-\varrho}| = |\Gamma(\beta + i\gamma)|\, |Y|^{-\beta} \exp\left(\gamma \operatorname{arc\,tan} \frac{\theta}{\eta}\right)$$

$$\leqq A|\gamma|^{\beta-\frac{1}{2}} |Y|^{-\beta} \exp\left(-\left(\frac{1}{2}\pi - \operatorname{arc\,tan} \frac{|\theta|}{\eta}\right)|\gamma|\right)$$

$$\leqq A|\gamma|^{\Theta-\frac{1}{2}} |Y|^{-\Theta} e^{-\delta|\gamma|}$$

(since $|Y| < A$ and, by hypothesis R, $\beta \leqq \Theta$). The number $M(T)$ of ϱ's for which $|\gamma|$ lies between T and $T+1$ $(T \geqq 0)$ is less than $A(\log(q+1))^A \log(T+2)$, by (2. 611). Hence

$$\sum_1 |\gamma|^{\Theta-\frac{1}{2}} e^{-\delta|\gamma|} \leqq A(\log(q+1))^A \sum_{n=0}^{\infty}(n+1)^{\Theta-\frac{1}{2}} \log(n+2)\, e^{-\delta n}$$

$$< A(\log(q+1))^A \delta^{-\Theta-\frac{1}{2}} \log\left(\frac{1}{\delta}+2\right),$$

$$\sum_1 |\Gamma(\varrho)\, Y^{-\varrho}| < A(\log(q+1))^A |Y|^{-\Theta} \delta^{-\Theta-\frac{1}{2}} \log\left(\frac{1}{\delta}+2\right). \tag{2. 826}$$

2. 83. Again, once more by (2. 611), $\sum_2$ has at most $A(\log(q+1))^A$ terms. We write

$$\sum_2 = \sum_{2,1} + \sum_{2,2}, \tag{2. 831}$$

$\sum_{2,1}$ applying to zeros for which $1-\Theta \leqq \beta \leqq \Theta$, and $\sum_{2,2}$ to those for which $\beta = 0$. Now, in $\sum_2$,

$$|Y^{-\varrho}| = |Y|^{-\beta} \exp\left(\gamma \operatorname{arc} \tan \frac{\theta}{\eta}\right) < A|Y|^{-\beta};$$

and in $\sum_{2,1}$, $|\Gamma(\varrho)| < A$. Hence

$$\left|\sum_{2,1}\right| < A|Y|^{-\beta} \sum_{2,1} |\Gamma(\varrho)| < A|Y|^{-\Theta} \sum_{2,1} 1 < A(\log(q+1))^A |Y|^{-\Theta}. \tag{2. 832}$$

Again, in $\sum_{2,2}$, $|Y| < A$ and

$$\frac{1}{|\varrho|} < Aq \log(q+1),$$

by (2. 716); so that

$$\left|\sum_{2,2}\right| < A \sum_{2,2} |\Gamma(\varrho)| = A \sum_{2,2} \frac{|\Gamma(1+\varrho)|}{|\varrho|} \tag{2. 833}$$

$$< A \sum_{2,2} \frac{1}{|\varrho|} < Aq(\log(q+1))^A.$$

From (2. 825), (2. 826), (2. 831), (2. 832), and (2. 833), we obtain

$$|G_k| < A(\log(q+1))^A \left(q + |Y|^{-\Theta} \delta^{-\Theta-\frac{1}{2}} \log\left(\frac{1}{\delta}+2\right)\right) = H_k, \tag{2. 834}$$

say; and from (2. 811), (2. 812), (2. 813), (2. 821), (2. 822) and (2. 834) we deduce

$$|\Phi| = \left|\sum_{k=1}^{h} C_k G_k + P\right|$$

$$< \sum_{k=1}^{h} |C_k G_k| + A\sqrt{q}\,(\log(q+1))^A \left(q + \eta^{-\frac{1}{2}} + |Y|^{\frac{1}{4}} \delta^{-\frac{1}{2}}\right)$$

$$< \frac{\sqrt{q}}{h} \sum_{k=1}^{h} H_k + A\sqrt{q}\,(\log(q+1))^A \left(q + \eta^{-\frac{1}{2}} + |Y|^{-\Theta} \delta^{-\Theta-\frac{1}{2}} \log\left(\frac{1}{\delta} + 2\right)\right)$$

$$< A\sqrt{q}\,(\log(q+1))^A \left(q + \eta^{-\frac{1}{2}} + |Y|^{-\Theta} \delta^{-\Theta-\frac{1}{2}} \log\left(\frac{1}{\delta} + 2\right)\right);$$

that is to say (2. 823).

2. 9. *Lemma 10. We have*

(2. 91) $$h = \varphi(q) > Aq\,(\log q)^{-A}.$$

We have in fact[1]

$$\varphi(q) > (1 - \delta)\, e^{-C} \frac{q}{\log\log q} \qquad (q > q_0(\delta))$$

for every positive δ, C being Euler's constant.

3. Proof of the main theorems.

Approximation to $\nu_r(n)$ by the singular series.

3. 11. **Theorem A.** *If r is an integer, $r \geqq 3$, and*

(3. 111) $$(f(x))^r = \sum \nu_r(n)\, x^n,$$

so that

(3. 112) $$\nu_r(n) = \sum_{\varpi_1 + \varpi_2 + \cdots + \varpi_r = n} \log \varpi_1 \log \varpi_2 \cdots \log \varpi_r,$$

then

(3. 113) $$\nu_r(n) = \frac{n^{r-1}}{(r-1)!} \mathfrak{S}_r + O\left(n^{r-1+\left(\Theta-\frac{3}{4}\right)} (\log n)^B\right) \sim \frac{n^{r-1}}{(r-1)!} \mathfrak{S}_r,$$

[1] Landau, p. 217.

where

(3. 114) $$S_r = \sum_{q=1}^{\infty} \left(\frac{\mu(q)}{\varphi(q)}\right)^r c_q(-n).$$

It is to be understood, here and in all that follows, that O's refer to the limit-process $n \to \infty$, and that their constants are functions of r alone.

If $n \geqq 2$, we have

(3. 115) $$\nu_r(n) = \frac{1}{2\pi i}\int (f(x))^r \frac{dx}{x^{n+1}},$$

the path of integration being the circle $|x| = e^{-H}$, where $H = \frac{1}{n}$, so that

$$1 - |x| = \frac{1}{n} + O\left(\frac{1}{n^2}\right) \sim \frac{1}{n}.$$

Using the Farey dissection of order $N = [\sqrt{n}]$, we have

(3. 116) $$\nu_r(n) = \sum_{q=1}^{N} \sum_{p<q,(p,q)=1} \frac{1}{2\pi i}\int_{\xi_{p,q}} (f(x))^r \frac{dx}{x^{n+1}}$$

$$= \sum e_q(-np) \frac{1}{2\pi i}\int_{\zeta_{p,q}} (f(x))^r \frac{dX}{X^{n+1}}$$

$$= \sum e_q(-np)\, j_{p,q},$$

say. Now

$$|f^r - \varphi^r| \leqq |\Phi|(|f^{r-1}| + |f^{r-2}\varphi| + \cdots + |\varphi^{r-1}|)$$
$$< B(|\Phi f^{r-1}| + |\Phi \varphi^{r-1}|).$$

Also $|X^{-n}| = e^{nH} < A$. Hence

(3. 117) $$j_{p,q} = l_{p,q} + m_{p,q},$$

where

(3. 118) $$l_{p,q} = \frac{1}{2\pi i}\int_{\zeta_{p,q}} \varphi^r \frac{dX}{X^{n+1}},$$

(3. 119) $$|m_{p,q}| = O\left(\int_{-\theta'_{p,q}}^{\theta_{p,q}} (|\Phi f^{r-1}| + |\Phi \varphi^{r-1}|)\, d\theta\right).$$

3. 12. We have $\eta = H = \frac{1}{n}$ and $q \leqq \sqrt{n}$, and so, by (2. 823),

$$|\Phi| < A n^{\frac{3}{4}} (\log n)^A + A (\log n)^A \sqrt{q} |Y|^{-\Theta} \delta^{-\Theta-\frac{1}{2}} \log\left(\frac{1}{\delta}+2\right), \tag{3. 121}$$

where $\delta = \text{arc tan} \frac{\eta}{|\theta|}$. We must now distinguish two cases. If $|\theta| \leqq \eta$, we have

$$|Y| > A\eta, \ \delta > A,$$

and

$$\sqrt{q} |Y|^{-\Theta} \delta^{-\Theta-\frac{1}{2}} \log\left(\frac{1}{\delta}+2\right) < A n^{\frac{1}{4}} \eta^{-\Theta} = A n^{\Theta+\frac{1}{4}}. \tag{3. 122}$$

If on the other hand $\eta < |\theta| \leqq \bar{\theta}_{p,q}$, we have

$$\delta > A \frac{\eta}{|\theta|} > \frac{A}{n}, \ |Y| > A |\theta|,$$

$$\sqrt{q} |Y|^{-\Theta} \delta^{-\Theta-\frac{1}{2}} \log\left(\frac{1}{\delta}+2\right) < A \sqrt{q} \, . \, |\theta|^{-\Theta} \, . \, \eta^{-\Theta-\frac{1}{2}} |\theta|^{\Theta+\frac{1}{2}} . \log n \tag{3. 123}$$

$$= A n^{\Theta+\frac{1}{2}} \log n \, (q|\theta|)^{\frac{1}{2}} < A n^{\Theta+\frac{1}{2}} \log n \, . \, n^{-\frac{1}{4}} = A n^{\Theta+\frac{1}{4}} \log n,$$

since $q|\theta| \leqq q \bar{\theta}_{p,q} < A n^{-\frac{1}{2}}$. Thus (3. 123) holds in either case. Also $\Theta \geqq \frac{1}{2}$ and so, by (3. 121),

$$|\Phi| < A n^{\Theta+\frac{1}{4}} (\log n)^A \tag{3. 124}$$

3. 13. Now, remembering that $r \geqq 3$, we have

$$\int_{-\theta'_{p,q}}^{\theta_{p,q}} |\varphi|^{r-1} d\theta < B h^{-(r-1)} \int_{-\theta'_{p,q}}^{\theta_{p,q}} |Y|^{-(r-1)} d\theta$$

$$< B h^{-(r-1)} \int_0^\infty (\eta^2 + \theta^2)^{-\frac{1}{2}(r-1)} d\theta$$

$$< B h^{-(r-1)} n^{r-2};$$

and so

$$(3.131)\qquad \sum_{p,q}\int_{-\theta'_{p,q}}^{\theta_{p,q}} |\Phi\varphi^{r-1}|\,d\theta < Bn^{r-2}\,(\text{Max}\,|\Phi|)\sum_{q} h^{-(r-2)}$$

$$< Bn^{r-2+\theta+\frac{1}{4}}(\log n)^B = Bn^{r-1+\left(\theta-\frac{3}{4}\right)}(\log n)^B,$$

by (3. 124) and (2. 91).

3. 14. Again, if $\arg x = \psi$, we have

$$\sum\int_{-\theta'_{p,q}}^{\theta_{p,q}} |f|^2\,d\theta = \int_0^{2\pi} |f|^2\,d\psi$$

$$= 2\pi\sum_{\varpi}(\log\varpi)^2\,|x|^{2\varpi} < A\sum_{m=2}^{\infty}\log m\,\Lambda(m)\,|x|^{2m}$$

$$< A(1-|x|^2)\sum_{m=2}^{\infty}\left(\sum_{k=2}^{m}\log k\,\Lambda(k)\right)|x|^{2m}$$

$$< A(1-|x|)\sum_{m=2}^{\infty} m\log m\,|x|^{2m}$$

$$< \frac{A}{1-|x|}\log\left(\frac{1}{1-|x|}\right) < An\log n.$$

Similarly

$$|f| \leq \sum_{\varpi}\log\varpi\,|x|^{\varpi} < \sum_{m}\Lambda(m)\,|x|^m < \frac{A}{1-|x|} < An.$$

Hence

$$(3.141)\qquad \sum_{p,q}\int_{-\theta'_{p,q}}^{\theta_{p,q}} |f|^{r-1}\,|\Phi|\,d\theta \leq \text{Max}\,|\Phi f^{r-3}|\int_0^{2\pi}|f|^2\,d\psi$$

$$< Bn^{\theta+\frac{1}{4}}\log n\,.\,n^{r-3}\,.\,n\log n$$

$$< Bn^{r-1+\left(\theta-\frac{3}{4}\right)}(\log n)^B.$$

From (3. 116), (3. 117), (3. 119), (3. 131) and (3. 141) we deduce

(3. 142) $$\nu_r(n) = \sum e_q(-np)\, l_{p,q} + O\left(n^{r-1+(\theta-\frac{3}{4})}(\log n)^B\right),$$

where $l_{p,q}$ is defined by (3. 118).

3. 15. In $l_{p,q}$ we write $X = e^{-Y}$, $dX = -e^{-Y}dY$, so that Y varies on the straight line from $\eta + i\theta_{p,q}$ to $\eta - i\theta'_{p,q}$. Then, by (2. 822) and (3. 118),

(3. 151) $$l_{p,q} = -\frac{1}{2\pi i}\left(\frac{\mu(q)}{h}\right)^r \int_{\eta+i\theta_{p,q}}^{\eta-i\theta'_{p,q}} Y^{-r} e^{nY} dY.$$

Now

(3. 152) $$-\int_{\eta+i\theta_{p,q}}^{\eta-i\theta'_{p,q}} = \int_{\eta-i\infty}^{\eta+i\infty} Y^{-r} e^{nY} dY + O\left(\int_{\theta_q}^{\infty} |\eta+i\theta|^{-r} d\theta\right)$$

$$= 2\pi i \frac{n^{r-1}}{(r-1)!} + O\left(\int_{\theta_q}^{\infty} |\eta+i\theta|^{-r} d\theta\right),$$

where

$$\theta_q = \operatorname*{Min}_{p<q}(\theta_{p,q}, \theta'_{p,q}) \geqq \frac{1}{2qN}.$$

Also

(3. 153) $$\int_{\theta_q}^{\infty} (\eta+i\theta)^{-r} d\theta < \int_{\theta_q}^{\infty} \theta^{-r} d\theta < B\theta_q^{1-r} < B(q\sqrt{n})^{r-1}.$$

From (3. 151), (3. 152) and (3. 153), we deduce

(3. 154) $$\sum e_q(-np)\, l_{p,q} = \frac{n^{r-1}}{(r-1)!} \sum_{p,q} \left(\frac{\mu(q)}{\varphi(q)}\right)^r e_q(-np) + Q,$$

where

(3. 155) $$|Q| < B\sum_{p,q} h^{-r} q^{r-1} n^{\frac{1}{2}(r-1)} < Bn^{\frac{1}{2}(r-1)} \sum_q \left(\frac{q}{h}\right)^{r-1}$$

$$< Bn^{\frac{1}{2}(r-1)} \sum_{q=1}^{N} (\log q)^B < Bn^{\frac{1}{2}r} (\log n)^B.$$

Since $r \geqq 3$ and $\Theta \geqq \frac{1}{2}$, $\frac{1}{2}r < r - 1 - \frac{1}{4} \leqq r - 1 + \left(\Theta - \frac{3}{4}\right)$; and from (3. 142), (3. 154), and (3. 155) we obtain

$$(3.\ 156)\qquad \nu_r(n) = \frac{n^{r-1}}{(r-1)!} \sum_{p,q} \left(\frac{\mu(q)}{\varphi(q)}\right)^r e_q(-np) + O\left(n^{r-1+\left(\Theta-\frac{3}{4}\right)} (\log n)^B\right)$$

$$= \frac{n^{r-1}}{(r-1)!} \sum_{q \leqq N} \left(\frac{\mu(q)}{\varphi(q)}\right)^r c_q(-n) + O\left(n^{r-1+\left(\Theta-\frac{3}{4}\right)} (\log n)^B\right).$$

3. 16. In order to complete the proof of Theorem A, we have merely to show that the finite series in (3. 156) may be replaced by the infinite series S_r. Now

$$\left| n^{r-1} \sum_{q>N} \left(\frac{\mu(q)}{\varphi(q)}\right)^r c_q(-n) \right| < B n^{r-1} \sum_{q>N} q^{1-r} (\log q)^B < B n^{\frac{1}{2}r} (\log n)^B,$$

and $\frac{1}{2}r < r - 1 + \left(\Theta - \frac{3}{4}\right)$. Hence this error may be absorbed in the second term of (3. 156), and the proof of the theorem is completed.

Summation of the singular series.

3. 21. *Lemma 11. If*

$$(3.\ 211)\qquad c_q(n) = \sum e_q(np),$$

where n is a positive integer and the summation extends over all positive values of p less than and prime to q, $p = 0$ being included when $q = 1$, but not otherwise, then

$$(3.\ 212)\qquad c_q(-n) = c_q(n);$$

$$(3.\ 213)\qquad c_{qq'}(n) = c_q(n)\, c_{q'}(n)$$

if $(q, q') = 1$; and

$$(3.\ 214)\qquad c_q(n) = \sum \delta \mu\left(\frac{q}{\delta}\right),$$

where δ is a common divisor of q and n.

The terms in p and $q - p$ are conjugate. Hence $c_q(n)$ is real. As $c_q(n)$ and $c_q(-n)$ are conjugate we obtain (3. 212).[1]

[1] The argument fails if $q = 1$ or $q = 2$; but $c_1(n) = c_1(-n) = 1$, $c_2(n) = c_2(-n) = -1$.

Again

$$c_q(n)c_{q'}(n) = \sum_{p,p'} \exp\left(2n\pi i\left(\frac{p}{q}+\frac{p'}{q'}\right)\right) = \sum_{p,p'} \exp\left(\frac{2nP\pi i}{qq'}\right),$$

where

$$P = pq' + p'q.$$

When p assumes a set of $\varphi(q)$ values, positive, prime to q, and incongruent to modulus q, and p' a similar set of values for modulus q', then P assumes a set of $\varphi(q)\varphi(q') = \varphi(qq')$ values, plainly all positive, prime to qq' and incongruent to modulus qq'. Hence we obtain (3. 213).

Finally, it is plain that

$$\sum_{d\mid q} c_d(n) = \sum_{h=0}^{q-1} e_q(nh),$$

which is zero unless $q\mid n$ and then equal to q. Hence, if we write

$$\eta(q) = q \quad (q\mid n), \qquad \eta(q) = 0 \quad (q \nmid n),$$

we have

$$\sum_{d\mid q} c_d(n) = \eta(q),$$

and therefore

$$c_q(n) = \sum_{d\mid q} \eta(d)\,\mu\left(\frac{q}{d}\right)$$

by the well-known inversion formula of Möbius.[1] This is (3. 214).[2]

3. 22. *Lemma 12. Suppose that $r \geqq 2$ and*

(3. 221) $$S_r = \sum_{q=1}^{\infty} \left(\frac{\mu(q)}{\varphi(q)}\right)^r c_q(-n).$$

Then

(3. 222) $$S_r = 0$$

[1] Landau, p. 577.

[2] The formula (3. 214) is proved by Ramanujan ('On certain trigonometrical sums and their applications in the theory of numbers', *Trans. Camb. Phil. Soc.*, vol. 22 (1918), pp. 259—276 (p. 260)). It had already been given for $n = 1$ by Landau (*Handbuch* (1909), p. 572: Landau refers to it as a known result), and in the general case by Jensen ('Et nyt Udtryk for den talteoretiske Funktion $\sum \mu(n) = M(n)$', *Den 3. Skandinaviske Matematiker-Kongres, Kristiania 1913*, Kristiania (1915), p. 145). Ramanujan makes a large number of very beautiful applications of the sums in question, and they may well be associated with his name.

if n and r are of opposite parity. But if n and r are of like parity then

(3. 223)
$$S_r = 2C_r \prod_{\mathfrak{p}} \left(\frac{(\mathfrak{p}-1)^r + (-1)^r(\mathfrak{p}-1)}{(\mathfrak{p}-1)^r - (-1)^r} \right),$$

where $\mathfrak{p}$ *is an odd prime divisor of n and*

(3. 224)
$$C_r = \prod_{\varpi=3}^{\infty} \left(1 - \frac{(-1)^r}{(\varpi-1)^r} \right).$$

Let

(3. 225)
$$\left(\frac{\mu(q)}{\varphi(q)} \right)^r c_q(-n) = A_q.$$

Then

$$\mu(qq') = \mu(q)\mu(q'),\ \varphi(qq') = \varphi(q)\varphi(q'),\ c_{qq'}(-n) = c_q(-n)\,c_{q'}(-n)$$

if $(q, q') = 1$; and therefore (on the same hypothesis)

(3. 226)
$$A_{qq'} = A_q A_{q'}.$$

Hence[1]

$$S_r = A_1 + A_2 + A_3 + \cdots = 1 + A_2 + \cdots = \prod_{\varpi} \chi_{\varpi}$$

where

(3. 227)
$$\chi_{\varpi} = 1 + A_{\varpi} + A_{\varpi^2} + A_{\varpi^3} + \cdots = 1 + A_{\varpi},$$

since $A_{\varpi^2}, A_{\varpi^3}, \cdots$ vanish in virtue of the factor $\mu(q)$.

3. 23. If $\varpi \nmid n$, we have

$$\mu(\varpi) = -1,\ \varphi(\varpi) = \varpi - 1,\ c_{\varpi}(n) = \mu(\varpi) = -1,$$

(3. 231)
$$A_{\varpi} = -\frac{(-1)^r}{(\varpi-1)^r}.$$

If on the other hand $\varpi \mid n$, we have

$$c_{\varpi}(n) = \mu(\varpi) + \varpi\mu(1) = \varpi - 1,$$

(3. 232)
$$A_{\varpi} = \frac{(-1)^r}{(\varpi-1)^{r-1}}.$$

---

[1] Since $|c_q(n)| \leq \sum \delta$, where $\delta \mid n$, we have $c_q(n) = O(1)$ when n is fixed and $q \to \infty$. Also by Lemma 10, $\varphi(q) > Aq(\log q)^{-A}$. Hence the series and products concerned are absolutely convergent.

Hence

(3. 233)
$$S_r = \prod_{\varpi \mid n} \left(1 + \frac{(-1)^r}{(\varpi - 1)^{r-1}}\right) \prod_{\varpi \nmid n} \left(1 - \frac{(-1)^r}{(\varpi - 1)^r}\right).$$

If n is even and r is odd, the first factor vanishes in virtue of the factor for which $\varpi = 2$; if n is odd and r even, the second factor vanishes similarly. Thus $S_r = 0$ whenever n and r are of opposite parity.

If n and r are of like parity, the factor corresponding to $\varpi = 2$ is in any case 2; and

$$S_r = 2 \prod_{\varpi=3}^{\infty} \left(1 - \frac{(-1)^r}{(\varpi - 1)^r}\right) \prod_{\mathfrak{p}} \left(\frac{(\mathfrak{p} - 1)^r + (-1)^r (\mathfrak{p} - 1)}{(\mathfrak{p} - 1)^r - (-1)^r}\right),$$

as stated in the lemma.

Proof of the final formulae.

3. 3. **Theorem B.** *Suppose that $r \geqq 3$. Then, if n and r are of unlike parity,*

(3. 31)
$$\nu_r(n) = o(n^{r-1}).$$

But if n and r are of like parity then

(3. 32)
$$\nu_r(n) \sim \frac{2C_r}{(r-1)!} n^{r-1} \prod_{\mathfrak{p}} \left(\frac{(\mathfrak{p} - 1)^r + (-1)^r (\mathfrak{p} - 1)}{(\mathfrak{p} - 1)^r - (-1)^r}\right),$$

where $\mathfrak{p}$ is an odd prime divisor of n and

(3. 33)
$$C_r = \prod_{\varpi=3}^{\infty} \left(1 - \frac{(-1)^r}{(\varpi - 1)^r}\right).$$

This follows immediately from Theorem A and Lemma 12.[1]

3. 4. *Lemma 13. If $r \geqq 3$ and n and r are of like parity, then*

$$\nu_r(n) > B n^{r-1},$$

for $n \geqq n_0(r)$.

[1] Results equivalent to these are stated in equations (5. 11)–(5. 22) of our note 2, but incorrectly, a factor

$$(\log n)^{-r}$$

being omitted in each, owing to a momentary confusion between $\nu_r(n)$ and $N_r(n)$. The $\nu_r(n)$ of 2 is the $N_r(n)$ of this memoir.

This lemma is required for the proof of Theorem C. If r is *even*

$$\prod\left(\frac{(p-1)^r+p-1}{(p-1)^r-1}\right)>1.$$

If r is *odd*

$$\prod\left(\frac{(p-1)^r-p+1}{(p-1)^r+1}\right)>\prod\left(\frac{(p-1)^r-p}{(p-1)^r}\right)>\prod_{\varpi=3}^{\infty}\left(1-\frac{\varpi}{(\varpi-1)^3}\right)=A.$$

In either case the conclusion follows from (3. 32).

3. 5. **Theorem C.** *If $r\geq 3$ and n and r are of like parity, then*

$$N_r(n)\sim\frac{\nu_r(n)}{(\log n)^r}. \tag{3. 51}$$

We observe first that

$$N_r(n)=\sum_{\varpi_1+\varpi_2+\cdots+\varpi_r=n} 1\leq\sum_{m_1+m_2+\cdots+m_r=n} 1<Bn^{r-1}$$

and

$$\nu_r(n)=\sum_{\varpi_1+\varpi_2+\cdots+\varpi_r=n}\log\varpi_1\cdots\log\varpi_r\leq(\log n)^r N_r(n)<Bn^{r-1}(\log n)^r. \tag{3. 511}$$

Write now

$$\nu_r=\nu'_r+\nu''_r,\quad N_r=N'_r+N''_r, \tag{3. 512}$$

where ν'_r and N'_r include all terms of the summations for which

$$\varpi_s\geq n^{1-\delta}\quad(0<\delta<1,\ s=1,2,\ldots,r).$$

Then plainly

$$\nu'_r(n)\geq(1-\delta)^r(\log n)^r N'_r(n). \tag{3. 513}$$

Again

$$N''_r(n)\leq r\sum_{\varpi_r<n^{1-\delta}}\left(\sum_{\varpi_1+\varpi_2+\cdots+\varpi_{r-1}=n-\varpi_r} 1\right)$$

$$<B\sum_{\varpi_r<n^{1-\delta}}N_{r-1}(n-\varpi_r)<Bn^{1-\delta}.n^{r-2}<Bn^{r-1-\delta},$$

$$\nu''_r(n)\leq(\log n)^r N''_r(n)<Bn^{r-1-\delta}(\log n)^r.$$

But $\nu_r(n)>Bn^{r-1}$ for $n\geq n_0(r)$, by Lemma 13; and so

$$(\log n)^r N''_r(n)=o(\nu_r(n)),\quad \nu''_r(n)=o(\nu_r(n)), \tag{3. 514}$$

for every positive δ.

From (3. 511), (3. 512), (3. 513), and (3. 514) we deduce

$$(1-\delta)^r (\log n)^r (N_r - N''_r) \leqq \nu_r - \nu''_r \leqq (\log n)^r N_r,$$

$$(1-\delta)^r (\log n)^r N_r \leqq \nu_r + o(\nu_r) \leqq (\log n)^r N_r,$$

$$(1-\delta)^r \leqq \underline{\lim} \frac{\nu_r}{(\log n)^r N_r}, \quad \overline{\lim} \frac{\nu_r}{(\log n)^r N_r} \leqq 1.$$

As δ is arbitrary, this proves (3. 51).

3. 6. **Theorem D.** *Every large odd number n is the sum of three odd primes. The asymptotic formula for the number of representations $\overline{N}_3(n)$ is*

$$\overline{N}_3(n) \sim C_3 \frac{n^2}{(\log n)^3} \prod \left(\frac{(\mathfrak{p}-1)(\mathfrak{p}-2)}{\mathfrak{p}^2 - 3\mathfrak{p} + 3}\right), \tag{3. 61}$$

where $\mathfrak{p}$ is a prime divisor of n and

$$C_3 = \prod_{\varpi=3}^{\infty} \left(1 + \frac{1}{(\varpi-1)^3}\right). \tag{3. 62}$$

This is an almost immediate corollary of Theorems B and C. These theorems give the corresponding formula for $N_3(n)$. If not all the primes are odd, two must be 2 and $n-4$ a prime. The number of such representations is one at most.

Theorem E. *Every large even number n is the sum of four odd primes (of which one may be assigned.) The asymptotic formula for the total number of representations is*

$$\overline{N}_4(n) \sim \frac{1}{3} C_4 \frac{n^3}{(\log n)^4} \prod \left(\frac{(\mathfrak{p}-1)(\mathfrak{p}^2 - 3\mathfrak{p} + 3)}{(\mathfrak{p}-2)(\mathfrak{p}^2 - 2\mathfrak{p} + 2)}\right), \tag{3. 63}$$

where $\mathfrak{p}$ is an odd prime divisor of n and

$$C_4 = \prod_{\varpi=3}^{\infty} \left(1 - \frac{1}{(\varpi-1)^4}\right). \tag{3. 64}$$

This is a corollary of the same two theorems. We have only to observe that the number of representations by four primes which are not all odd is plainly $O(n)$. There are evidently similar theorems for any greater value of r.

4. Remarks on 'Goldbach's Theorem'.

4. 1. Our method fails when $r = 2$. It does not fail *in principle*, for it leads to a definite result which appears to be correct; but we cannot overcome the difficulties of the proof, even if we assume that $\Theta = \frac{1}{2}$. The best upper bound that we can determine for the error is too large by (roughly) a power $n^{\frac{1}{4}}$.

The formula to which our method leads is contained in the following

Conjecture A. *Every large even number is the sum of two odd primes. The asymptotic formula for the number of representatives is*

$$N_2(n) \sim 2C_2 \frac{n}{(\log n)^2} \prod_{\mathfrak{p}} \left(\frac{\mathfrak{p}-1}{\mathfrak{p}-2}\right) \tag{4. 11}$$

where $\mathfrak{p}$ *is an odd prime divisor of* n, *and*

$$C_2 = \prod_{\varpi=3}^{\infty} \left(1 - \frac{1}{(\varpi-1)^2}\right). \tag{4. 12}$$

We add a few words as to the history of this formula, and the empirical evidence for its truth.[1]

The first definite formulation of a result of this character appears to be due to SYLVESTER[2], who, in a short abstract published in the *Proceedings of London Mathematical Society* in 1871, suggested that

$$N_2(n) \sim \frac{2n}{\log n} \prod \left(\frac{\varpi-2}{\varpi-1}\right), \tag{4. 13}$$

where

$$3 \leqq \varpi < \sqrt{n}, \quad \varpi \nmid n.$$

Since

$$\prod_{\varpi<\sqrt{n}} \left(\frac{\varpi-2}{\varpi-1}\right) = \prod_{\varpi<\sqrt{n}} \left(1 - \frac{1}{(\varpi-1)^2}\right) \prod_{\varpi<\sqrt{n}} \left(1 - \frac{1}{\varpi}\right) \sim C_2 \prod_{\varpi<\sqrt{n}} \left(1 - \frac{1}{\varpi}\right),$$

[1] As regards the earlier history of 'Goldbach's Theorem', see L. E. DICKSON, *History of the Theory of Numbers*, vol. 1 (Washington 1919), pp. 421—425.

[2] J. J. SYLVESTER, 'On the partition of an even number into two primes', *Proc. London Math. Soc.*, ser. 1, vol. 4 (1871), pp. 4—6 (*Math. Papers*, vol. 2, pp. 709—711). See also 'On the Goldbach-Euler Theorem regarding prime numbers', *Nature*, vol. 55 (1896—7), pp. 196—197, 269 (*Math. Papers*, vol. 4, pp. 734—737).

We owe our knowledge of Sylvester's notes on the subject to Mr. B. M. WILSON of Trinity College, Cambridge. See, in connection with all that follows, Shah and Wilson, 1, and Hardy and Littlewood, 2.

and [1]

$$\prod_{\varpi < \sqrt{n}} \left(1 - \frac{1}{\varpi}\right) \sim \frac{2e^{-C}}{\log n}, \tag{4. 14}$$

where C is Euler's constant, (4. 13) is equivalent to

$$N_2(n) \sim 4e^{-C} C_2 \frac{n}{(\log n)^2} \prod_{\mathfrak{p}} \left(\frac{\mathfrak{p}-1}{\mathfrak{p}-2}\right), \tag{4. 15}$$

and contradicts (4. 11), the two formulae differing by a factor $2e^{-C} = 1.123\ldots$ We prove in 4. 2 that (4. 11) is the only formula of the kind that can possibly be correct, so that Sylvester's formula is erroneous. But Sylvester was the first to identify the factor

$$\prod \left(\frac{\mathfrak{p}-1}{\mathfrak{p}-2}\right), \tag{4. 16}$$

to which the *irregularities* of $N_2(n)$ are due. There is no sufficient evidence to show how he was led to his result.

A quite different formula was suggested by STÄCKEL[2] in 1896, viz.,

$$N_2(n) \sim \frac{n}{(\log n)^2} \prod \left(\frac{\mathfrak{p}}{\mathfrak{p}-1}\right).$$

This formula does not introduce the factor (4. 16), and does not give anything like so good an approximation to the facts; it was in any case shown to be incorrect by LANDAU[3] in 1900.

In 1915 there appeared an uncompleted essay on Goldbach's Theorem by MERLIN.[4] MERLIN does not give a complete asymptotic formula, but recognises (like Sylvester before him) the importance of the factor (4. 16).

About the same time the problem was attacked by BRUN[5]. The formula to which Brun's argument naturally leads is

---

[1] Landau, p. 218.

[2] P. STÄCKEL, 'Über Goldbach's empirisches Theorem: Jede grade Zahl kann als Summe von zwei Primzahlen dargestellt werden', *Göttinger Nachrichten*, 1896, pp. 292—299.

[3] E. LANDAU, 'Über die zahlentheoretische Funktion $\varphi(n)$ und ihre Beziehung zum Goldbachschen Satz', *Göttinger Nachrichten*, 1900, pp. 177—186.

[4] J. MERLIN, 'Un travail sur les nombres premiers', *Bulletin des sciences mathématiques*, vol. 39 (1915), pp. 121—136.

[5] V. BRUN, 'Über das Goldbachsche Gesetz und die Anzahl der Primzahlpaare', *Archiv for Mathematik* (Christiania), vol. 34, part 2 (1915), no. 8, pp. 1—15. The formula (4. 18) is not actually formulated by Brun: see the discussion by Shah and Wilson, 1, and Hardy and Littlewood, 2. See also a second paper by the same author, 'Sur les nombres premiers de la forme $ap + b$', *ibid.*, part. 4 (1917), no. 14, pp. 1—9; and the postscript to this memoir.

(4. 17)
$$N_2(n) \backsim 2Hn \prod_{\mathfrak{p}} \left(\frac{\mathfrak{p}-1}{\mathfrak{p}-2}\right),$$

where

(4. 171)
$$H = \prod_{3 \leq \varpi < \sqrt{n}} \left(1 - \frac{2}{\varpi}\right).$$

This is easily shown to be equivalent to

(4. 18)
$$N_2(n) \backsim 8\, e^{-2\gamma} C_2 \frac{n}{(\log n)^2} \prod_{\mathfrak{p}} \left(\frac{\mathfrak{p}-1}{\mathfrak{p}-2}\right),$$

and differs from (4. 11) by a factor $4e^{-2C} = 1.263\ldots$ The argument of 4. 2 will show that this formula, like Sylvester's, is incorrect.

Finally, in 1916 STÄCKEL[1] returned to the subject in a series of memoirs published in the *Sitzungsberichte der Heidelberger Akademie der Wissenschaften*, which we have until very recently been unable to consult. Some further remarks concerning these memoirs will be found in our final postscript.

4. 2. We proceed to justify our assertion that the formulae (4. 15) and (4. 18) cannot be correct.

Theorem F. *Suppose it to be true that*[2]

(4. 21)
$$N_2(n) \backsim A \frac{n}{(\log n)^2} \prod_{\mathfrak{p}} \left(\frac{\mathfrak{p}-1}{\mathfrak{p}-2}\right)$$

if

$$n = 2^a \mathfrak{p}^a \mathfrak{p}'^{a'} \ldots \qquad (\alpha > 0,\ a,\ a', \ldots > 0),$$

and

(4. 22)
$$N_2(n) = o\left(\frac{n}{(\log n)^2}\right)$$

if n is odd. Then

(4. 23)
$$A = 2C_2 = \prod_{\varpi=3}^{\infty} \left(1 - \frac{1}{(\varpi-1)^2}\right).$$

[1] P. STÄCKEL, 'Die Darstellung der geraden Zahlen als Summen von zwei Primzahlen', 8 August 1916; 'Die Lückenzahlen r-ter Stufe und die Darstellung der geraden Zahlen als Summen und Differenzen ungerader Primzahlen', I. Teil 27 Dezember 1917, II. Teil 19 Januar 1918, III. Teil 19 Juli 1918.

[2] Throughout 4. 2 A is *the same* constant.

Write

(4. 24) $$\Omega(n) = An\prod_{\mathfrak{p}}\left(\frac{\mathfrak{p}-1}{\mathfrak{p}-2}\right)\ (n\ \textit{even}),\quad \Omega(n) = 0\ (n\ \textit{odd}).$$

Then, by (4. 21) and Theorem C, now valid in virtue of (4. 21),

(4. 25) $$\nu_2(n) = \sum_{\varpi+\varpi'=n}\log\varpi\log\varpi' \sim \Omega(n),$$

it being understood that, when n is odd, this formula means

$$\nu_2(n) = o(n).$$

Further let

$$f(s) = \sum\frac{\Omega(n)}{n^s} = \sum\frac{\Omega(n)}{n^{1+u}},$$

these series being absolutely convergent if $\Re(s) > 2$, $\Re(u) > 1$. Then

(4. 26) $$f(s) = A\sum_{n\equiv 0\ (\mathrm{mod.}\ 2)} n^{-u}\prod_{\mathfrak{p}}\left(\frac{\mathfrak{p}-1}{\mathfrak{p}-2}\right)$$

$$= A\sum_{a>0} 2^{-au}\,\mathfrak{p}^{-au}\,\mathfrak{p}'^{-a'u}\ldots\frac{(\mathfrak{p}-1)(\mathfrak{p}'-1)\ldots}{(\mathfrak{p}-2)(\mathfrak{p}'-2)\ldots}$$

$$= \frac{2^{-u}A}{1-2^{-u}}\prod_{\varpi=3}^{\infty}\left(1+\frac{\varpi-1}{\varpi-2}\,\frac{\varpi^{-u}}{1-\varpi^{-u}}\right) = \frac{2^{-u}A}{1-2^{-u}}\xi(u),$$

say. Suppose now that $u \to 1$, and let

$$\eta(u) = \prod_{\varpi=3}^{\infty}\left(1+\frac{\varpi^{-u}}{1-\varpi^{-u}}\right) = \prod_{\varpi=3}^{\infty}\left(\frac{1}{1-\varpi^{-u}}\right) = (1-2^{-u})\zeta(u).$$

Then

$$\frac{\xi(u)}{\eta(u)} = \prod\left(\left(1+\frac{\varpi-1}{\varpi-2}\,\frac{\varpi^{-u}}{1-\varpi^{-u}}\right)\Big/\left(1+\frac{\varpi^{-u}}{1-\varpi^{-u}}\right)\right)$$

$$\to \prod\left(\left(1+\frac{1}{\varpi-2}\right)\Big/\left(1+\frac{1}{\varpi-1}\right)\right) = \prod\left(\frac{(\varpi-1)^2}{\varpi(\varpi-2)}\right)$$

$$= \prod\left(\frac{(\varpi-1)^2}{(\varpi-1)^2-1}\right) = \frac{1}{C_2}.$$

Hence

(4. 27) $$f(s) \sim A\xi(u) \sim \frac{A}{C_2}\eta(u) \sim \frac{A}{2C_2}\zeta(u) \sim \frac{A}{2C_2(u-1)} = \frac{A}{2C_2(s-2)}.$$

On the other hand, when $x \to 1$,

$$\sum \nu_2(n) x^n \sim \left(\sum \log \varpi\, x^{\varpi}\right)^2 \sim \frac{1}{(1-x)^2},$$

and so[1]

(4. 28) $$\nu_2(1) + \nu_2(2) + \cdots + \nu_2(n) \sim \frac{1}{2} n^2.$$

It is an elementary deduction[2] that

$$g(s) = \sum \frac{\nu_2(n)}{n^s} \sim \sum \frac{1}{n^{s-1}} \sim \frac{1}{s-2}$$

when $s \to 2$; and hence[2] that (under the hypotheses (4. 21) and (4. 22))

(4. 29) $$f(s) \sim \frac{1}{s-2}.$$

Comparing (4. 27) and (4. 29), we obtain the result of the theorem.

4. 3. The fact that both Sylvester's and Brun's formulae contain an erroneous constant factor, and that this factor is in each case a simple function of the number e^{-C}, is not so remarkable as it may seem.

In the first place we observe that any formula in the theory of primes, *deduced from considerations of probability*, is likely to be erroneous in just this way. Consider, for example, the problem '*what is the chance that a large number n should be prime?*' We know that the answer is that the chance is approximately $\dfrac{1}{\log n}$.

Now the chance that n should not be divisible by any prime less than a *fixed* number x is asymptotically equivalent to

$$\prod_{\varpi < x}\left(1 - \frac{1}{\varpi}\right);$$

[1] We here use Theorem 8 of our paper 'Tauberian theorems concerning power series and Dirichlet's series whose coefficients are positive', *Proc. London Math. Soc.*, ser. 2, vol. 13, pp. 174—192. This is the quickest proof, but by no means the most elementary. The formula (4. 28) is equivalent to the formula

$$\sum_{1}^{n} N_2(m) \sim \frac{n^2}{2(\log n)^2}$$

used by Landau in his note quoted on p. 33.

[2] For general theorems including those used here as very special cases, see K. Knopp, 'Divergenzcharactere gewisser Dirichlet'scher Reihen', *Acta Mathematica*, vol. 34, 1909, pp. 165—204 (*e. g.* Satz III, p. 176).

and it would be natural to infer[1] that the chance required is asymptotically equivalent to

$$\prod_{\varpi < \sqrt{n}} \left(1 - \frac{1}{\varpi}\right).$$

But[2]

$$\prod_{\varpi > \sqrt{n}} \left(1 - \frac{1}{\varpi}\right) \sim \frac{2e^{-C}}{\log n};$$

and our inference is incorrect, to the extent of a factor $2e^{-C}$.

It is true that Brun's argument is not stated in terms of probabilities[3], but it involves a heuristic passage to the limit of exactly the same character as that in the argument we have just quoted. Brun finds first (by an ingenious use of the 'sieve of Eratosthenes') an asymptotic formula for the number of representations of n as the sum of two numbers, *neither divisible by any fixed number of primes*. This formula is correct and the proof valid. So is the first stage in the argument above; it rests on an enumeration of cases, and all reference to 'probability'[4] is easily eliminated. It is in the passage to the limit that error is introduced, and the nature of the error is the same in one case as in the other.

4. 4. Shah and Wilson have tested Conjecture A extensively by comparison with the empirical data collected by Cantor, Aubry, Haussner, and Ripert. We reprint their table of results; but some preliminary remarks are required. In the first place it is essential, in a numerical test, to work with a formula $N_2(n)$, such as (4. 11), and not with one for $\nu_2(n)$, such as (4. 25). In our analysis, on the other hand, it is $\nu_2(n)$ which presents itself first, and the formula for $N_2(n)$ is secondary. In order to derive the asymptotic formula for $N_2(n)$, we write

$$\nu_2(n) = \sum_{\varpi + \varpi' = n} \log \varpi \log \varpi' \sim (\log n)^2 N_2(n).$$

The factor $(\log n)^2$ is certainly in error to an order $\log n$, and it is more natural[5] to replace $\nu_2(n)$ by

$$((\log n)^2 - 2 \log n + \cdots) N_2(n).$$

[1] One might well replace $\varpi < \sqrt{n}$ by $\varpi < n$, in which case we should obtain a probability half as large. This remark is in itself enough to show the unsatisfactory character of the argument.

[2] Landau, p. 218.

[3] Whether Sylvester's argument was or was not we have no direct means of judging.

[4] *Probability* is not a notion of pure mathematics, but of philosophy or physics.

[5] Compare Shah and Wilson, *l. c.*, p. 238. The same conclusion may be arrived at in other ways.

For the *asymptotic* formula, naturally, it is indifferent which substitution we adopt. But, for purposes of *verification within the limits of calculation*, it is by no means indifferent, for the term in $\log n$ is by no means of negligible importance; and it will be found that is makes a vital difference in the plausibility of the results. Bearing these considerations in mind, Shah and Wilson worked, not with the formula (4. 11), but with the modified formula

$$N_2(n) \backsim \varrho(n) = 2\,C_2 \frac{n}{(\log n)^2 - 2\log n} \prod_{p} \left(\frac{p-1}{p-2}\right).$$

Failure to make allowances of this kind has been responsible for a good deal of misapprehension in the past. Thus (as is pointed out by Shah and Wilson [1]) Sylvester's erroneous formula gives, for values of n within the limits of Table I, decidedly *better* results than those obtained from the *unmodified* formula (4. 11).

There is another point of less importance. The function which presents itself most naturally in our analysis is not

$$f(x) = \sum \log \varpi\, x^{\varpi}$$

but

$$g(x) = \sum \varLambda(n)\, x^n = \sum_{\varpi, l} \log \varpi\, x^{\varpi^l}.$$

The corresponding numerical functions are not $\nu_2(n)$ and $N_2(n)$, but

$$g_2(n) = \sum_{m+m'=n} \varLambda(m)\, \varLambda(m'),\ Q_2(n) = \sum_{\varpi^l + \varpi'^{l'} = n} 1$$

(so that $Q_2(n)$ is the number of decompositions of n *into two primes or two powers of primes*). Here again, $N_2(n)$ and $Q_2(n)$ are asymptotically equivalent; the difference between them is indeed of lower order than errors which we are neglecting in any case; but there is something to be said for taking the latter as the basis for comparison, when (as is inevitable) the values of n are not very large.

In the table the decompositions into primes, and powers of primes, are reckoned separately; but it is the total which is compared with $\varrho(n)$. The value of the constant $2\,C_2$ is 1 . 3203. It will be seen that the correspondence between the calculated and actual values is excellent.

[1] *l. c.*, p. 242.

Table I.

n	$Q_2(n)$	$\rho(n)$	$Q_2(n):\rho(n)$
$30 = 2.3.5$	$6 + 4 = 10$	22	0.45
$32 = 2^5$	$4 + 7 = 11$	8	1.38
$34 = 2.17$	$7 + 6 = 13$	9	1.44
$36 = 2^2.3^2$	$8 + 8 = 16$	17	0.94
$210 = 2.3.5.7$	$42 + 0 = 42$	49	0.85
$214 = 2.107$	$17 + 0 = 17$	16	1.07
$216 = 2^3.3^3$	$28 + 0 = 28$	32	0.88
$256 = 2^8$	$16 + 3 = 19$	17	1.10
$2{,}048 = 2^{11}$	$50 + 17 = 67$	63	1.06
$2{,}250 = 2.3^2.5^3$	$174 + 26 = 200$	179	1.11
$2{,}304 = 2^8.3^2$	$134 + 8 = 142$	136	1.04
$2{,}306 = 2.1153$	$67 + 20 = 87$	69	1.26
$2{,}310 = 2.3.5.7.11$	$228 + 16 = 244$	244	1.00
$3{,}888 = 2^4.3^5$	$186 + 24 = 210$	197	1.06
$3{,}898 = 2.1949$	$99 + 6 = 105$	99	1.06
$3{,}990 = 2.3.5.7.19$	$328 + 20 = 348$	342	1.02
$4{,}096 = 2^{12}$	$104 + 5 = 109$	102	1.06
$4{,}996 = 2^2.1249$	$124 + 16 = 140$	119	1.18
$4{,}998 = 2.3.7^2.17$	$228 + 20 = 308$	305	1.01
$5{,}000 = 2^3.5^4$	$150 + 26 = 176$	157	1.12
$8{,}190 = 2.3^2.5.7.13$	$578 + 26 = 604$	597	1.01
$8{,}192 = 2^{13}$	$150 + 32 = 182$	171	1.06
$8{,}194 = 2.17.241$	$192 + 10 = 202$	219	0.92
$10{,}008 = 2^3.3^2.139$	$388 + 30 = 418$	396	1.06
$10{,}010 = 2.5.7.11.13$	$384 + 36 = 420$	384	1.09
$10{,}014 = 2.3.1669$	$408 + 8 = 416$	396	1.05
$30{,}030 = 2.3.5.7.11.13$	$1{,}800 + 54 = 1854$	1795	1.03
$36{,}960 = 2^5.3.5.7.11$	$1{,}956 + 38 = 1994$	1937	1.03
$39{,}270 = 2.3.5.7.11.17$	$2{,}152 + 36 = 2188$	2213	0.99
$41{,}580 = 2^2.3^3.5.7.11$	$2{,}140 + 44 = 2184$	2125	1.03
$50{,}026 = 2.25013$	$702 + 8 = 710$	692	1.03
$50{,}144 = 2^5.1567$	$607 + 32 = 706$	694	1.02
$170{,}166 = 2.3.79.359$	$3{,}734 + 46 = 3780$	3762	1.00
$170{,}170 = 2.5.7.11.13.17$	$3{,}784 + 8 = 3792$	3841	0.99
$170{,}172 = 2^2.3^2.29.163$	$3{,}732 + 48 = 3780$	3866	0.98

Noted by the editor: We omit the remaining part of the paper, where a lot of conjectures on the other additive problems are given by the circle method on considering only the major arcs.

Comptes Rendus (Doklady) de l'Académie des Sciences de l'URSS
1937. Volume XV, № 6—7

MATHEMATICS

REPRESENTATION OF AN ODD NUMBER AS A SUM OF THREE PRIMES

By I. M. VINOGRADOW, Member of the Academy

Some simple examples of application of my method to the theory of primes were given in 1934 (1).

In the present paper I give the application of the same method to the estimation of the sum

$$\sum_{p<N} e^{2\pi i \alpha p}$$

and with help of this estimation and using a new theorem concerning the distribution of primes in an arithmetical progression (2) (the difference of the progression grows slowly simultaneously with the increasing of the number of terms), I deduce an asymptotical formula for the number of representations of an odd number $N>0$ in the form

$$N = p_1 + p_2 + p_3.$$

It follows directly that every odd number from a certain point onwards can be represented as a sum of three primes. This is the complete resolution of Goldbach's problem for odd numbers.

The estimations of the present note can be replaced by much more exact estimations.

Notations. $N>0$ is an odd and sufficiently great number; $n = \log N$.

$h, h_1, h_2, \ldots$ are arbitrary large constants >3;

$$\tau = Nn^{-3h}; \quad \tau_1 = Nn^{-h};$$

θ is a real number and $|\theta| \leqslant 1$;

$$A \ll B; \quad A = O(B)$$

denotes that the ratio $\frac{|A|}{B}$ does not exceed a certain constant;

(d) denotes a set of divisors $d \leqslant N$ of the product H of all primes $\leqslant \sqrt{N}$; (d_0) denotes the part of this set consisting of all d with an even number of prime divisors; (d_1) is the part of the same set consisting of all d with an odd number of prime divisors. The set (d) is divided also into two sets (d') and (d''). The first consists of the numbers d satisfying the condition that all prime divisors are

$$\leqslant n^{3h},$$

the second consists of all the remaining numbers d.

The sets (d_0) and (d_1) are correspondingly divided into sets (d_0'), (d_0'') and (d_1'), (d_1'').

Lemma 1. Let (x) and (y) denote two sets of increasing positive integral numbers;

$$1 < U_0 < U_1 \leqslant N_1 \leqslant N;$$

m is integral and > 0.

$$\alpha = \frac{a}{q} + \frac{\theta}{q\tau}; (a, q) = 1;\ 0 < q \leqslant \tau;\ m = m_1\delta;\ q = q_1\delta;\ \delta = (m, q);$$

$$T = \sum_x \sum_y e^{2\pi i\alpha mxy}$$

where x runs over the numbers (x) satisfying the condition

$$U_0 < x \leqslant U_1$$

and y for a given x runs over the numbers (y) satisfying the condition

$$0 < y \leqslant \frac{N_1}{x}.$$

Then we have

$$T \ll N_1 n \sqrt{\frac{n}{U_0} + \frac{U_1}{N_1} + \frac{q_1 n}{N_1} + \frac{1}{q_1} + \frac{m_1}{\tau}}.$$

Theorem 1. Let

$$\alpha = \frac{a}{q} + \frac{\theta}{q\tau}; (a, q) = 1;\ n^{3h} \leqslant q \leqslant \tau.$$

Then we have

$$S = \sum_{p \leqslant N} e^{2\pi i\alpha p} \ll N n^{2-h}.$$

Proof. We have

$$S = \sum_{(d)} \mu(d) S_d + O(\sqrt{N});\quad S_d = \sum_{m=1}^{\frac{N}{d}} e^{2\pi i\alpha md}. \tag{1}$$

Hence we find

$$S = \sum_{d > \tau_1} \mu(d) S_d + O(Nn^{-h+1}) =$$

$$= T_0 - T_1 + O(Nn^{-h+1});\quad T_0 = \sum_{(d_0)} S_d;\quad T_1 = \sum_{(d_1)} S_d, \tag{2}$$

where d runs over the values $> \tau_1$. We estimate only T_0 as the estimation of T_1 is performed in the same way.

By change of the order of the summation we get

$$T_0 = \sum_m T(m);\quad T(m) = \sum_d e^{2\pi i\alpha md}, \tag{3}$$

where m runs over the numbers

$$m = 1, \ldots, [n^h]$$

and d for every given m runs over the numbers

$$\tau_1 < d \leqslant \frac{N}{m}.$$

Further we find

$$T(m) = T''(m) + O\left(\frac{N}{m} n^{-h}\right) \tag{4}$$

where $T''(m)$ consists only of those terms of the sum $T(m)$, which correspond to the values of d from the set (d_0''). For, the part $T'(m)$ of $T(m)$ corresponding to the values of d from d_0' does not exceed the number of those terms of the set (d') which are not exceeding $\frac{N}{m}$. But the order of this number is significantly less than

$$\frac{N}{m} n^{-h}.$$

Now if d belongs to (d_0'') and k is the number of the prime divisors of d exceeding n^{3h}, then

$$k < n.$$

Therefore

$$T''(m) = \sum_{k<n} T_k(m), \tag{5}$$

where $T_k(m)$ consists of the terms of $T''(m)$ with d containing exactly k prime divisors $> n^{3h}$. Further we find

$$T_k(m) = \frac{1}{k} T_{k0}(m) + O\left(\frac{N}{mk} n^{-3h}\right), \tag{6}$$

where

$$T_{k0}(m) = \sum_u \sum_v e^{2\pi i a m u v}$$

and u runs over the primes $\geqslant n^{3h}$ belonging to (d) and v for a given u runs over the numbers belonging to (d_1) and satisfying the condition

$$\frac{\tau_1}{u} < v \leqslant \frac{N}{mu}.$$

To the sum $T_{k0}(m)$ we can directly apply the lemma 1. We obtain

$$T_{k0}(m) \ll N \frac{n^{\frac{3}{2} - \frac{3}{2}h}}{\sqrt{m}},$$

and then from (6), (5), (4), (3) and (2) we deduce the theorem 1.

Theorem 2. For the number I_N of the representations of N in the form

$$N = p_1 + p_2 + p_3$$

we have the formula

$$I_N = RS + O(N^2 n^{-c}),$$

where c is an arbitrary large constant > 3 and

$$S = \sum_{q=1}^{\infty} \frac{\mu(q)}{q_1^3} \sum_{\substack{0<a<q \\ (a,q)=1}} e^{2\pi i \frac{a}{q} N}; \quad R = \frac{N^2}{2n^3}(1+\lambda); \quad \lim_{N\to\infty} \lambda = 0; \quad q_1 = \varphi(q).$$

Proof. a) We have

$$I_N = \int_0^1 S_\alpha^3 e^{-2\pi i \alpha N} \, d\alpha; \quad S_\alpha = \sum_{p<N} e^{2\pi i \alpha p}.$$

The interval of integration we divide into intervals of two classes

1. $\alpha = \frac{a}{q} + z; \quad (a, q) = 1; \quad 0 < q \leqslant n^{3h}; \quad -\frac{1}{\tau} \leqslant z \leqslant \frac{1}{\tau}.$

2. The remaining intervals; for them

$$\alpha = \frac{a}{q} + z; \quad (a, q) = 1; \quad n^{3h} < q \leqslant \tau; \quad |z| \leqslant \frac{1}{q\tau}.$$

Correspondingly this division into intervals we have

$$I_N = I_{N1} + I_{N2}. \tag{7}$$

b) Applying the theorem 1 we find

$$I_{N2} \ll Nn^{2-h} \int_0^1 |S_\alpha|^2 \, d\alpha \ll Nn^{2-h} \int_0^1 \sum_{p<N} \sum_{p_1<N} e^{2\pi i \alpha (p-p_1)} d\alpha \ll$$

$$\ll Nn^{2-h} \frac{N}{n} \ll N^2 n^{1-h}. \tag{8}$$

c) The calculation of I_{N1} we perform without difficulty. This is done in the same way as in the Waring's problem. But here we use the now theorem on the distribution of primes in an arithmetical progression. If α belongs to the interval of the first class then we find

$$S_\alpha = \frac{\mu(q)}{q_1} V(z) + O(Nn^{-h_1}); \quad V(z) = \int_2^N \frac{e^{2\pi i z x}}{\log x} \, dx.$$

Hence the part of I_{N1} corresponding the given fraction $\frac{a}{q}$ is represented in the form

$$R \frac{\mu(q)}{q_1^3} e^{-2\pi i \frac{a}{q} N} + O(Nn^{-h_2}); \quad R = \int_{-\frac{1}{\tau}}^{\frac{1}{\tau}} [V(z)]^3 e^{-2\pi i z N} \, dz,$$

where R can be expressed in the form

$$R = \frac{N^2}{2n^3}(1 + \lambda); \quad \lim_{N \to \infty} \lambda = 0.$$

Hence we find without difficulty:

$$I_{N1} = RS + O(N^2 n^{-h_3})$$

and by (7) and (8) the theorem follows directly.

V. Stekloff Institute of Mathematics.
Academy of Sciences of the USSR.
Moscow.

Received
19.V.1937.

REFERENCES

[1] И. М. Виноградов, ДАН, III, 1; IV, 4 (1934). [2] A. Walfitz, Math. ZS., 40 (1936).

A New Proof of the Goldbach-Vinogradov Theorem

Ju. V. Linnik

§1. In my note 'On the possibility of a method for some 'additive' and 'distributive' problems in the theory of prime numbers" [1], I sketch a proof of the Goldbach problem by the pure Riemann-Hadamard's method of L-series and contour integration with some theorems on the density of zeros of L-series.

In this paper, I gave the detailed proof of the three primes theorem by the Riemann-Hadamard's method, thereby the Hardy-Littlewood's conditional solution is completed.

§2. Our basic instrument is the following lemma, and its detailed proof is contained in my paper "On the density of the zeros of L-series" [3].

Fundamental lemma. Let q be a natural number, $\chi(n)$ a primitive character (mod q) and $L(\omega, \chi)$ its L-series. Let

$$\omega = \sigma + it\ , \qquad T \geq q^{50}\ , \qquad \beta \geq 1 \quad \text{and} \quad \nu = \beta - \frac{1}{2} \geq 0\ .$$

Then the number of zeros of $L(\omega, \chi)$ in the rectangle $\beta \leq \sigma \leq 1$, $|t| \leq T$ will be

$$Q(\beta, T) < c_1 q^{2\nu} T^{1-(\nu/1-\nu)} \ln^{10} T + c_2 q^{30}\ , \tag{1}$$

where c_1 and c_2 are absolute constants.

§3. Let

$$S(N, \theta) = \sum_{n=1}^{\infty} \Lambda(n)\, e^{-(n/N)}\, e^{-2\pi i n\theta}$$

where N is an odd number which we wish to decompose as the sum of three prime numbers. Then

$$Q(N) = e \int_0^1 S(N, \theta)^3 e^{2\pi i N\theta} d\theta + o(N^{3/2+\varepsilon}) \quad ,$$

where

$$Q(N) = \sum_{p+p'+p''=N} \ln p \ln p' \ln p'' \quad .$$

Let

$$r = \ln N \quad , \quad \tau = r^{10,000} \quad , \quad H_1 = \tau^{100} \quad .$$

For each $\theta \in [0,1]$, we use the approximation by continued fraction

$$\theta = \frac{a}{q} + \alpha \ , \quad |\alpha| \le \frac{1}{q\tau} \ , \quad q \le \tau \tag{2}$$

The set $\mathcal{M}$ formed by those θ with $|\alpha| \le H_1 N^{-1} = \tau^{100} N^{-1}$ is called the "major arcs" |2|.

The asymptotic behaviour of $S(N, \theta)$ for $\theta \in \mathcal{M}$ is well established by the classical Riemann-Hadamard's method with the aid of Siegel's theorem [4] or Page's theorem [5]. Hence the integral

$$\int_{\mathcal{M}} S(N, \theta)^3 e^{2\pi i N\theta} d\theta$$

forms the principal term of our problem.

We use m to denote the complement of $\mathcal{M}$ with respect to $[0,1]$. For $\theta \in m$, we have

$$\theta = \frac{a}{q} + \alpha \ , \quad \frac{1}{q\tau} \ge |\alpha| \ge \frac{H_1}{N} \ , \quad q \le \tau \ . \tag{3}$$

Now we shall prove that for $\theta \in m$, $S(N, \theta)$ can also be estimated by the Riemann-Hadamard's method.

§4. We use χ to denote a primitive character (mod q), where q satisfies (3); $E(\chi) = 1$ if χ is the principal character, $E(\chi) = 0$ otherwise, and ρ denotes a critical zero of $L(\omega, \chi)$.

Suppose that x is a number with $\operatorname{Re} x > 0$. It follows by Littlewood's argument [6] that if $L(0, \chi) \ne 0$, then

$$S(N, \alpha, \chi) = \sum_{n=1}^{\infty} \chi(n)\, \Lambda(n)\, e^{-nx}$$

$$= E(\chi)x^{-1} - \sum_{\rho} x^{-\rho}\, \Gamma(\rho) - \frac{L'}{L}(0, \chi)$$

$$+ \frac{1}{2\pi i} \int_{-\frac{1}{2} - i\infty}^{-\frac{1}{2} + i\infty} x^{-\omega} \left(- \frac{L'}{L}(\omega, \chi)\right) \Gamma(\omega) d\omega \quad ,$$

and it remains no essential alternation if $L(0, \chi) = 0$.

Let $x = N^{-1} + 2\pi i\alpha$, where α satisfies (3). Then $|x| < 1$.

In order to estimate the remainder term

$$R = \frac{1}{2\pi i} \int_{-\frac{1}{2} - i\infty}^{-\frac{1}{2} + i\infty} x^{-\omega} \left(- \frac{L'}{L}(\omega, \chi)\right) \Gamma(\omega) d\omega \quad ,$$

we notice that for $\sigma = -\frac{1}{2}$,

$$\frac{L'}{L}(\omega, \chi) \ll \ln q\,(|t| + 2) \ , \qquad x^{-\omega} = e^{-\omega \ln|x| - i\omega \operatorname{arc} x} \quad ,$$

$$\left| e^{-\omega \ln|x|} \right| < 1 \quad , \qquad \left| e^{-i\omega \operatorname{arc} x} \right| \le e^{|t| \operatorname{arc} x} \quad ,$$

$$\Gamma(\omega) \ll |t|^{-1}\, e^{-(\pi/2)|t|} \quad .$$

Take $\eta = \frac{\pi}{2} - \operatorname{arc} x = \operatorname{arc\,tg} \frac{1}{2\pi N\alpha}$. Then

$$R \ll \int_{2}^{\infty} e^{(\operatorname{arc} x - (\pi/2))t} \cdot \frac{\ln qt}{t}\, dt \ll \ln^3 \frac{1}{\eta} \quad .$$

For $\theta \in m$,

$$\operatorname{arc\,tg} \frac{1}{2\pi N\alpha} > \frac{1}{4\pi N\alpha} \ , \qquad R \ll (\ln N\alpha)^3 \quad .$$

Since $\frac{L'}{L}(0, \chi) \ll q$ and $x^{-1} \ll \alpha^{-1}$, we have

$$S(N, \alpha, \chi) \ll \alpha^{-1} + (\ln N\alpha)^3 + \left| \sum_{\rho} x^{-\rho}\, \Gamma(\rho) \right| \quad . \qquad (4)$$

§5. Let $\nu_0 = \frac{\ln\ln N}{\ln N}$. In order to estimate $\left|\sum_\rho x^{-\rho}\,\Gamma(\rho)\right|$, we divide the critical strip σ into the sum of strips σ_0: $0 \le \sigma \le \frac{1}{2} + \nu_0 = \beta_0$, and those σ_ρ: $\beta \le \sigma \le \beta + \frac{1}{\ln N}$, $\beta \ge \frac{1}{2} + \nu_0$. Let $\alpha > 0$ and $N_0 \ge N\alpha$. It is well-known [5] that the trivial estimation for the number of zeros of $L(\omega, \chi)$ in the rectangle $0 \le \sigma \le \beta$, $|t| \le N_0$ will be

$$Q_L(\beta, N_0) << N_0 \ln(q N_0)$$

Set $\rho_k = \beta_k + it_k$. Since $|x| \sim 2\pi\alpha$ and

$$|\Gamma(\beta + it)| < c_3 t^{\beta - \frac{1}{2}} e^{-(\pi/2)|t|}, \quad |t| \ge 1, \quad -\frac{1}{2} \le \sigma \le 1 , \tag{5}$$

we have

$$\left|\sum_{\rho_k \in \sigma_{\rho_0}} x^{-\rho_k}\,\Gamma(\rho_k)\right|$$

$$<< \alpha^{-\beta_0} \sum_{\rho_k \in \sigma_{\beta_0}} e^{(\operatorname{arc} x - (\pi/2))|t_k|}\, |t_k|^{\beta_k - \frac{1}{2}}$$

$$<< \alpha^{-\beta_0} \sum_{\rho_k \in \sigma_{\beta_0}} e^{-(|t_k| / 4\pi N\alpha)}\, |t_k|^{\beta_0 - \frac{1}{2}}$$

$$<< \alpha^{-\beta_0}\, N\alpha \ln(N\alpha)(N\alpha)^{\nu_0} << \alpha^{\frac{1}{2} - \nu_0} N^{2\nu_0} N ,$$

where the constant implicit in symbol $<<$ is uniform on χ, N, α, ν.

Since $\alpha = \frac{1}{q\tau}$, we have

$$\alpha^{-\nu_0} << (\ln N)^{20{,}000\,\nu_0} << 1, \quad N^{2\nu_0} = (\ln N)^2 = r^2 ,$$

and therefore

$$\alpha^{\frac{1}{2} - \nu_0} N^{2\nu_0} N << \frac{Nr^2}{(q\tau)^{\frac{1}{2}}} < \frac{N}{q^{\frac{1}{2}}\,\tau^{\frac{1}{4}}} . \tag{6}$$

§6. Suppose that $\frac{1}{2}+\nu_0 \le \beta \le 0.6$, i.e. $\nu_0 \le \nu \le 0.1$. Then by the fundamental lemma (inequality (1)), we have

$$Q_L(\beta, N_0) < c_1 q^{2\nu} N_0^{1-(\nu/1-\nu)} \ln^{10} N_0 + c_2 q^{30} \quad .$$

Notice that $N_0 \ge N\alpha > H_1 = \tau^{100} \ge q^{100}$. Hence

$$\left|\sum_{\rho_k \in \sigma_\beta} x^{-\rho_k} \Gamma(\rho_k)\right| << \alpha^{-\frac{1}{2}-\nu} \sum_{\rho_k \in \sigma_\beta} e^{-(|t_k|/4\pi N\alpha)} |t_k|^{\nu}$$

$$<< (N\alpha)^{1-(\nu/1-\nu)} q^{2\nu}(N\alpha)^{\nu} \alpha^{-\frac{1}{2}-\nu} \ln^{10} N$$

$$<< (N\alpha)^{1-\nu^2} q^{2\nu} \alpha^{-\frac{1}{2}-\nu} r^{10}$$

$$= N^{1-\nu^2} \alpha^{\frac{1}{2}-\nu-\nu^2} r^{10} q^{2\nu} \le \frac{Nq^{2\nu} r^{10}}{(q\tau)^{\frac{1}{2}-\nu-\nu^2}} << \frac{N}{q\tau^{\frac{1}{4}}} \quad . \tag{7}$$

§7. Suppose that $0.1 \le \nu \le \frac{1}{3}$. Then $\frac{3}{2} - \frac{1}{1-\nu} \ge 0$, and so

$$\left|\sum_{\rho_k \in \sigma_\beta} x^{-\rho_k} \Gamma(\rho_k)\right| << \alpha^{-\frac{1}{2}-\nu} (N\alpha)^{1-(\nu/1-\nu)} (N\alpha)^{\nu} q^{2\nu} \ln^{10} N$$

$$<< N^{1-\nu^2} \alpha^{(3/2)-(1/1-\nu)} q^{2\nu} << N^{1-0.01} q^{2\nu} \quad .$$

Since $q \le \tau$, we have

$$\left|\sum_{\rho_k \in \sigma_\beta} x^{-\rho_k} \Gamma(\rho_k)\right| << \frac{N}{q^{\frac{1}{2}} N^{0.005}} \quad . \tag{8}$$

Suppose that $\frac{1}{3} \le \nu \le 0.4$. Then $\frac{3}{2} - \frac{1}{1-\nu} < 0$, and the maximum estimation is obtained by the minimum of $\alpha \ge \frac{H_1}{N}$, i.e., the right-hand side of (8) is

$$\ll N^{1-(\nu^2/1-\nu)}\ r^{10}\ q^{2\nu}\left(\frac{N}{H_1}\right)^{(1/1-\nu)-(3/2)}$$

$$\ll \frac{N^{\frac{1}{2}+\nu}\ q^{2\nu}\ r^{10}}{H_1^{(1/1-\nu)-(3/2)}} < N^{0.9}\ qr^{10} < \frac{N}{q^{\frac{1}{2}}\ N^{0.05}} . \qquad (9)$$

Finally, for $0.4 \le \nu \le \frac{1}{2}$, the sum is dominated by

$$\alpha^{-\frac{1}{2}-\nu}\ (N\alpha)^{1-(\nu/1-\nu)}\ r^{10}\ q^{2\nu}\ (N\alpha)^{\nu}$$

$$< N^{1-(\nu^2/1-\nu)}\ r^{10}\ q^{2\nu}\left(\frac{N}{H_1}\right)^{(1/1-\nu)-(3/2)}$$

$$\ll \frac{N^{\frac{1}{2}+\nu}\ q^{2\nu}\ r^{10}}{H_1^{(5/3)-(3/2)}} \ll \frac{N}{q\,H_1^{0.1}} . \qquad (10)$$

§8. For $\theta = \frac{a}{q} + \alpha$ $(\theta \in m)$, it follows by (4),...,(10) that

$$\sum_{n=1}^{\infty} \chi(n)\ \Lambda(n)\ e^{-(n/N)}\ e^{-2\pi i n\alpha}$$

$$\ll r\left(|\alpha|^{-1} + (\ln N\alpha)^3 + \frac{N}{q^{\frac{1}{2}}\,\tau^{\frac{1}{4}}} + \frac{N}{q^{\frac{1}{2}}\ N^{0.005}} + \frac{N}{q^{\frac{1}{2}}\ N^{0.05}} + \frac{N}{q\,H_1^{0.1}}\right) ;$$

$$|\alpha|^{-1} \ll \frac{N}{q\,H_1^{\frac{1}{2}}} ,$$

and thus there is a small number $c_5 > 0$ such that

$$\sum_{n=1}^{\infty} \chi(n)\ \Lambda(n)\ e^{-(n/N)}\ e^{-2\pi i n\alpha} \ll \frac{N}{q^{\frac{1}{2}+c_5}\ \tau^{0.1}} . \qquad (11)$$

Consequently, for $\theta = \frac{a}{q} + \alpha$ $(\theta \in m)$, we have

$$S(N,\theta) = \sum_{n=1}^{\infty} \Lambda(n)\, e^{-(n/N)}\, e^{-2\pi i n\theta}$$

$$= \sum_{n=1}^{\infty} \Lambda(n)\, e^{-(n/N)}\, e^{2\pi i(a/q+\alpha)n}$$

$$= \sum_{\substack{(\ell,q)=1 \\ \ell(\mathrm{mod}\, q)}} e^{-2\pi i(a/q)\ell} \sum_{n\equiv \ell(\mathrm{mod}\ q)} \Lambda(n)\, e^{-(n/N)}\, e^{-2\pi i n\alpha}$$

$$+ O(q^{\varepsilon})$$

$$= \frac{1}{\phi(q)} \sum_{\chi} \left(\sum_{\ell} \bar{\chi}(\ell)\, e^{-(2\pi i a\ell/q)} \right)$$

$$\cdot \sum_{n=1}^{\infty} \chi(n)\, \Lambda(n)\, e^{-(n/N)}\, e^{-2\pi i n\alpha} + O(q^{\varepsilon}) \quad .$$

Since

$$\sum_{\ell} \bar{\chi}(\ell)\, e^{-(2\pi i a\ell/q)} \ll q^{\frac{1}{2}+\varepsilon} \quad ,$$

we have by (11),

$$S(N,\theta) \ll \frac{q^{\frac{1}{2}}\,\phi(q)}{\phi(q)} \cdot \frac{q^{\varepsilon} N}{q^{\frac{1}{2}+c_5}\,\tau^{0.1}} \ll \frac{N}{\tau^{0.1}} < \frac{N}{(\ln N)^{1,000}} \quad . \tag{12}$$

It is sufficient for the solution of Goldbach problem.

References

[1]. Ju. V. Linnik, Dokl. Akad. Nauk SSSR, 48, (1945) 3-7.

[2]. E. Landau, Vorlesungen über Zahlentheorie, Bd. II (1927).

[3]. Ju. V. Linnik, Nzv. Akad. Nauk SSSR, Ser. Mat; 10 (1946) 35-46.

[4]. C. L. Siegel, Acta Arith; 1 (1935) 83-86.

[5]. A. Page, Proc. London Math. Soc.; 39 (1935) 116-141.

[6]. J. E. Littlewood, Proc. London Math. Soc.; 27 (1928) 358-371.

(See Mat. Sbornik, 19 (1946) 3-8).

Translated by Wang Yuan

A New Proof on the Three Primes Theorem

Pan Cheng Biao

(A) By the circle method of Hardy and Littlewood and his method on the estimation of trigonometrical sum with prime variables, I. M. Vinogradov [1] first proved in 1937 that every large odd number is the sum of three prime numbers which is usually called the Goldbach-Vinogradov theorem or the three primes theorem. Later, Ju. V. Linnik [2] and N. G. Tchudakov [3] gave another two proofs on this theorem based on the estimation of the density of zeros of L-functions. Recently, H. L. Montgomery [4] and M. N. Huxley [5] gave two simplified proofs which are also based on the estimation of the density of zeros of L-functions, and in their proofs, the approximate functional equation of L-function and a mean value theorem on the fourth moment of L-function are used.[a] In this paper, a new simplified analytic proof of the three primes theorem will be given which is not based on the Vinogradov's estimation and the density theorem of zeros of L-function, and only some well-known simple facts on L-function are used.

(B) We use N to denote large integers, p, p_1, p_2, p_3 the prime numbers, and $e(x) = e^{2\pi i x}$. Let

$$S(x, N) = \sum_{p \le N} e(px) \quad . \tag{1}$$

Then

$$r(N) = \sum_{p_1+p_2+p_3 = N} 1 = \int_0^1 S^3(x, N)\, e(-Nx)dx \tag{2}$$

denotes the number of representations of N as the sum of three

[a]Recently, K. Ramachandra [7] gave a simplified proof for the mean value theorem on the fourth moment of L-function.

primes. The three primes theorem is equivalent to $r(N) > 0$ for N is odd and sufficiently large. It is well known that the proof of $r(N) > 0$ is reduced to show that for any given positive integer c and

$$\log^c N < q \leq N \log^{-c} N \quad , \qquad (h, q) = 1 \quad , \tag{3}$$

we have

$$S(\frac{h}{q}, N) \ll N \log^{-3} N \quad . \tag{4}$$

In this paper, we prove the following

<u>Theorem</u>. Let

$$T_1(x, N) = \sum_{n \leq N} \Lambda(n) \log \frac{N}{n} e(nx) \quad . \tag{5}$$

If $1 \leq q \leq N$ and $(h, q) = 1$, then

$$T_1(\frac{h}{q}, N) \ll Nq^{-(1/2)} \log^{10} N + N^{(3/4)} q^{(1/4)} \log^{(13/2)} N \quad . \tag{6}$$

We shall show that (4) can be drived by our Theorem, and therefore the three primes theorem. Wẹ need the following well-known lemma (Cf. [4], Theorem 6.2).

<u>Lemma 1</u>. Let $\chi(n)$ denote a character mod q. Then

$$\sum_{\chi} \left| \sum_{n=n_0+1}^{n_0+k} a_n \chi(n) \right|^2 \leq (q+k) \sum_{n=n_0+1}^{n_0+k} |a_n|^2 \quad , \tag{7}$$

where $\sum_{\chi}$ denotes a sum over all characters mode q.

<u>The proof of Theorem</u>. For $(h, q) = 1$, we have

$$T_1(\frac{h}{q}, N) = \sum_{\substack{\ell=1 \\ (\ell,q)=1}}^{q} e(\frac{h\ell}{q}) \sum_{\substack{n \leq N \\ N \equiv \ell (\mathrm{mod}\, q)}} \Lambda(n) \log \frac{N}{n}$$

$$+ \sum_{\substack{n \leq N \\ (n,q)=1}} \Lambda(n) \log \frac{N}{n} e(\frac{h\ell}{q})$$

$$= \frac{1}{\phi(q)} \sum_{\chi} \tau(\bar{\chi})\, \chi(h)\, \psi_1(N, \chi) + O(\log^2 N \log q) \quad , \tag{8}$$

where $\phi(q)$ denotes the Euler function,

$$\tau(\chi) = \sum_{h=1}^{q} \chi(h)\, e\left(\frac{h}{q}\right) , \tag{9}$$

and

$$\psi_1(N, \chi) = \sum_{n \le N} \Lambda(n)\, \chi(n) \log \frac{N}{n} \ . \tag{10}$$

Since $\tau(\chi_0) = \mu(q)$, where χ_0 denotes the principal character mod q, $|\tau(\chi)| \le \sqrt{q}$ if $\chi \ne \chi_0$, and $\phi(q) \gg q \log^{-1} q$, we have

$$T_1\left(\frac{h}{q}, N\right) \ll \frac{\log q}{q}\, \psi_1(N, \chi_0) + \frac{\log q}{\sqrt{q}} \sum_{\chi \ne \chi_0} |\psi_1(N, \chi)| + \log^2 N \log q \tag{11}$$

It is easy to prove that for $\alpha > 1$,

$$\psi_1(N, \chi) = \frac{1}{2\pi i} \int_{\alpha - i\infty}^{\alpha + i\infty} - \frac{L'}{L}(s, \chi) \frac{N^s}{s^2} ds$$

$$= \frac{1}{2\pi i} \int_{(\alpha)} - \frac{L'}{L}(s, \chi) \frac{N^s}{s^2} ds \quad , \quad \text{say} \ . \tag{12}$$

Let $A(\le N)$ be a constant which will be determined in the later. Let

$$M(s, \chi) = \sum_{n \le A} \frac{\mu(n)\, \chi(n)}{n^s} \tag{13}$$

where $\mu(n)$ denotes the Möbius function. We use the identity [6]

$$- \frac{L'}{L}(s, \chi) = - \frac{L'}{L}(s, \chi) \Big(1 - L(s, \chi)\, M(s, \chi) \Big) - L'(s, \chi)\, M(s, \chi) \ . \tag{14}$$

Set $\alpha = 1 + \log^{-1} N$ and $B = [6 \log^2 N]$. Then

$$- \frac{L'}{L}(s, \chi) = f_1(s, \chi) + f_2(s, \chi) + O(N^{-3}) \quad , \tag{15}$$

where

$$f_1(s, \chi) = \sum_{n \le A} \frac{\Lambda(n)\ \chi(n)}{n^s} ,$$

$$f_2(s, \chi) = \sum_{A \le n \le 2^B A} \frac{\Lambda(n)\ \chi(n)}{n^s} \tag{16}$$

Since for $\mathrm{Re}\, s = \alpha$, $L(s, \chi) \ll \log N$ and $M(s, \chi) \ll \log N$, it follows from (14) and (15) that for $\mathrm{Re}\, s = \alpha$,

$$-\frac{L'}{L}(s, \chi) = f_1(1 - LM) + f_2(1 - LM) - L'M + O(N^{-2}) \quad . \tag{17}$$

From (12) and (17), we have

$$\psi_1(N, \chi) = \frac{1}{2\pi i} \int_{(\alpha)} \left(f_1(1 - LM) + f_2(1 - LM) - L'M \right) \frac{N^s}{s^2} ds$$
$$+ O(N^{-1}) \quad . \tag{18}$$

If $\chi \ne \chi_0$, the integrals corresponding to the first and third terms of the integrand may be shifted to the line $\mathrm{Re}\, s = \frac{1}{2}$. Therefore

$$\psi_1(N, \chi) = \frac{1}{2\pi i} \int_{(\frac{1}{2})} (f_1(1 - LM) - L'M) \frac{N^s}{s^2} ds$$
$$+ \frac{1}{2\pi i} \int_{(\alpha)} f_2(1 - LM) \frac{N^s}{s^2} ds + O(N^{-1})$$
$$\ll \int_{(\frac{1}{2})} (|f_1| + |f_1 LM| + |L'M|) \frac{N^{\frac{1}{2}}}{|s|^{\frac{1}{2}}} |ds|$$
$$+ \int_{(\alpha)} |f_2|\ |1 - LM| \frac{N}{|s|^2} |ds| + O(N^{-1}) , \tag{19}$$

and by Hölder inequality, we have

$$\sum_{\chi\neq\chi_0} |\psi_1(N,\chi)| << N^{\frac12} q^{\frac12} \sup_{\mathrm{Re}\, s=\frac12} \Big(\sum_{\chi\neq\chi_0} |f_1|^2 \Big)^{\frac12}$$

$$+ N^{\frac12} \sup_{\mathrm{Re}\, s=\frac12} \Big(\sum_{\chi\neq\chi_0} |f_1|^4 \Big)^{\frac14}$$

$$\cdot \sup_{\mathrm{Re}\, s=\frac12} \Big(\sum_{\chi\neq\chi_0} |M|^4 \Big)^{\frac14} \int_{(\frac12)} \Big(\sum_{\chi\neq\chi_0} |L|^2 \Big)^{\frac12} \frac{|ds|}{|s|^2}$$

$$+ N^{\frac12} \sup_{\mathrm{Re}\, s=\frac12} \Big(\sum_{\chi\neq\chi_0} |M|^2 \Big)^{\frac12} \int_{(\frac12)} \Big(\sum_{\chi\neq\chi_0} |L'|^2 \Big)^{\frac12} \frac{|ds|}{|s|^2}$$

$$+ N \sup_{\mathrm{Re}\, s=\alpha} \Big(\sum_{\chi\neq\chi_0} |f_2|^2 \Big)^{\frac12} \sup_{\mathrm{Re}\, s=\alpha} \Big(\sum_{\chi\neq\chi_0} |1-LM|^2 \Big)^{\frac12} + qN^{-1} \quad . \tag{20}$$

Since

$$\sum_{\chi\neq\chi_0} |L(s,\chi)|^2 << q|s| \log^2 q|s| \quad , \quad (s = \frac{1}{2} + it) \tag{21}$$

and

$$\sum_{\chi\neq\chi_0} |L(s,\chi)|^2 << q|s| \log^2 q|s| \quad , \quad (s = \frac{1}{2} + it) \tag{22}$$

which will be proved in (D), we have

$$\int_{(\frac12)} \Big(\sum_{\chi\neq\chi_0} |L|^2 \Big)^{\frac12} \frac{|ds|}{|s|^2} << \sqrt{q} \log q \tag{23}$$

and

$$\int_{(\frac12)} \Big(\sum_{\chi\neq\chi_0} |L'|^2 \Big)^{\frac12} \frac{|ds|}{|s|^2} << \sqrt{q} \log^2 q \quad . \tag{24}$$

Now we proceed to estimate the sums in the right hand side of (20) by the use of Lemma 1. Hereafter we assume that $q \le N$ and $A \le N$.

(a) By (16) and Lemma 1,

$$\sum_{\chi} |f_1(\frac{1}{2} + it, \chi)|^2 \le (q + A) \log^3 N \quad . \tag{25}$$

(b) By (13) and Lemma 1,

$$\sum_{\chi} |M(\tfrac{1}{2}+it,\chi)|^2 \leq (q+A)\log N \quad . \tag{26}$$

(c) By (16),

$$f_1^2(s,\chi) = \sum_{n\leq A^2} \frac{a_n\,\chi(n)}{n^s}, \qquad |a_n| \leq d(n)\log^2 n \quad ,$$

where $d(n)$ denotes the divisor function, and therefore by Lemma 1 and $\sum_{n\leq x} \frac{d^2(n)}{n} \ll \log^4 x$, we have

$$\sum_{\chi} |f_1(\tfrac{1}{2}+it,\chi)|^2 \ll (q+A^2)\log^8 N \quad . \tag{27}$$

(d) By (13),

$$M^2(s,\chi) = \sum_{n\leq A^2} \frac{b_n\,\chi(n)}{n^s}, \qquad |b_n| \leq d(n) \quad ,$$

and therefore

$$\sum_{\chi} |M(\tfrac{1}{2}+it,\chi)|^4 \ll (q+A^2)\log^4 N \quad . \tag{28}$$

(e) By (16), we have for $\operatorname{Re} s = \alpha$,

$$\sum_{\chi} |f_2(s,\chi)|^2 = \sum_{\chi} \left| \sum_{j=0}^{B-1} \sum_{2^jA\leq n\leq 2^{j+1}A} \frac{\Lambda(n)\,\chi(n)}{n^s} \right|^2$$

$$\leq B \sum_{j=0}^{B-1} \sum_{\chi} \left| \sum_{2^jA< n\leq 2^{j+1}A} \frac{\Lambda(n)\,\chi(n)}{n^s} \right|^2$$

$$\ll \log^2 N \sum_{j=0}^{B-1} (q+2^jA) \sum_{2^jA<n\leq 2^{j+1}A} \frac{\Lambda^2(n)}{n^s}$$

$$\ll (\tfrac{q}{A} + \log^2 N)\log^6 N \quad . \tag{29}$$

(f) For $\operatorname{Re} s = \alpha$, we have

$$1 - LM = \sum_{A < n \le 2^B A} \frac{c_n \chi(n)}{n^s} + O(N^{-1}) , \qquad |c_n| \le d(n) ,$$

and therefore by $\sum_{n \le x} d^2(n) \ll x \log^3 x$,

$$\sum_{\chi} |1 - LM|^2 \ll \left(\frac{q}{A} + \log^2 N\right) \log^8 N . \tag{30}$$

From (20) and (23)-(30), we have

$$\sum_{\chi \ne \chi_0} |\psi_1(N, \chi)| \ll N^{\frac{1}{2}} q^{\frac{1}{2}} (q + A^2)^{\frac{1}{2}} \log^4 N + N\left(\frac{q}{A} + \log^2 N\right) \log^7 N . \tag{31}$$

Take $A = N^{\frac{1}{4}} q^{\frac{1}{4}} \log^{(3/2)} N$. Then it follows by (11) and (31) that $\psi_1(N, \chi_0) \ll N$, and therefore the theorem is proved.

From our theorem, it yields

Lemma 2. Suppose that c is an integer > 42. Then for

$$\log^c N < q \le N \log^{-c} N , \qquad (h, q) = 1 , \tag{32}$$

we have

$$T_1\left(\frac{h}{q}, N\right) \ll N \log^{-4} N . \tag{33}$$

(C) To prove (4), we shall need

Lemma 3[b]. Let c be an integer > 46 and

$$T_0(x, N) = \sum_{n \le N} \Lambda(n) e(nx) . \tag{34}$$

Then for $\log^c N < q \le N \log^{-c} N$ and $(h, q) = 1$, we have

$$T_0\left(\frac{h}{q}, N\right) \ll N \log^{-2} N . \tag{35}$$

---

[b] This lemma was proposed by Prof. Din Xia Qi.

Proof. Let $\lambda = \log^{-2} N$. Then

$$T_1(\frac{h}{q}, N+\lambda N) - T_1(\frac{h}{q}, N)$$

$$= \log(1+\lambda)\, T_0(\frac{h}{q}, N) + \sum_{N<n\le N+\lambda N} \Lambda(n) \log \frac{N+\lambda N}{n} e(nx) . \tag{36}$$

By Lemma 2 and (36),

$$\log(1+\lambda)\, T_0(\frac{h}{q}, N) << N \log^{-4} N + \lambda N \log(1+\lambda) . \tag{37}$$

Since $\log(1+x) > \frac{1}{2}x$ if $0 < x < \frac{1}{2}$, we have

$$T_0(\frac{h}{q}, N) << \lambda^{-1} N \log^{-4} N + \lambda N << N \log^{-2} N . \tag{38}$$

This lemma is proved.

It follows by Lemma 3 and the summation by parts that for

$$\log^c N < q \le N \log^{-c} N , \qquad (h, q) = 1, \qquad c > 42 , \tag{39}$$

we have

$$\sum_{2\le n\le N} \frac{\Lambda(n)}{\log n} e(\frac{nh}{q}) << N \log^{-3} N . \tag{40}$$

This is equivalent to (4), and thus the three primes theorem is proved.

(D) The proofed of (21) and (22). Let $\chi \ne \chi_0$, $H = [q|s|]$ and $F(x) = \sum_{H<n\le x} \chi(n)$. By Polya's theorem, we have

$$F(x) << \sqrt{q} \log q .$$

Therefore

$$\sum_{n=H+1}^{\infty} \frac{\chi(n)}{n^{\frac{1}{2}+it}} = \int_H^{\infty} \frac{dF(x)}{x^{\frac{1}{2}+it}} = \int_H^{\infty} (\frac{1}{2}+it) \frac{F(x)}{x^{(3/2)+it}} dx$$

$$<< |s| \sqrt{q} \log q \int_H^{\infty} \frac{dx}{x^{3/2}} << \sqrt{|s|} \log q , \tag{41}$$

and by Lemma 1, we have

$$\sum_{\chi\neq\chi_0} |L(\frac{1}{2}+it,\chi)|^2 << \sum_{\chi\neq\chi_0}\left(\left|\sum_{n=1}^{H}\frac{\chi(n)}{n^{\frac{1}{2}+it}}\right|^2 + |s|\log^2 q\right)$$

$$<< (q+H)\log H + q|s|\log^2 q << q|s|\log^2 q|s| \quad . \qquad (42)$$

(21) is proved. The proof of (22) is similar.

References

[1]. I. M. Vinogradov, Dokl. Akad. Nauk SSSR, 15 (1937) 291-294.

[2]. Ju. V. Linnik, Dokl. Akad. Nauk SSSR, 48 (1945) 3-7.

[3]. N. G. Tchudakov, Ann. of Math.; 48 (1947) 515-545.

[4]. H. L. Montgomery, Topics in Multiplicative Number Theory, Lec. Notes in Math.; Springer-Verlag, 227 (1971).

[5]. M. N. Huxley, The Distribution of Prime Numbers, Oxford, Clarendon Press (1972).

[6]. Pan Cheng Dong and Din Xia Qi, Acta, Math. Sinica, 18, 4 (1975) 254-262.

[7]. K. Ramachandra, Ann. Scuola Norm. Sup. Pisa, Cl. Sci.; 4 (1974) 81-97.

(See Acta Math. Sinica, 20 (1977) 206-211).

Translated by Wang Yuan

An Elementary Method in Prime Number Theory

R. C. VAUGHAN

Mathematics Department, Imperial College,
Cromwell Road, London SW7 2AZ, England

1. INTRODUCTION

Let

$$T(Y,Q)=\sum_{q\leq Q}\frac{q}{\phi(q)}\sum_{\chi}{}^{*}\max_{X\leq Y}|\psi(X,\chi)| \tag{1}$$

where

$$\psi(X,\chi)=\sum_{n\leq X}\Lambda(n)\chi(n) \tag{2}$$

and $\sum^*$ denotes summation over primitive characters modulo q. An estimate for T is an essential ingredient in the Bombieri–Vinogradov theorem on primes in arithmetical progressions. Also, let

$$H_r(Y,Q)=\sum_{q\leq Q}\frac{q}{\phi(q)}\sum_{\chi}{}^{*}\max_{X\leq Y}|M_r(X,\chi)| \tag{3}$$

where

$$M_r(X,\chi)=\sum_{\substack{n\leq X\\(n,r)=1}}\mu(n)\chi(n). \tag{4}$$

The purpose of this note is to adumbrate proofs of the following two theorems based on ideas contained in [**5**], [**6**].

THEOREM 1. *Let* $Q\geq 1$, $Y\geq 2$, $\mathscr{L}=\log YQ$. *Then*

$$T(Y,Q)\ll(Y+Y^{\frac{5}{6}}Q+Y^{\frac{1}{2}}Q^2)\mathscr{L}^4. \tag{5}$$

THEOREM 2. *Let* $Q \geq 1$, $Y \geq 2$, $r \geq 1$, $\mathscr{L} = \log YQ$. *Then*

$$H_r(Y, Q) \ll (Y + d(r) Y^{\frac{5}{6}} Q + Y^{\frac{1}{2}} Q^2) \mathscr{L}^4. \tag{6}$$

Theorem 1 combined with the Siegel–Walfisz theorem easily gives

THEOREM 3 (*Bombieri–Vinogradov*). *Let* $Q \geq 1$, $Y \geq 2$, $\mathscr{L} = \log YQ$. *Then*

$$\sum_{q \leq Q} \sup_{\substack{a, X \\ (a,q)=1, X \leq Y}} \left| \psi(X, q, a) - \frac{X}{\phi(q)} \right| \ll_A Y (\log Y)^{-A} + Y^{\frac{1}{2}} Q \mathscr{L}^4. \tag{7}$$

Similarly Theorem 2 gives

THEOREM 4. *Let* $Q \geq 1$, $Y \geq 2$, $\mathscr{L} = \log YQ$. *Then*

$$\sum_{q \leq Q} \sup_{\substack{a, X \\ X \leq Y}} \left| \sum_{\substack{n \leq X \\ n \equiv a \pmod{q}}} \mu(n) \right| \ll_A Y (\log Y)^{-A} + Y^{\frac{1}{2}} Q \mathscr{L}^4. \tag{8}$$

2. PROOFS OF THEOREMS 1 AND 2

LEMMA 1. *Suppose that* a_m $(m = 1, \ldots, M)$ *and* $b_n (n = 1, \ldots, N)$ *are complex numbers. Then*

$$\sum_{q \leq Q} \frac{q}{\phi(q)} \sum_{\chi}{}^{*} \left| \sum_{m=1}^{M} \sum_{n=1}^{N} a_m b_n \chi(mn) \right| \ll \left((M + Q^2)(N + Q^2) \sum_m |a_m|^2 \sum_n |b_n|^2 \right)^{\frac{1}{2}}.$$

This is an immediate consequence of the large sieve inequality (see, for example, Gallagher [1], or (1.4) of [2]) and Cauchy's inequality.

LEMMA 2. *On the premises of Lemma* 1,

$$\sum_{q \leq Q} \frac{q}{\phi(q)} \sum_{\chi}{}^{*} \sup_{X \leq Y} \left| \sum_{\substack{m=1 \\ mn \leq X}}^{M} \sum_{n=1}^{N} a_m b_n \chi(mn) \right|$$

$$\ll \left((M + Q^2)(N + Q^2) \sum_m |a_m|^2 \sum_n |b_n|^2 \right)^{\frac{1}{2}} \log YMN. \tag{9}$$

Proof. Let

$$C = \int_{-\infty}^{\infty} \frac{\sin \alpha}{\alpha} \, d\alpha$$

and $\gamma > 0$. Define $\delta(\beta) = 1$ when $0 \leq \beta < \gamma$ and $\delta(\beta) = 0$ when $\beta > \gamma$. Then $C > 0$ and it is easily seen that for $A \geq 1$, $\beta \geq 0$, $\beta \neq \gamma$, one has

$$\delta(\beta) = \int_{-A}^{A} e^{i\beta\alpha} \frac{\sin \gamma\alpha}{C\alpha} \, d\alpha + O(A^{-1} |\gamma - \beta|^{-1}).$$

Let $\gamma = \log([X]+\frac{1}{2})$, $\beta = \log mn$. Thus

$$\sum_{\substack{m \\ mn \leq X}}\sum_{n} a_m b_n \chi(mn) = \int_{-A}^{A} \sum_m \sum_n a_m m^{i\alpha} b_n n^{i\alpha} \chi(mn) \frac{\sin \gamma\alpha}{C\alpha}\, d\alpha$$

$$+ O\Big(XA^{-1} \sum_m \sum_n |a_m b_n|\Big).$$

The desired conclusion now follows easily from Lemma 1 on taking $A = YMN$.

If $Q^2 > Y$, then Theorem 1 follows at once from Lemma 2 on taking $M = 1$, $a_1 = 1$, $b_n = \Lambda(n)$. Hence it may be assumed that $Q^2 \leq Y$.

Let

$$u = \min(Q^2, Y^{\frac{1}{3}}, YQ^{-2}). \tag{10}$$

By applying Lemma 2 as in the case $Q^2 > Y$ it is easily seen that

$$\sum_{q \leq Q} \frac{q}{\phi(q)} \sum_{\chi}{}^{*} \sup_{X \leq u^2} |\psi(X, \chi)| \ll (u^2 Q + uQ^2)\mathscr{L}^2. \tag{11}$$

Consider the identity

$$\sum_{u < n \leq X} \Lambda(n) f(n) = S_1 - S_2 - S_3 \tag{12}$$

where

$$S_1 = \sum_{m \leq u} \sum_{n \leq X/m} \mu(m)(\log n) f(mn), \tag{13}$$

$$S_2 = \sum_{m \leq u^2} \sum_{n \leq X/m} c_m f(mn), \qquad c_m = \sum_{\substack{a \leq u, b \leq u \\ ab = m}} \mu(a)\Lambda(b), \tag{14}$$

$$S_3 = \sum_{\substack{m > u \\ mn \leq X}} \sum_{n > u} \tau_m \Lambda(n) f(mn), \qquad \tau_m = \sum_{\substack{d \mid m \\ d \leq u}} \mu(d), \tag{15}$$

which is most readily obtained by inspecting the coefficients in the Dirichlet series identity

$$\Big(-\frac{\zeta'}{\zeta}(s) - F(s)\Big) = G(s)(-\zeta'(s)) - F(s)G(s)\zeta(s)$$

$$-(\zeta(s)G(s) - 1)\Big(-\frac{\zeta'}{\zeta}(s) - F(s)\Big) \tag{16}$$

where

$$F(s) = \sum_{n \leq u} \Lambda(n) n^{-s}, \qquad G(s) = \sum_{n \leq u} \mu(n) n^{-s}. \tag{17}$$

On writing $f(n)=\chi(n)$ in (12), one sees that it suffices to show that for $j=1$, 2, 3 the sum

$$T_j=\sum_{q\leq Q}\frac{q}{\phi(q)}\sum_{\chi}{}^{*}\sup_{u^2<X\leq Y}|S_j|$$

satisfies (5) with T replaced by T_j. Note that the terms in $\sum_{n\leq X}\Lambda(n)\chi(n)$ with $n\leq u$ can be taken care of by (11).

By (15),

$$T_3\quad\sum_{\leq M\in\mathcal{M}}T_3(M)$$

where $\mathcal{M}=\{2^k u:k=0,1,\ldots;2^k u^2\leq Y\}$ and

$$T_3(M)=\sum_{q\leq Q}\frac{q}{\phi(q)}\sum_{\chi}{}^{*}\sup_{u^2<X\leq Y}|S_3(M)|$$

with

$$S_3(M)=\sum_{M<m\leq 2M}\sum_{u<n\leq X/m}\tau_m\Lambda(n)\chi(mn).$$

By Lemma 2,

$$T_3(M)\ll\left((M+Q^2)(YM^{-1}+Q^2)\sum_{m\leq 2M}d(m)^2\sum_{n\leq Y/M}\Lambda(n)^2\right)^{\frac{1}{2}}\log Y$$
$$\ll(Y+Y^{\frac{1}{2}}M^{\frac{1}{2}}Q+YM^{-\frac{1}{2}}Q+Y^{\frac{1}{2}}Q^2)(\log Y)^3$$

which easily gives the desired conclusion.

By (13), on writing $\log n=\int_1^n(d\alpha/\alpha)$ and interchanging the order of summation and integration, one obtains

$$S_1=\int_1^X\sum_{m\leq\min(u,X/\alpha)}\mu(m)\chi(m)\sum_{\alpha\leq n\leq X/m}\chi(n)\frac{d\alpha}{\alpha}.$$

Using the Pólya–Vinogradov inequality (Schur's proof [3] is elementary) when $q>1$ gives one

$$T_1\ll(Y+uQ^{\frac{5}{2}})(\log Y)^2$$

which with (10) again gives a suitable estimate.

The expression T_2 is estimated by combining the above arguments. The sum S_2 is divided into two parts

$$S_2=S_2'+S_2''$$

where S_2' contains the terms with $m\leq u$ and S_2'' the terms with $u<m\leq u^2$. Then S_2' is treated like S_1 and S_2'' like S_3. This provides an appropriate upper bound for T_2 and completes the proof of Theorem 1.

Theorem 3 follows from Theorem 1 in the same manner that Corollary 1.1.1 of [**4**] is deduced from Theorem 1 therein.

2. PROOFS OF THEOREMS 2 AND 4

The proof of Theorem 2 is similar to that of Theorem 1, using instead the identity

$$\sum_{n\leqslant X}\mu(n)f(n)=2S_1-S_2-S_3 \tag{18}$$

where

$$S_1=\sum_{n\leqslant u}\mu(n)f(n) \tag{19}$$

$$S_2=\sum_{m\leqslant u^2}\sum_{n\leqslant X/m}c_mf(mn),\qquad c_m=\sum_{\substack{a\leqslant u,b\leqslant u\\ ab=m}}\mu(a)\mu(b), \tag{20}$$

$$S_3=\sum_{\substack{m>u\ n>u\\ mn\leqslant X}}\sum \tau_m\mu(n)f(mn),\qquad \tau_m=\sum_{\substack{d\mid m\\ d\leqslant u}}\mu(d). \tag{21}$$

This is an immediate consequence of the identity

$$\frac{1}{\zeta(s)}=2G(s)-G(s)^2\zeta(s)-(\zeta(s)G(s)-1)\left(\frac{1}{\zeta(s)}-G(s)\right) \tag{22}$$

where $G(s)$ satisfies (17).

The case $Q^2>Y$ of Theorem 2 can be treated as in the proof of Theorem 1. Let u satisfy (10). Then, as before, (11) holds with $\psi(X,\chi)$ replaced by $M_r(X,\chi)$. Now in (18) let $f(n)=\chi(n)$ when $(n,r)=1$ and $f(n)=0$ when $(n,r)>1$. Then it suffices to bound

$$T_j=\sum_{q\leqslant Q}\frac{q}{\phi(q)}\sum_{\chi}{}^{*}\sup_{u^2<X\leqslant Y}|S_j|\qquad (j=1,2,3).$$

The sum T_1 can be bounded at once by appealing to the analogue of (11). Also the sum T_3 can be estimated in the same manner as the corresponding sum occurring in the proof of Theorem 2. Similarly T_2 can be estimated by dividing S_2 into two parts S_2' and S_2'' according as $m\leqslant u$ or $m>u$. Thus $T_2\leqslant T_2'+T_2''$ where T_2' and T_2'' correspond to T_2 with S_2 replaced by S_2' and S_2'' respectively. Now T_2'' can be treated in the same manner as T_3. It remains, therefore, to consider T_2'.

By the Pólya–Vinogradov inequality, when χ is a non-principal character with modulus $q>1$,

$$\sum_{\substack{n\leq Z\\(n,r)=1}}\chi(n)=\sum_{d\mid r}\mu(d)\chi(d)\sum_{m\leq Z/d}\chi(m)$$

$$\ll d(r)q^{\frac{1}{2}}\log q.$$

Hence

$$T_2'\ll(Y+d(r)uQ^{\frac{5}{2}})\mathscr{L}^2.$$

The proof of Theorem 2 is completed by observing that, by (10), $uQ^{\frac{5}{2}}\leq Y^{\frac{5}{6}}Q$.

The proof of Theorem 4 is rather more involved than that of Theorem 3, there being an extra difficulty in the reduction to primitive characters.

Observe that

$$\sup_a\sup_{X\leq Y}\left|\sum_{\substack{n\leq X\\n\equiv a\,(\mathrm{mod}\,q)}}\mu(n)\right|\leq\sum_{r\mid q}\sup_{\substack{b\\(b,q/r)=1}}\sup_{X\leq Y/r}\left|\sum_{\substack{m\leq X\\m\equiv b\,(\mathrm{mod}\,q/r)\\(m,r)=1}}\mu(m)\right|.$$

Hence

$$\sum_{q\leq Q}\sup_a\sup_{X\leq Y}\left|\sum_{\substack{n\leq X\\n\equiv a\,(\mathrm{mod}\,q)}}\mu(n)\right|\leq\sum_{r\leq Q}F_r(Y/r,Q/r)\tag{23}$$

where

$$F_r(Y,Q)=\sum_{q\leq Q}\sup_{\substack{a\\(a,q)=1}}\sup_{X\leq Y}\left|\sum_{\substack{n\leq X\\n\equiv a\,(\mathrm{mod}\,q)\\(n,r)=1}}\mu(n)\right|.$$

When $(a,q)=1$,

$$\sum_{\substack{n\leq X\\n\equiv a\,(\mathrm{mod}\,q)\\(n,r)=1}}\mu(n)=\frac{1}{\phi(q)}\sum_{\chi\,\mathrm{mod}\,q}\bar{\chi}(a)\sum_{\substack{n\leq X\\(n,r)=1}}\chi(n)\mu(n).$$

Therefore

$$\left|\sum_{\substack{n\leq X\\n\equiv a\,(\mathrm{mod}\,q)\\(n,r)=1}}\mu(n)\right|\leq\frac{1}{\phi(q)}\sum_{d\mid q}\sum_{\chi\,\mathrm{mod}\,d}^{*}\left|\sum_{\substack{n\leq X\\(n,rq/d)=1}}\chi(n)\mu(n)\right|,$$

whence

$$F_r(Y,Q)\leq\sum_{k\leq Q}\frac{1}{\phi(k)}G_{rk}(Y,Q/k)\tag{24}$$

where

$$G_r(Y,Q)=\sum_{q\leq Q}\frac{1}{\phi(q)}\sum_{\chi}^{*}\sup_{X\leq Y}\left|\sum_{\substack{n\leq X\\(n,r)=1}}\chi(n)\mu(n)\right|.\tag{25}$$

Let $R \leqslant Q$. Then, by partial integration, (3) and (4),

$$G_r(Y, Q) - G_r(Y, R) \leqslant Q^{-1}H_r(Y, Q) + \int_R^Q \alpha^{-2}H_r(Y, \alpha)\, d\alpha.$$

Therefore, by Theorem 2,

$$G_r(Y, Q) - G_r(Y, R) \ll (YR^{-1} + Y^{\frac{1}{2}}Q)\mathscr{L}^4 + d(r)Y^{\frac{5}{6}}\mathscr{L}^5. \tag{26}$$

Suppose that $q \leqslant (\log Z)^A$ and χ is a character modulo q. Then a standard application of the theory of Dirichlet L-functions gives

$$\sum_{\substack{n \leqslant Z \\ (n,r)=1}} \chi(n)\mu(n) \ll_A d(r) Z \exp(-c(\log Z)^{\frac{1}{2}})$$

where C is a positive constant. Hence, by (25),

$$G_r(Y, (\log Y)^B) \ll_B d(r) Y \exp(-\tfrac{1}{2}c(\log Y)^{\frac{1}{2}}).$$

This combined with (26) and a suitable choice of B gives

$$G_r(Y, Q) \ll_A (Y\mathscr{L}^{-A-4} + Y^{\frac{1}{2}}Q\mathscr{L}^4)\, d(r).$$

Hence, by (24),

$$F_r(Y, Q) \ll_A (Y\mathscr{L}^{-A-2} + Y^{\frac{1}{2}}Q\mathscr{L}^4)\, d(r).$$

Therefore, by (23), when $Q \leqslant Y^{\frac{1}{2}}$,

$$\sum_{q \leqslant Q} \sup_{\substack{a, X \\ X \leqslant Y}} \Bigg| \sum_{\substack{n \leqslant X \\ n \equiv a \pmod q}} \mu(n) \Bigg| \ll_A Y\mathscr{L}^{-A} + Y^{\frac{1}{2}}Q\mathscr{L}^4.$$

The proof of Theorem 4 is completed by noting that the conclusion is trivial when $Q > Y^{\frac{1}{2}}$.

REFERENCES

[1] Gallagher, P. X.
The large sieve. *Mathematika* **14** (1967), 14–20.

[2] Montgomery, H. L. and Vaughan, R. C.
The large sieve. *Mathematika* **20** (1973), 119–134.

[3] Schur, I.
Einige Bemerkungen zu der vorstehenden Arbeit des Herr G. Pólya: Über die Verteilung der quadratischen Reste und Nichtreste, Göttinger Nachrichten 1918, 30–36.

[4] Vaughan, R. C.
Mean value theorems in prime number theory. *J. London Math. Soc.* (2) **10** (1975), 153–162.

[5] Vaughan, R. C.
Sommes trigonométriques sur les nombres premiers. *Comptes Rendus Acad. Sci. Paris*, Serie A, **285** (1977), 981–983.

[6] Vaughan, R. C.
On the distribution of αp modulo 1. *Mathematika* **24** (1977), 135–141.

(See "Recent Progress in Analytic Number Theory", edited by H. Halberstam and C. Hooley, Acad. Press, 1981, pp. 241-248.)

Noted by Pan Cheng Biao: From (12), we can easily derive the following estimation for $S(\alpha) = \sum_{n \le x} \Lambda(n)e(n\alpha)$, namely if $|\alpha - \frac{a}{q}| < q^{-2}$, $(a,q) = 1$, then $S(\alpha) \ll (xq^{-1/2} + x^{4/5} + x^{1/2}q^{1/2})\log^{7/2}x$. We may assume without loss of generality that $q \le x$. Since

$$\sum_{m \le y} \max_{\omega} \left| \sum_{\omega \le n \le x/m} e(mn\alpha) \right| \ll \sum_{m \le y} \min\left(\frac{x}{m}, \frac{1}{\|m\alpha\|}\right) \ll (xq^{-1} + y + q)\log qy,$$

where $\|\xi\|$ denotes the least distance from ξ to an integer, we have from (13), (14) and (15) with $f(n) = e(n\alpha)$ the following estimations

$$S_1 \ll \log x \sum_{m \le u} \max_{\omega} \left| \sum_{\omega \le n \le x/m} e(mn\alpha) \right| \ll (xq^{-1} + u + q)\log^2 x,$$

$$S_2 \ll \log x \sum_{m \le u^2} \left| \sum_{n \le x/m} e(mn\alpha) \right| \ll (xq^{-1} + u^2 + q)\log^2 x$$

and

$$S_3 \ll \log x \max_{u < M < x/u} \left| \sum_{M < m \le 2M} \tau_m \sum_{u < n \le x/m} \Lambda(n)e(mn\alpha) \right|$$

$$\ll \log^{5/2}x \max_{u < M < x/u} M^{1/2} \left(\sum_{M < m \le 2M} \left| \sum_{u < n \le x/m} \Lambda(n)e(mn\alpha) \right|^2 \right)^{\frac{1}{2}}$$

$$\ll x^{1/2}\log^3 x \max_{u < M < x/u} \max_{u < n_1 \le x/M} \left(\sum_{u < n_2 \le x/M} \left| \sum_{\substack{M < m \le 2M \\ m \le x/n_1 \\ m \le x/n_2}} e((n_1 - n_2)m\alpha) \right| \right)^{\frac{1}{2}}$$

$$\ll x^{1/2}\log^3 x \max_{u<M<x/u}\ \max_{u<n_1\le x/M}\left(\sum_{u<n_2\le x/M}\min\left(M, \frac{1}{\|(n_1-n_2)\alpha\|}\right)\right)^{\frac{1}{2}}$$

$$\ll x^{1/2}\log^3 x \max_{u<M<x/u}\left(M+\sum_{1<m\le x/M}\min\left(\frac{x}{m}, \frac{1}{\|m\alpha\|}\right)\right)^{\frac{1}{2}}$$

$$\ll (xq^{-1/2}+xu^{-1/2}+x^{1/2}q^{1/2})\log^{7/2}x.$$

Take $u = x^{2/5}$. The assertion follows.

II. REPRESENTATION OF AN EVEN NUMBER AS THE SUM OF TWO ALMOST PRIMES (ELEMENTARY APPROACH)

The Sieve of Eratosthenes and the Theorem of Goldbach

Viggo Brun

§1. The theorem of Goldbach is well-known that one can write every even number as a sum of two prime numbers. In a letter of 1742, Euler has written: "I believe it is a completely acceptable theorem, although I cannot prove it." This theorem has still not been proved, and it is the same about the following theorem: The sequence of the twin prime numbers[1] is infinite. In an address delivered at the International Congress of Mathematics, Cambridge, 1912, E. Landau had said that he regarded these problems as "unattainable problems in modern science."

However, one has now a starting point for the treatment of these problems, after which one has discovered that the prime numbers of Goldbach and twin prime numbers can be determined by a method analogous to that of Eratosthenes. The first who had paid attention to this fact should be Jean Merlin.[2]

The method consists of a double employing the Eratosthenes sieve. Let us, for example, give the partition of the even number 26. We write the following two sequences of numbers

$$\underline{0}\ 1\ 2\ 3\ \underline{4}\ 5\ \underline{6}\ 7\ \underline{8}\ 9\ \underline{10}\ 11\ \underline{12}\ 13\ \underline{14}\ \underline{15}\ \underline{16}\ 17\ \underline{18}\ 19\ \underline{20}\ \underline{21}\ \underline{22}\ 23\ \underline{24}\ \underline{25}\ \underline{26}$$

$$\underline{26}\ \underline{25}\ \underline{24}\ 23\ \underline{22}\ \underline{21}\ \underline{20}\ 19\ \underline{18}\ 17\ \underline{16}\ \underline{15}\ \underline{14}\ 13\ \underline{12}\ 11\ \underline{10}\ \underline{9}\ \underline{8}\ 7\ \underline{6}\ 5\ \underline{4}\ 3\ 2\ 1\ \underline{0}\,.$$

---

[1] That is to say that the couples of the prime numbers having the difference 2. See P. Stäckel in "Sitzungsberichte der Heidelberger Akademie Abt. A., Jahrg; 1916, 10 Abh.

[2] See Bulletin des Sciences mathematiques T. 39, I partie, 1915. See also Viggo Brun in "Archiv for Mathematik og Naturvidenskab" 1915, B. 34, nr. 8: "Über das Goldbachsche Gesetz und die Anzahl der Primzahlpaare."

The prime numbers not exceeding $\sqrt{26}$ are 2, 3 and 5. We efface the numbers of the form 2λ, 3λ and 5λ in our two sequences. The sum of a number of the first line and the number immediately below in the second line is 26. If these two numbers are not effaced, they are prime numbers, and give then a Goldbachian partition of 26. It is not necessary to write the second sequence. One can only choose the numbers 26 and 0 of the first sequence as the starting points of the effacements. By this method we obtain all the partitions of an even number x into a sum of two prime numbers lying between $\sqrt{x}$ and $x - \sqrt{x}$. On choosing 0 and 2 as the starting points, we can determine the twin prime numbers. We do not know if a treatment by this method can lead to a proof of these theorems; but we see that the method can at least lead to very profound results.

§2. We study at first the method of Eratosthenes, on giving it the following form:

Suppose that the series:

$$\begin{array}{cccccccccccc}
\underline{0} & \underline{1} & \underline{2} & \underline{3} & \underline{4} & \underline{5} & \underline{6} & \underline{7} & \underline{8} & \underline{9} & \underline{10} & \underline{\ldots x} \\
0 & & 2 & & 4 & & 6 & & 8 & & 10 & \ldots \\
0 & & & 3 & & & 6 & & & 9 & & \\
 & & & \ldots & & & & & & & & \\
0 & & & p_n & & & 2p_n & & & 3p_n & & \ldots \lambda p_n
\end{array}$$

are given, where x denotes an integer and p_n the n-th prime number:

$$p_n \le \sqrt{x} < p_{n+1} \quad ,$$

and λ an integer:

$$\lambda p_n \le x < (\lambda+1)p_n \quad .$$

The terms of the first series, which are different from all the terms of the other series, are the prime numbers lying between $\sqrt{x}$ and x and the number 1.

These are the terms not effaced by the Eratosthenes sieve. We generalize, on studying the following arithmetical progression

Δ	$\Delta + D$	$\Delta + 2D$	...
a_1	a_1+p_1	a_1+2p_1	...
	...		
a_r	a_r+p_r	a_r+2p_r	...

The progressions are extended from 0 to x. D denotes an integer prime to the prime numbers $p_1,\dots,p_r$ (successive or not, but different).

Δ and $a_1,\dots,a_r$ are integers:

$$0 < \Delta \le D \ , \qquad 0 < a_i < p_i \ .$$

We raise the following problem:

How many terms different from all the terms of the other lines does the first line contain?

We denote this number by

$$N(\Delta,\ D,\ x,\ a_1,\ p_1,\dots,a_r,\ p_r)$$

or often more briefly by

$$N(D,\ x,\ p_1,\dots,p_r) \ .$$

We obtain the fundamental formula:

$$N(\Delta,\ D,\ x,\ a_1,\ p_1,\dots,a_r,\ p_r)$$

$$= N(\Delta,\ D,\ x,\ a_1,\ p_1,\dots,a_{r-1},\ p_{r-1})$$

$$- N(\Delta',\ Dp_r,\ x,\ a_1,\ p_1,\dots,a_{r-1},\ p_{r-1}) \ ,$$

where

$$0 < \Delta' \le Dp_r$$

or more briefly

$$N(D, x, p_1,\ldots,p_r) = N(D, x, p_1,\ldots,p_{r-1})$$
$$- N(Dp_r, x, p_1,\ldots,p_{r-1}) \qquad (1)$$

on studying at first our arithmetical progressions up to the progression $a_{r-1} + \lambda p_{r-1}$, and on subjoining then the progression $a_r + \lambda p_r$. Suppose that $N(\Delta, D, x, a_1, p_1,\ldots,a_{r-1}, p_{r-1})$ is known. We deduce $N(\Delta, D, x, a_1, p_1,\ldots,a_r, p_r)$ from it on subtracting the number of the terms of the last progression, which are identical to the terms of the first progression, but not identical to the terms of the intermediate progressions.

We see that the number is equal to $N(\Delta', Dp_r, x, a_1, p_1,\ldots,p_{r-1})$ on noting that the terms of the last progression $a_r + \lambda p_r$, which are identical to the first progression $\Delta + \mu D$, are the terms between 0 and x of the arithmetical progression

$$\Delta' \quad \Delta' + Dp_r \quad \Delta' + 2Dp_r \; . \; . \; . \quad ,$$

where

$$0 < \Delta' \leq Dp_r \quad ,$$

Δ' being the smallest positive term of the progression.

The indeterminate equation

$$a_r + \lambda p_r = \Delta + \mu D$$

or

$$p_r\lambda - D\mu = \Delta - a_r$$

always has, as one knows, solutions, because p_r and D are relatively prime. The solutions are

$$\lambda = \lambda_0 + tD \; , \qquad \mu = \mu_0 + tp_r \quad ,$$

whenever λ_0, μ_0 are solutions and t runs through the values $0, \pm 1, \pm 2, \ldots$.

The terms of the last progression, which are identical to the terms of the first progression, are then all the terms

$$a_r + \lambda p_r = a_r + \lambda_0 p_r + tDp_r \quad , \quad \text{where} \quad t = 0, \pm 1, \pm 2, \ldots \quad .$$

These are the terms of an arithmetical progression having the difference Dp_r.

We define particularly $N(\Delta, D, x)$ or briefly $N(D, x)$ as the numbers of the terms between 0 and x of the progression

$$\Delta \qquad \Delta + D \qquad \Delta + 2D \; . \; . \; . \; \Delta + \lambda D \quad ,$$

where

$$0 < \Delta \leq D \;, \qquad \Delta + \lambda D \leq x < \Delta + (\lambda+1)D \quad .$$

Hence we deduce that

$$\lambda + 1 = N(D, x) = \frac{x}{D} + \theta \;, \qquad \text{where} \quad -1 < \theta < 1 \quad .$$

We give an example, choosing

$\Delta = 2 \quad D = 7 \quad x = 60 \quad a_1 = 2 \quad p_1 = 2 \quad a_2 = 1 \quad p_2 = 3 \quad a_3 = 4 \quad p_3 = 5$

(A) 2 9 16 23 30 37 44 51 58

(B) 2 4 6 8 10 12 14 16 18 20 22 24 26 28 30 32 34 36 38 40 42 44 46 48 50 52 54 56 58 60

(C) 1 4 7 10 13 16 19 22 25 28 31 34 37 40 43 46 49 52 55 58

(D) 4 9 14 19 24 29 34 39 44 49 54 59

The numbers of (A) which are different from the numbers of (B) and (C) are 9, 23, 51. We subjoin then the progression (D). The numbers of (A) and (D), which are identical, are 9 and 44, having the difference 7·5. We obtain then

$$N(7, 60, 2, 3, 5) = N(7, 60, 2, 3) - N(7 \cdot 5, 60, 2, 3)$$

or $2 = 3 - 1$.

From the formula (1) we deduce the following

$$N(D, x, p_1, \ldots, p_r) = N(D, x) - N(Dp_1, x) - N(Dp_2, x, p_1) - \ldots - N(Dp_r, x, p_1, \ldots, p_{r-1}) \qquad (2)$$

and

$$N(D, x, p_1,\dots,p_r) = N(D, x) - N(Dp_1, x) - \dots - N(Dp_r, x)$$
$$+ N(Dp_2p_1, x)$$
$$+ N(Dp_3p_1, x) + N(Dp_3p_2, x, p_1)$$
$$+ \dots$$
$$+ N(Dp_rp_1, x) + N(Dp_rp_2, x, p_1)$$
$$+ \dots + N(Dp_rp_{r-1}, x, p_1,\dots,p_{r-2}) \quad (3)$$

We give the last formula a concise form

$$N(D, x, p_1,\dots,p_r) = N(D, x) - \sum_{a \le r} N(Dp_a, x) + \sum_{a \le r} \sum_{b < a} N(Dp_ap_b, x, p_1,\dots,p_{b-1}). \quad (3')$$

When the question is to determine a lower bound for $N(D, x, p_1,\dots,p_r)$ we can set aside as many positive terms as we want in the formula (3). One can choose these terms in several different ways[3)], for example, the terms which lie on the right of a vertical line. In general we obtain the formula

$$N(D, x, p_1,\dots,p_r) > N(D, x) - \sum_{a \le r} N(Dp_a, x) + \sum_{\omega_1}\sum N(Dp_ap_b, x, p_1,\dots,p_{b-1}), \quad (4)$$

where we have chosen for p_ap_b a domain ω_1 which lies in the interior of the following domain

$$\begin{array}{llll} p_2p_1 & & & \\ p_3p_1 & p_3p_2 & & \\ \dots & & & \\ p_rp_1 & p_rp_2 & \cdots & p_rp_{r-1} \end{array}$$

---

3) See: "Nyt tidsskrift" 1918: Une formule exacte pour la determination du nombre des nombres premiers audessous de x, etc. by Viggo Brun.

On applying the formula (4) twice we obtain the new formula

$$N(D, x, p_1,\dots,p_r) > N(D, x) - \sum_{a \le r} N(Dp_a, x)$$

$$+ \sum_{\omega_1}\sum \left(N(Dp_ap_b, x) - \sum_{c<b} N(Dp_ap_bp_c, x)\right)$$

$$+ \sum_{\omega_1'}\sum \ \sum_{\omega_2}\sum N(Dp_ap_bp_cp_d, x, p_1,\dots,p_{d-1}) \quad ,$$

where $\omega_1' \le \omega_1$ and ω_2 denotes the domain for p_cp_d.

On continuing and applying

$$N(d, x) = \frac{x}{d} + \theta, \qquad \text{where} \quad -1 < \theta < 1 \ ,$$

we obtain at last the general formula

$$\frac{D}{x} N(D, x, p_1,\dots,p_r) > 1 - \sum_{a \le r} \frac{1}{p_a} + \sum_{\omega_1}\sum \frac{1}{p_ap_b}\left(1 - \sum_{c<b} \frac{1}{p_c}\right)$$

$$+ \sum_{\omega_1'}\sum \ \sum_{\omega_2}\sum \frac{1}{p_ap_bp_cp_d}\left(1 - \sum_{e<d} \frac{1}{p_e}\right) + \dots - \frac{RD}{x} \quad , \qquad (5)$$

where R denotes the number of terms, and where $\omega_1' \le \omega_1$ etc.

We can also give the formula (5) the following form, on supposing particularly $p_1 = 2$, $p_2 = 3$, $p_3 = 5$ etc.:

$$N(D, x, 2, 3, 5,\dots,p_r) > \frac{x}{D}\Bigg[1 - \frac{1}{2} - \frac{1}{3} - \frac{1}{5} - \dots - \frac{1}{p_r}$$

$$+ \frac{1}{3\cdot 2}$$

$$+ \frac{1}{5\cdot 2} + \frac{1}{5\cdot 3}\left(1 - \frac{1}{2}\right)$$

$$+ \frac{1}{7\cdot 2} + \frac{1}{7\cdot 3}\left(1 - \frac{1}{2}\right) + \frac{1}{7\cdot 5}\begin{pmatrix} 1 - \frac{1}{2} - \frac{1}{3} \\ + \frac{1}{3\cdot 2} \end{pmatrix}$$

$$+ \dots$$

$$+ \frac{1}{p_r \cdot 2} + \frac{1}{p_r \cdot 3}\left(1 - \frac{1}{2}\right) + \frac{1}{p_r \cdot 5}\left(\begin{matrix} 1 - \frac{1}{2} - \frac{1}{3} \\ + \frac{1}{3 \cdot 2} \end{matrix}\right)$$

$$\left. + \frac{1}{p_r \cdot 7}\left(\begin{matrix} 1 - \frac{1}{2} - \frac{1}{3} - \frac{1}{5} \\ + \frac{1}{3 \cdot 2} \\ + \frac{1}{5 \cdot 2} + \frac{1}{5 \cdot 3}\left(1 - \frac{1}{2}\right) \end{matrix}\right) + \ldots \right] - R\,,$$

where one can set aside every term (the subsequent parenthesis included), which follows the sign + .

R denotes the number of terms employed.

We obtain the better lower bound for N, when we aside those terms, which multiplied by $\frac{x}{D}$ are less than the number of terms employed.

We give an example, choosing $x = 1{,}000$, $D = 1$ and $p_r = 31$ which is the greatest prime number not exceeding $\sqrt{x}$.

$$N(1, 10^3, 2, 3, \ldots, 31) > 10^3 \left[1 - \frac{1}{2} - \frac{1}{3} - \ldots - \frac{1}{31} + \frac{1}{3 \cdot 2} \right.$$

$$+ \frac{1}{5 \cdot 2} + \frac{1}{5 \cdot 3}\left(1 - \frac{1}{2}\right) + \frac{1}{7 \cdot 2} + \frac{1}{7 \cdot 3}\left(1 - \frac{1}{2}\right) + \frac{1}{7 \cdot 5}\left(1 - \frac{1}{2} - \frac{1}{3} + \frac{1}{3 \cdot 2}\right)$$

$$+ \frac{1}{11 \cdot 2} + \frac{1}{11 \cdot 3}\left(1 - \frac{1}{2}\right) + \frac{1}{11 \cdot 5}\left(1 - \frac{1}{2} - \frac{1}{3} + \frac{1}{3 \cdot 2}\right)$$

$$+ \frac{1}{13 \cdot 2} + \frac{1}{13 \cdot 3}\left(1 - \frac{1}{2}\right) + \frac{1}{13 \cdot 5}\left(1 - \frac{1}{2} - \frac{1}{3} + \frac{1}{3 \cdot 2}\right)$$

$$+ \frac{1}{17 \cdot 2} + \frac{1}{17 \cdot 3}\left(1 - \frac{1}{2}\right) + \frac{1}{19 \cdot 2} + \frac{1}{19 \cdot 3}\left(1 - \frac{1}{2}\right) + \frac{1}{23 \cdot 2} + \frac{1}{23 \cdot 3}\left(1 - \frac{1}{2}\right)$$

$$\left. + \frac{1}{29 \cdot 2} + \frac{1}{29 \cdot 3}\left(1 - \frac{1}{2}\right) + \frac{1}{31 \cdot 2} + \frac{1}{31 \cdot 3}\left(1 - \frac{1}{2}\right) \right] - 52$$

We have set aside the term $\frac{1}{17 \cdot 5}\left(1 - \frac{1}{2} - \frac{1}{3} - \frac{1}{3 \cdot 2}\right) = 0.0039\ldots$

since $10^3 \cdot 0.0039\ldots = 3.9\ldots$ is less than 4, the number of terms employed. In the term $\frac{1}{11\cdot 7}\left(1 - \frac{1}{2} - \frac{1}{3} - \frac{1}{5} + \frac{1}{3\cdot 2} + \frac{1}{5\cdot 2} + \frac{1}{5\cdot 3}(1 - \frac{1}{2})\right)$, we would at first set aside $\frac{1}{5\cdot 3}(1 - \frac{1}{2})$ since $\frac{10^3}{11\cdot 7\cdot 5\cdot 3}(1 - \frac{1}{2}) = 0.4\ldots$ is less than 2, and we should also set aside the term $\frac{1}{11\cdot 7}\left(1 - \frac{1}{2} - \frac{1}{3} - \frac{1}{5} + \frac{1}{3\cdot 2} + \frac{1}{5\cdot 2}\right) = 0.003\ldots$ since $10^3 \cdot 0.003\ldots = 3.\ \ldots$ is less than 6.

We obtain then

$$N(1, 10^3, 2, 3, \ldots, 31) > 109 - 52 = 57 \quad .$$

We can express this result in the following way:

When we efface among 1,000 numbers all the multiples of two, three, five up to 31, there remain still at least 57 numbers. Thence we deduce particularly that there exist more than 56 prime numbers between 31 and 1000, on observing that

$$N(1, 10^3, 2, 3, \ldots, 31) = \pi(10^3) - \pi(\sqrt{10^3}) + 1$$

when we choose 0 as the starting point of the effacements.

Here $\pi(x)$ denotes the number of prime numbers not exceeding x.

Here we have chosen the domains ω in a way to obtain the most suitable lower bound. If we choose the domains ω by the same principle, we find

$$N(1, 10^3, 2, 3, \ldots, 31) > 109 - 52 = 57,$$

$$\text{while} \quad \pi(10^3) - \pi(\sqrt{10^3}) = 158 \ ,$$

$$N(1, 10^4, 2, 3, \ldots, 97) > 820 - 284 = 536 \ ,$$

$$\text{while} \quad \pi(10^4) - \pi(\sqrt{10^4}) = 1{,}206 \ ,$$

$$N(1, 10^5, 2, 3, \ldots, 313) > 5{,}733 - 1{,}862 = 3{,}871 \ ,$$

$$\text{while} \quad \pi(10^5) - \pi(\sqrt{10^5}) = 9{,}528 \ .$$

In the sequel we will choose the domains ω by simpler principles.

To illustrate the principles sought after we give at first three examples:

Eg. 1)
$$N(1, x, 2, 3, 5, 7) > x\left[1-\frac{1}{2}-\frac{1}{3}-\frac{1}{5}-\frac{1}{7}+\frac{1}{3\cdot 2}+\frac{1}{5\cdot 2}+\frac{1}{5\cdot 3}\left(1-\frac{1}{2}\right)+\frac{1}{7\cdot 2}+\frac{1}{7\cdot 3}\left(1-\frac{1}{2}\right)+\frac{1}{7\cdot 5}\begin{pmatrix}1-\frac{1}{2}-\frac{1}{3}\\ +\frac{1}{3\cdot 2}\end{pmatrix}\right]-16$$

$$= x\left(1-\frac{1}{2}\right)\left(1-\frac{1}{3}\right)\left(1-\frac{1}{5}\right)\left(1-\frac{1}{7}\right)-2^4$$

We have set aside no terms.

Eg. 2)
$$N(1, x, 2, 3, 5, 7, 11) > x\left[1-\frac{1}{2}-\frac{1}{3}-\frac{1}{5}-\frac{1}{7}-\frac{1}{11}+\frac{1}{3\cdot 2}+\frac{1}{5\cdot 2}+\frac{1}{5\cdot 3}\left(1-\frac{1}{2}\right)+\frac{1}{7\cdot 2}+\frac{1}{7\cdot 3}\left(1-\frac{1}{2}\right)+\frac{1}{7\cdot 5}\left(1-\frac{1}{2}-\frac{1}{3}\right)+\frac{1}{11\cdot 2}+\frac{1}{11\cdot 3}\left(1-\frac{1}{2}\right)+\frac{1}{11\cdot 5}\left(1-\frac{1}{2}-\frac{1}{3}\right)+\frac{1}{11\cdot 7}\left(1-\frac{1}{2}-\frac{1}{3}-\frac{1}{5}\right)\right]-26\ ,$$

where the terms set aside are added on a small scale. One can also write

$$N(1, x, 2, 3, 5, 7, 11) > x\left[\left(1-\frac{1}{2}\right)\left(1-\frac{1}{3}\right)\left(1-\frac{1}{5}\right)\left(1-\frac{1}{7}\right)\left(1-\frac{1}{11}\right)-\left(\frac{1}{7\cdot 5\cdot 3\cdot 2}+\frac{1}{11\cdot 5\cdot 3\cdot 2}+\frac{1}{11\cdot 7\cdot 3\cdot 2}+\frac{1}{11\cdot 7\cdot 5\cdot 2}+\frac{1}{11\cdot 7\cdot 5\cdot 3}\right)+\left(\frac{1}{11\cdot 7\cdot 5\cdot 3\cdot 2}\right)\right]-\left(1+5+\frac{5\cdot 4}{1\cdot 2}+\frac{5\cdot 4\cdot 3}{1\cdot 2\cdot 3}\right)$$

$$= x\left[0.2078 - 0.0121 + 0.0004\right] - 26 = 0.1961x - 26.$$

Here we have set aside all terms of the form $\frac{1}{p_a p_b p_c p_d}$ and of the form $\frac{1}{p_a p_b p_c p_d p_e}$.

Eg. 3) $N(1,\, x,\, 2,\, 3,\, 5,\, 7,\, 11,\, 13,\, 17,\, 19) > x\Big[\, 1 - \frac{1}{2} - \frac{1}{3} - \frac{1}{5}$

$$- \frac{1}{7} - \frac{1}{11} - \frac{1}{13} - \frac{1}{17} - \frac{1}{19} + \frac{1}{3\cdot 2} + \frac{1}{5\cdot 2} + \frac{1}{5\cdot 3}\left(1 - \frac{1}{2}\right) + \frac{1}{7\cdot 2}$$

$$+ \frac{1}{7\cdot 3}\left(1 - \frac{1}{2}\right) + \frac{1}{7\cdot 5}\left(1 - \frac{1}{2} - \frac{1}{3} + \frac{1}{3\cdot 2}\right)$$

$$+ \frac{1}{11\cdot 2} + \frac{1}{11\cdot 3}\left(1 - \frac{1}{2}\right) + \frac{1}{11\cdot 5}\begin{pmatrix} 1 - \frac{1}{2} - \frac{1}{3} \\ + \frac{1}{3\cdot 2} \end{pmatrix} + \frac{1}{11\cdot 7}\begin{pmatrix} 1 - \frac{1}{2} - \frac{1}{3} - \frac{1}{5} \\ + \frac{1}{3\cdot 2} \\ + \frac{1}{5\cdot 2} \end{pmatrix}$$

$$+ \frac{1}{13\cdot 2} + \frac{1}{13\cdot 3}\left(1 - \frac{1}{2}\right) + \frac{1}{13\cdot 5}\begin{pmatrix} 1 - \frac{1}{2} - \frac{1}{3} \\ + \frac{1}{3\cdot 2} \end{pmatrix} + \frac{1}{13\cdot 7}\begin{pmatrix} 1 - \frac{1}{2} - \frac{1}{3} - \frac{1}{5} \\ + \frac{1}{3\cdot 2} \\ + \frac{1}{5\cdot 2} \end{pmatrix}$$

$$+ \frac{1}{17\cdot 2} + \frac{1}{17\cdot 3}\left(1 - \frac{1}{2}\right) + \frac{1}{17\cdot 5}\begin{pmatrix} 1 - \frac{1}{2} - \frac{1}{3} \\ + \frac{1}{3\cdot 2} \end{pmatrix} + \frac{1}{17\cdot 7}\begin{pmatrix} 1 - \frac{1}{2} - \frac{1}{3} - \frac{1}{5} \\ + \frac{1}{3\cdot 2} \\ + \frac{1}{5\cdot 2} \end{pmatrix}$$

$$+ \frac{1}{19\cdot 2} + \frac{1}{19\cdot 3}\left(1 - \frac{1}{2}\right) + \frac{1}{19\cdot 5}\begin{pmatrix} 1 - \frac{1}{2} - \frac{1}{3} \\ + \frac{1}{3\cdot 2} \end{pmatrix} + \frac{1}{19\cdot 7}\begin{pmatrix} 1 - \frac{1}{2} - \frac{1}{3} - \frac{1}{5} \\ + \frac{1}{3\cdot 2} \\ + \frac{1}{5\cdot 2} \end{pmatrix}\Bigg] - 72$$

$$= 0.163x - 72 \,.$$

Here we have set aside the terms on the right of the vertical lines. One see that the expression is of the form

$$1 - \sum \frac{1}{p_a} + \sum\sum \frac{1}{p_a p_b} - \sum\sum\sum \frac{1}{p_a p_b p_c} + \sum\sum\sum\sum \frac{1}{p_a p_b p_c p_d} ,$$

where p_a, p_b, p_c and p_d run through the following values

p_a	2	3	5	7	11	13	17	19
p_b	2	3	5	7				
p_c	2	3	5	7				
p_d	2							

in which $a > b > c > d$.

§3. We study at first the method employed for example 2.

We do not apply the general formula (5), but we deduce directly from the formula (3'):

$$N(D, x, p_1, \ldots, p_r) = N(D, x) - \sum_{a \le r} N(Dp_a, x) + \sum_{a \le r} \sum_{b < a} N(Dp_a p_b, x, p_1, \ldots, p_{b-1}) .$$

On employing this formula twice, we obtain

$$\begin{aligned} N(D, x, p_1, \ldots, p_r) = N(D, x) &- \sum_{a \le r} N(Dp_a, x) \\ &+ \sum_{a \le r} \sum_{b < a} N(Dp_a p_b, x) \\ &- \sum_{a \le r} \sum_{b < a} \sum_{c < b} N(Dp_a p_b p_c, x) \\ &+ \sum_{a \le r} \sum_{b < a} \sum_{c < b} \sum_{d < c} \\ &\cdot N(Dp_a p_b p_c p_d, x, p_1, \ldots, p_{d-1}) . \quad (6) \end{aligned}$$

The last sum is positive (or 0). On applying

$$N(d, x) = \frac{x}{d} + \theta , \qquad \text{where } -1 \le \theta < 1 ,$$

thence we conclude:

$$N(D,\ x,\ p_1,\ldots,p_r) > \frac{x}{D}\left[1 - \sum_{a\le r}\frac{1}{p_a} + \sum_{a\le r}\ \sum_{b<a}\frac{1}{p_a p_b} - \sum_{a\le r}\ \sum_{b<a}\ \sum_{c<b}\frac{1}{p_a p_b p_c}\right] - R\ , \tag{7}$$

or more briefly

$$N(D,\ x,\ p_1,\ldots,p_r) > \frac{x}{D}\left[1 - \Sigma_1 + \Sigma_2 - \Sigma_3\right] - R\ , \tag{7'}$$

where Σ_1 is equal to the sum of the terms of the first of the following three lines

$$\begin{array}{l} \frac{1}{p_1} + \frac{1}{p_2} + \ldots + \frac{1}{p_r} = \sigma \\ \frac{1}{p_1} + \frac{1}{p_2} + \ldots + \frac{1}{p_r} \\ \frac{1}{p_1} + \frac{1}{p_2} + \ldots + \frac{1}{p_r}\ , \end{array} \tag{A}$$

Σ_2 is equal to the sum of the terms formed by multiplication of every term of the first line by those terms of the second line, which lie on the left of this term, and Σ_3 can be defined similarly.

We will say, in the sequel, that we calculate the expression

$$1 - \Sigma_1 + \Sigma_2 - \Sigma_3$$

by means of diagram (A) or more briefly by means of the diagram

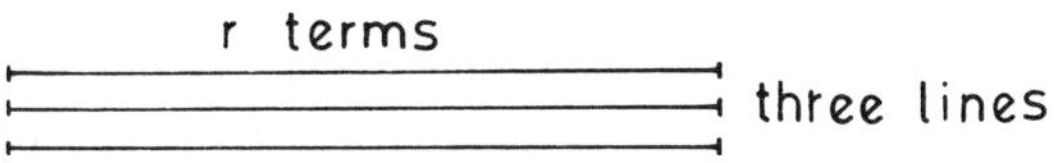

We compare Σ_2 and σ^2:

$$\sigma^2 = \left(\frac{1}{p_1}\right)^2 + \left(\frac{1}{p_2}\right)^2 + \ldots + \left(\frac{1}{p_r}\right)^2 + 2\Sigma_2 > 2\Sigma_2$$

$$\text{or} \quad \sigma\Sigma_1 > 2\Sigma_2\ .$$

We will also prove that

$$\sigma\sum_2 > 3\sum_3 \quad \text{or} \quad \left(\sum_{c\le r}\frac{1}{p_c}\right)\left(\sum_{a\le r}\ \sum_{b<a}\frac{1}{p_a p_b}\right)$$

$$> 3\left(\sum_{a\le r}\ \sum_{b<a}\ \sum_{c<b}\frac{1}{p_a p_b p_c}\right)$$

Any term $\frac{1}{p_\alpha p_\beta p_\gamma}$, where $\gamma < \beta < \alpha \le r$, is represented once in $\sum_3$ but, as we see, three times in $\sigma\sum_2$.

We search at first $\frac{1}{p_\alpha}$ in $\sum_{c\le r}\frac{1}{p_c}$ and $\frac{1}{p_\beta p_\gamma}$ in $\sum_{a\le r}\ \sum_{b<a}\cdot\frac{1}{p_a p_b}$, and then $\frac{1}{p_\beta}$ in $\sum_{c\le r}\frac{1}{p_c}$ and $\frac{1}{p_\alpha p_\gamma}$ in $\sum_{a\le r}\ \sum_{b<a}\frac{1}{p_a p_b}$, and at last $\frac{1}{p_\gamma}$ in $\sum_{c\le r}\frac{1}{p_c}$ and $\frac{1}{p_\alpha p_\beta}$ in $\sum_{a\le r}\ \sum_{b<a}\frac{1}{p_a p_b}$.

The term $\frac{1}{p_\alpha p_\beta p_\gamma}$ is therefore represented three times in $\sigma\sum_2$, which contains also terms of the form $\frac{1}{p_\alpha^2 p_\beta}$ etc. Hence we conclude that $\sigma\sum_2 > 3\sum_3$.

We can generalize the formula (7), on calculating the last sum in (6) by means (6). On continuing we obtain a formula analogous to (7) or more briefly analogous to (7'):

$$N(D,\ x,\ p_1,\ldots,p_r) > \frac{x}{D}\left[1 - \sum_1 + \sum_2 - \ldots - \sum_m\right] - R\ , \qquad (8)$$

where m is an odd number satisfying $m \le r$, and where the expression $1 - \sum_1 + \sum_2 - \ldots - \sum_m$ is calculated by means of the diagram

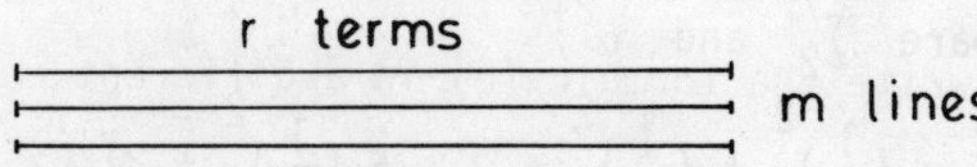

We can, in the special case $m = r$, calculate this expression:

$$1 - \sum_1 + \sum_2 - \dots + (-1)^r \sum_r$$

$$= (1 - \frac{1}{p_1})\ (1 - \frac{1}{p_2})\ \dots\ (1 - \frac{1}{p_r})$$

$$= 1 - \sum_{a \le r} \frac{1}{p_a} + \sum_{a \le r} \ \sum_{b < a} \frac{1}{p_a p_b} - \dots \quad ,$$

where r may be even or odd. The number of terms is 2^r in this case. We obtain then the formula

$$N(D, x, p_1,\dots,p_r) > \frac{x}{D} (1 - \frac{1}{p_1})\ (1 - \frac{1}{p_2})\ \dots\ (1 - \frac{1}{p_r}) - 2^r \ . \tag{9}$$

In general case we will determine a lower bound for the expression

$$1 - \sum_1 + \sum_2 - \dots - \sum_m \ .$$

We can, as before, prove that

$$\sigma = \sum_1 \ , \qquad \sigma \sum_i > (i+1) \sum_{i+1} \qquad (1 \le i \le m-1)$$

whence $\sigma^m > m! \sum_m$.

Hence we conclude

$$\sum_m < \frac{\sigma}{m} \sum_{m-1} \tag{10}$$

and

$$\sum_m < \frac{\sigma^m}{m!} < \left(\frac{e\sigma}{m}\right)^m \tag{11}$$

on applying the Stirling formula

$$m! = \left(\frac{m}{e}\right)^m (\sqrt{2\pi m} + \theta) \quad , \qquad -1 < \theta < 1 \ .$$

We now write the formula (8) in a different way

$$N(D, x, p_1,\dots,p_r) > \frac{x}{D} \Big[(1 - \sum_1 + \sum_2 - \dots + (-1)^r \sum_r)$$

$$- (\sum_{m+1} - \sum_{m+2} + \dots + (-1)^r \sum_r)\Big] - R \ .$$

We know the value of the first parenthesis in the form of a product. The second parenthesis is composed of a series of decreasing terms, whenever $m+2 > \sigma$, and then it has a value less than $\sum_{m+1}$, which is less than $\left(\frac{e\sigma}{m+1}\right)^{m+1}$.

We can therefore write

$$N(D, x, p_1,\ldots,p_r) > \frac{x}{D}\left[(1-\frac{1}{p_1}) \ldots (1-\frac{1}{p_r}) - (\frac{e\sigma}{m+1})^{m+1}\right] - R .$$

It is not difficult to determine the value of R[4]:

$$R = 1 + \binom{r}{1} + \binom{r}{2} + \ldots + \binom{r}{m}$$

$$< 1 + r + r^2 + \ldots + r^m < r^{m+1} .$$

We obtain then the formula

$$N(D, x, p_1,\ldots,p_r) > \frac{x}{D}\left[(1-\frac{1}{p_1}) \ldots (1-\frac{1}{p_r}) - (\frac{e\sigma}{m+1})^{m+1}\right] - r^{m+1} \tag{12}$$

whenever

$$m+2 > \sigma = \frac{1}{p_1} + \ldots + \frac{1}{p_r} .$$

This formula is more useful than (9), the growth of r^{m+1} being not so great as that of 2^r. But the growth of the term R is still too great for our purpose.

§4. For this reason we shall choose the domains ω in another way, setting aside all terms on the right of the vertical lines, as in the example 3 (§2).

At first we set aside in the formula (3) all positive terms on the right on a vertical line. We obtain then the following formula

---

[4] See, for example, Landau: Handbuch der Lehre von der Verteilung der Primzahlen, I, p. 67.

$$N(D, x, p_1,\dots,p_r) > N(D, x) - \sum_{a \le r} N(Dp_a, x) + \sum_{a \le r} \sum_{\substack{b < a \\ b < t}} N(Dp_a p_b, x, p_1,\dots,p_{b-1}) , \tag{13}$$

where t is an integer less than r.

The terms of the last sum can be calculated by means of the same formula, whence one deduces

$$N(D, x, p_1,\dots,p_r) > N(D, x) - \sum_{a \le r} N(Dp_a, x)$$

$$+ \sum_{a \le r} \sum_{\substack{b < a \\ b < t}} N(Dp_a p_b, x) - \sum_{a \le r} \sum_{\substack{b < a \\ b < t}} \sum_{\substack{c < b \\ c < t}} N(Dp_a p_b p_c, x)$$

$$+ \sum_{a \le r} \sum_{\substack{b < a \\ b < t}} \sum_{\substack{c < b \\ c < t}} \sum_{\substack{d < c \\ d < u}} N(Dp_a p_b p_c p_d, x, p_1,\dots,p_{d-1}) ,$$

where u is an integer less than t.

On continuing, and on applying

$$N(d, x) = \frac{x}{d} + \theta , \qquad -1 < \theta < 1 ,$$

we obtain at last the formula

$$N(D, x, p_1,\dots,p_r) > \frac{x}{D} \Bigg[1 - \sum_{a \le r} \frac{1}{p_r} + \sum_{a \le r} \sum_{\substack{b < a \\ b < t}} \frac{1}{p_a p_b}$$

$$- \sum_{a \le r} \sum_{\substack{b < a \\ b < t}} \sum_{\substack{c < b \\ c < t}} \frac{1}{p_a p_b p_c}$$

$$+ \sum_{a \le r} \sum_{\substack{b < a \\ b < t}} \sum_{\substack{c < b \\ c < t}} \sum_{\substack{d < c \\ d < u}} \frac{1}{p_a p_b p_c p_d} - \dots \Bigg] - R \tag{14}$$

or more briefly

$$N(D, x, p_1,\dots,p_r) > \frac{x}{D} \Big[1 - S_1 + S_2 - \dots - S_{2n-1} \Big] - R , \tag{14'}$$

where the expression

$$E_n = 1 - S_1 + S_2 - \dots - S_{2n-1}$$

is calculated by means of the diagram in the form of stairs

$$\begin{array}{l}
\overbrace{\frac{1}{p_1} + \dots + \frac{1}{p_{w-1}}}^{\sigma_n} + \dots + \overbrace{\frac{1}{p_u} + \dots + \frac{1}{p_{t-1}}}^{\sigma_2} \quad \overbrace{\frac{1}{p_t} + \dots + \frac{1}{p_r}}^{\sigma_1} \\
\frac{1}{p_1} + \dots + \frac{1}{p_{w-1}} + \dots + \frac{1}{p_u} + \dots + \frac{1}{p_{t-1}} \\
\frac{1}{p_1} + \dots + \frac{1}{p_{w-1}} + \dots + \frac{1}{p_u} + \dots + \frac{1}{p_{t-1}} \\
\dots\dots \\
\frac{1}{p_1} + \dots + \frac{1}{p_{w-1}} \\
\frac{1}{p_1} + \dots + \frac{1}{p_{w-1}} .
\end{array}$$

We choose the prime numbers of the diagram as successive prime numbers lying in the interior of the following intervals

$$R_r^{\frac{1}{\alpha^n}} \quad p_1 \quad p_r^{\frac{1}{\alpha^{n-1}}} \quad \dots \quad p_r^{\frac{1}{\alpha^2}} \quad p_r^{\frac{1}{\alpha}} \quad p_r$$

where $\alpha > 1$.

We apply the Mertens' formulas, giving them the following forms:

$$\sum_2^x \frac{1}{p} = \log\log x + 0.261 \dots + \theta \frac{5}{\log x} \quad , \quad -1 < \theta < 1$$

$$\prod_2^x \left(1 - \frac{1}{p}\right) = e^{7\Theta/\log x} \, \frac{0.561\dots}{\log x} \quad , \quad -1 < \Theta < 1$$

where log denotes the natural logarithm.

---

5) See, "Journal fur die reine und angewandte Mathematik" B.78, 1874, or Landau, Handbuch, I, p. 201.

Hence we conclude

$$\sum_{x}^{x^{\alpha}} \frac{1}{p} = \log \alpha + \theta \frac{5(1+\frac{1}{\alpha})}{\log x} , \qquad \prod_{x}^{x^{\alpha}} (1-\frac{1}{p}) = \frac{1}{\alpha} e^{(1+1/\alpha)7\Theta/\log x} .$$

But in that case we can choose p_1 sufficiently large for which

$$\sigma_1 = \frac{1}{p_t} + \ldots + \frac{1}{p_r} < \log \alpha_0 ,$$

$$\sigma_2 = \frac{1}{p_u} + \ldots + \frac{1}{p_{t-1}} < \log \alpha_0 , \ldots$$

$$\sigma_n = \frac{1}{p_1} + \ldots + \frac{1}{p_{w-1}} < \log \alpha_0 \tag{15}$$

and

$$\pi_1 = (1-\frac{1}{p_t}) \ldots (1-\frac{1}{p_r}) > \frac{1}{\alpha_0} ,$$

$$\pi_2 = (1-\frac{1}{p_u}) \ldots (1-\frac{1}{p_{t-1}}) > \frac{1}{\alpha_0} , \ldots$$

$$\pi_n = (1-\frac{1}{p_1}) \ldots (1-\frac{1}{p_{w-1}}) > \frac{1}{\alpha_0} , \tag{16}$$

whenever $\alpha_0 > \alpha$.

We suppose particularly $\log \alpha_0 < 1$.

We try to realize a successive calculation of the sums, to which the diagrams in the form of stairs give rise.

Suppose that we have calculated by means of the diagram

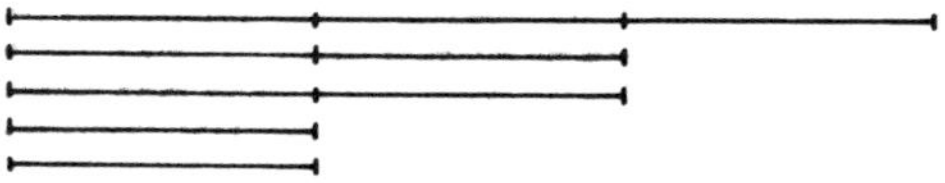

(2m-1) lines

giving rise to the expression $E_m = 1 - S_1 + S_2 - \ldots - S_{2m-1}$.

We subjoin then $2m+1$ lines on the left, (which only taken gives rise to the expression $1 - \sum_1 + \sum_2 - \ldots - \sum_{2m+1}$):

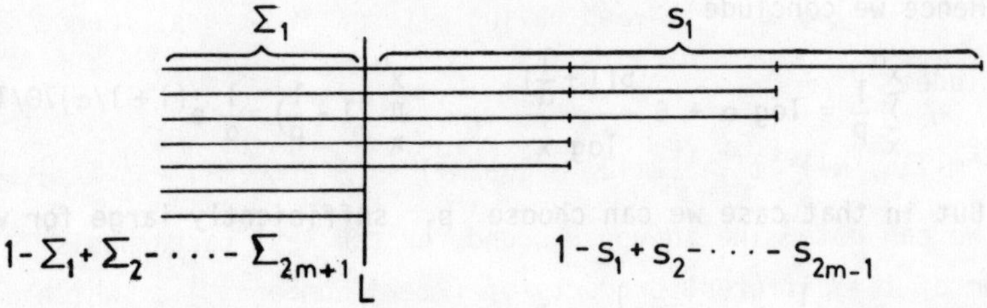

The sum $\sum \frac{1}{p_a}$ is now equal to $\sum_1 + S_1$. We see also that the new sum $\sum\sum \frac{1}{p_a p_b}$ is equal to $\sum_2 + S_1\sum_1 + S_2$ on studying the three possible cases:

p_a occurs on the left of L and p_b on the left of L $(\sum_2)$

p_a occurs on the left of L and p_b on the right of L $(S_1\sum_1)$

p_a occurs on the right of L and p_b on the right of L (S_2) .

In general we can calculate the new expression E_{m+1} by the following way:

$$E_{m+1} = 1 - \left(\sum_1 + S_1\right) + \left(\sum_2 + S_1\sum_1 + S_2\right) - \left(\sum_3 + S_1\sum_2 + S_2\sum_1 + S_3\right)$$

$$+ \ldots - \left(\sum_{2m+1} + S_1 \sum_{2m} + \ldots + S_{2m-1} \sum_2\right).$$

We compare this expression with the following product

$$(1 - \sum_1 + \sum_2 - \ldots \pm \sum_\nu)(1 - S_1 + S_2 - \ldots - S_{2m-1})$$

$$= 1 - (\sum_1 + S_1) + (\sum_2 + S_1\sum_1 + S_2) - \ldots$$

$$- (\sum_{2m+1} + S_1\sum_{2m} + \ldots + S_{2m-1} \sum_2)$$

$$+ (\sum_{2m+2} + S_1 \sum_{2m+1} + \ldots + S_{2m-1} \sum_3) - \ldots \quad .$$

The first factor contains as many terms as possible, that is to say, ν is equal to the number of the terms in $\sum_1$. The product contains, as one sees, all the terms of E_{m+1} and in addition a series of parentheses, whose values, by (10), are decreasing, since

$\sum_1 = \sigma_{m+1} < \log \alpha_0 < 1$, and having alternative signs. Hence we conclude

$$E_{m+1} > \pi_{m+1} E_m - (E_{2m+2} + S_1 \textstyle\sum_{2m+1} + \dots + S_{2m-1} \sum_3) . \qquad (17)$$

We can determine an upper bound for the last parenthesis. It is a sum of the different products of (2m+2) numbers $\frac{1}{p}$, which all occur in the two sums S_1 and $\sum_1$. But we obtain the sum of all possible products of that form, on forming the sum

$$(S_1 + \textstyle\sum_1)_{2m+2}$$

calculating by means of the diagram

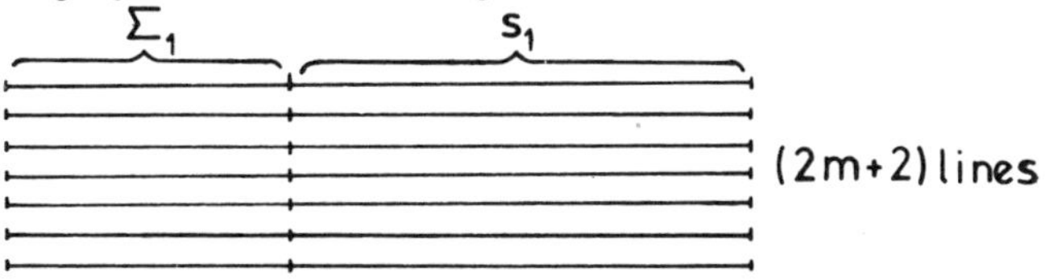

But by (11) and (15) we obtain

$$(S_1 + \textstyle\sum_1)_{2m+2} < \left(\dfrac{e(S_1 + \sum_1)}{2m+2} \right)^{2m+2} < \left(\dfrac{e(m+1) \log \alpha_0}{2(m+1)} \right)^{2m+2}$$

$$= \left(\frac{e \log \alpha_0}{2} \right)^{2m+2}$$

Our parenthesis (in (17)) is then still less, whence we conclude that

$$E_{m+1} > \pi_{m+1} E_m - \left(\frac{e \log \alpha_0}{2} \right)^{2m+2}$$

We obtain then particularly, since $E_1 = 1 - S_1$,

$$E_1 > 1 - \log \alpha_0 ,$$

$$E_2 > \pi_2 E_1 - \left(\frac{e \log \alpha_0}{2} \right)^4 > \pi_2 \left(1 - \log \alpha_0 - \alpha_0 \left(\frac{e \log \alpha_0}{2} \right)^4 \right)$$

on applying (16). On continuing in the same way, we obtain at last

$$E_n > \pi_2 \pi_3 \ldots \pi_n \left(1 - \log \alpha_0 - \alpha_0 \left(\frac{e \log \alpha_0}{2} \right)^4 - \ldots - \alpha_0^{n-1} \left(\frac{e \log \alpha_0}{2} \right)^{2n} \right),$$

or, since $\pi_1 < 1$:

$$E_n > \pi_1 \pi_2 \ldots \pi_n \left(1 - \log \alpha_0 - \frac{\alpha_0 \left(\frac{e \log \alpha_0}{2} \right)^4}{1 - \alpha_0 \left(\frac{e \log \alpha_0}{2} \right)^2} \right)$$

whenever $\alpha_0 \left(\frac{e \log \alpha_0}{2} \right)^2 < 1$.

Choose particularly

$$\alpha = \frac{3}{2} \quad \text{and} \quad \alpha_0 = 1.51 \ .$$

We obtain

$$E_n > 0.3(1 - \frac{1}{p_1}) \ldots (1 - \frac{1}{p_r}) \tag{19}$$

We study the number (R) of terms in E_n, on forming the following product

$$(1 - \frac{1}{p_1} - \ldots - \frac{1}{p_r}) \, (1 - \frac{1}{p_1} - \ldots - \frac{1}{p_{t-1}})^2 \ldots (1 - \frac{1}{p_1} - \ldots - \frac{1}{p_{w-1}})^2 .$$

This product contains all the terms of E_n and more. The number $(r+1)$ of terms in the first factor is less than p_r, and in the second less than $p_r^{1/\alpha}$ etc. We obtain the number of terms of the product, on substituting all the terms $-\frac{1}{p}$ by $+1$, whence we conclude

$$R < p_r \cdot p_r^{2/\alpha} \ldots p_r^{2/\alpha^n} < p_r^{(\alpha+1)/(\alpha-1)} = p_r^5 .$$

We can then give (14') the following form

$$N(D,\, x,\, p_1,\ldots,p_r) > \frac{x}{D}\, 0.3\left(1-\frac{1}{p_1}\right) \ldots \left(1-\frac{1}{p_r}\right) - p_r^5 \,. \qquad (20)$$

This formula is valid for all successive prime numbers $p_1,\ldots,p_r$ with $p_1 \geq p_e$, where p_e denotes a determinable prime number.

Suppose particularly $p_1 = p_{e+1}$, the (e+1)-th prime number.

When the question is to calculate $N(D, x, 2,\ldots,p_e, p_1,\ldots,p_r)$, we can subjoin to our diagram (under (14)) the following:

$$\frac{1}{2} + \frac{1}{3} + \ldots + \frac{1}{p_e}$$

$$\cdots\cdots$$

$$\frac{1}{2} + \frac{1}{3} + \ldots + \frac{1}{p_e}$$

which gives rise to the expression

$$\left(1-\frac{1}{2}\right) \ldots \left(1-\frac{1}{p_e}\right) = 1 - \sum_1 + \sum_2 - \ldots \pm \sum_e$$

containing 2^e terms, whenever the number of the lines are $\geq e$.

We obtain then the new diagram

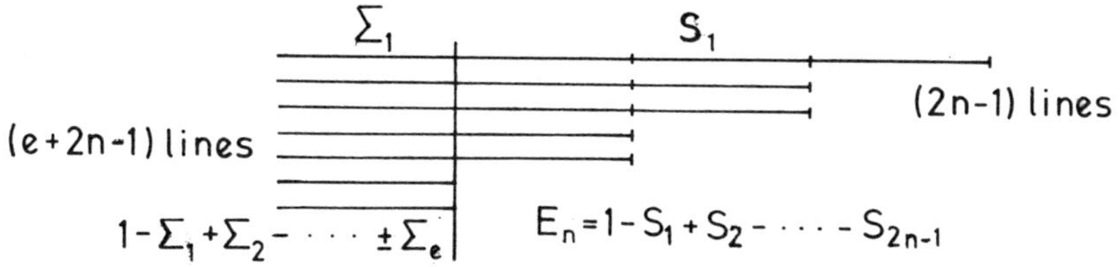

giving rise to the new expression E_{n+1}:

$$\begin{aligned} E_{n+1} = 1 &- \left(\sum_1 + S_1\right) + \left(\sum_2 + S_1\sum_1 + S_2\right) - \ldots \\ &+ \left(\sum_e + S_1 \sum_{e-1} + \ldots + S_e\right) \\ &- \left(S_1\sum_e + S_2 \sum_{e-1} + \ldots + S_{e+1}\right) + \ldots \\ &+ \left(S_{2n-e} \sum_e + \ldots + S_{2n-1} \sum_1\right) + \ldots + \left(S_{2n-1} \sum_e\right) \end{aligned}$$

or

$$E_{n+1} = (1-\sum_1+\sum_2 - \ldots + \sum_e)(1-S_1+S_2 - \ldots + S_{2n-1})$$
$$= (1-\frac{1}{2}) \ldots (1-\frac{1}{p_e})E_n \quad ,$$

where we have supposed e to be even.

We obtain then by means of (19) the formula

$$N(D, x, 2, 3, \ldots, p_r) > \frac{x}{D}\, 0.3\, (1-\frac{1}{2})(1-\frac{1}{3}) \ldots (1-\frac{1}{p_r}) - 2^e p_r^5 \qquad (21)$$

valid for all $r > e$, where e denotes a determinable number, on noting that every term of $(1-\frac{1}{2})(1-\frac{1}{3}) \ldots (1-\frac{1}{p_r})$ is multiplied by every term of E_n.

But in that case we can determine, by the Mertens' formula, a number c in a way that

$$N(D, x, 2, 3, \ldots, p_r) > \frac{0.168\, x}{D \log p_r} - 2^e p_r^5 \qquad (22)$$

for all $r > c$, where c denotes a determinable number ($c \geq e$).

If we choose $D = 1$ and $P_r = p(\sqrt[6]{x})$, i.e.; the greatest prime number not exceeding $\sqrt[6]{x}$: $p_r \leq \sqrt[6]{x} < p_{r+1}$, we obtain particularly:

$$N\left(1, x, 2, 3, \ldots, p(\sqrt[6]{x})\right) > \frac{1.008\, x}{\log x} - 2^e\, x^{5/6} > \frac{x}{\log x}$$

for all $x > x_0$.

We can then state the following theorem:

When we efface from x consecutive numbers the terms from two to two, then from three to three, etc; finally from $p(\sqrt[6]{x})$ to $p(\sqrt[6]{x})$, there remain always more than $\frac{x}{\log x}$ terms, provided $x > x_0$.

The starting points of the effacements can be chosen as one would have it. x_0 denotes a determinable number.

We can also deduce, by means of the formula (22), the following theorem:

There exists always a number between n and $n+\sqrt{n}$, whose number of prime factors does not exceed eleven whenever $n > n_0$.

Choose in the formula (22)

$$D = 1, \qquad x = \sqrt{n} \qquad \text{and} \qquad p_r = p(n^{1/11}) .$$

We obtain then

$$N(1, \sqrt{n}, 2,3,\ldots,p(n^{1/11})) > \frac{1.8\sqrt{n}}{\log n} - 2^e\, n^{5/11} > 1$$

for all $n > n_0$.

When we efface in the interval $[n, n+\sqrt{n}]$ all the multiples of two, three, etc. up to $p(n^{1/11})$, there remains therefore at least one number. We choose n as a starting point of the effacements. The numbers not effaced cannot be composed of 12 or more prime factors, because in that case one of these factors would be less than $\sqrt[12]{n+\sqrt{n}}$, and therefore less than $\sqrt[11]{n}$ for all $n > n_0$. But all these numbers being divisible by 2, 3,..., or $p(n^{1/11})$ are effaced.

§5. We have supposed that

$$2, 3,\ldots,p_r$$

in the formula (21) are successive prime numbers.

We generalize easily on studying the non-successive prime numbers

$$q_1, q_2,\ldots,q_{\alpha-1}, q_{\alpha+1},\ldots,q_{\gamma-1}, q_{\gamma+1},\ldots,q_r$$

forming a part of the successive prime numbers

$$q_1, q_2,\ldots,q_{\alpha-1}, q_\alpha, q_{\alpha+1},\ldots,q_{\gamma-1}, q_\gamma, q_{\gamma+1},\ldots,q_r ,$$

where $q_1 = 2$ etc;

and we obtain as before (see (21)):

$$N(D, x, q_1,\ldots,q_{\alpha-1}, q_{\alpha+1},\ldots,q_r)$$

$$> \frac{x}{D} \cdot 0.3(1-\frac{1}{q_1}) \ldots (1-\frac{1}{q_{\alpha-1}})(1-\frac{1}{q_{\alpha+1}}) \ldots (1-\frac{1}{q_r}) - 2^e q_r^5$$

or

$$N(D, x, q_1,\ldots,q_{\alpha-1}, q_{\alpha+1},\ldots,q_r)$$

$$> \frac{x}{D} \cdot 0.3 \frac{(1-\frac{1}{q_1}) \ldots (1-\frac{1}{q_r})}{(1-\frac{1}{q_\alpha}) \ldots (1-\frac{1}{q_\gamma})} - 2^e q_r^5 .$$

Hence we conclude

$$N(D, x, q_1,\ldots,q_{\alpha-1}, q_{\alpha+1},\ldots,q_r)$$

$$> \frac{0.168\,x}{D \log q_r} \cdot \frac{1}{(1-\frac{1}{q_\alpha}) \ldots (1-\frac{1}{q_\gamma})} - 2^e q_r^5 .$$

We study now an arithmetical progression extended from 0 to x:

$$\Delta \qquad \Delta + D \qquad \Delta + 2D \;\ldots. \qquad ,$$

Δ and D being relatively prime. Suppose

$$D = q_\alpha^a \ldots q_\gamma^c .$$

We efface now the numbers being divisible by

$$q_1,\ldots,q_{\alpha-1}, q_{\alpha+1},\ldots,q_{\gamma-1}, q_{\gamma+1},\ldots,q_r$$

on choosing $q_r = q(\sqrt[6]{x})$. We obtain

$$N(D, x, q_1,\ldots,q_{\alpha-1}, q_{\alpha+1},\ldots,q_r) > \frac{0.168\,x}{\phi(D) \log q_r} - 2^e q_r^5$$

$$> \frac{1.008\,x}{\phi(D) \log x} - 2^e x^{5/6} > \frac{1}{\phi(D)} \cdot \frac{x}{\log x}$$

for all $x > x_0$.

The numbers not effaced are indivisible by

$$q_1,\ldots,q_{\alpha-1},\ q_{\alpha+1},\ldots,q_{\gamma-1},\ q_{\gamma+1},\ldots,q_r$$

but they are also indivisible by

$$q_\alpha,\ldots,q_r\ ,$$

since Δ and D are relatively prime. The numbers not effaced contain therefore five or less prime factors.

Hence we deduce the following theorem analogous to that of Dirichlet:

Every arithmetical progression, whose first term and difference are relatively prime, contains an infinity of terms, whose number of prime factors does not exceed five.

§6. Now we study the Merlin's sieve, where one efface double all the multiples of three, five, etc. up to p_r. On generalizing, we study the following arithmetical progression

Δ	$\Delta + D$	$\Delta + 2D$	...
a_1	$a_1 + p_1$	$a_1 + 2p_1$	...
b_1	$b_1 + p_1$	$b_1 + 2p_1$	...
	...	...	
a_r	$a_r + p_r$	$a_r + 2p_r$	...
b_r	$b_r + p_r$	$b_r + 2p_r$	...

All the letters are defined in §2. Moreover we suppose $a_i \neq b_i$ and $p_1 \geq 3$. Denote by

$$P(\Delta,\ D,\ x,\ a_1,\ b_1,\ p_1,\ldots,a_r,\ b_r,\ p_r)$$

or more briefly by

$$P(D,\ x,\ p_1,\ldots,p_r)$$

the number of the terms of the first progression, which are different from all the terms of the other progressions. We deduce as before the fundamental formula

$$P(\Delta, x, a_1, b_1, p_1, \ldots, a_r, b_r, p_r)$$

$$= P(\Delta, D, x, a_1, b_1, p_1, \ldots, a_{r-1}, b_{r-1}, p_{r-1})$$

$$- P(\Delta', Dp_r, x, a_1, b_1, p_1, \ldots, a_{r-1}, b_{r-1}, p_{r-1})$$

$$- P(\Delta'', Dp_r, x, a_1, b_1, p_1, \ldots, a_{r-1}, b_{r-1}, p_{r-1}) \;,$$

or more briefly

$$P(D, x, p_1, \ldots, p_r) = P(D, x, p_1, \ldots, p_{r-1})$$

$$- 2P(Dp_r, x, p_1, \ldots, p_{r-1}) \;. \qquad (23)$$

It can give rise to no misunderstanding, since we have written $2P(Dp_r, x, p_1, \ldots, p_{r-1})$ when one remembers that it denotes a sum of two expressions of the form $P(\Delta, Dp_r, x, a_1, b_1, p_1, \ldots, a_{r-1}, b_{r-1}, p_{r-1})$.

We obtain as before, by means (23), the general formula analogous to (5)

$$\frac{D}{x} P(D, x, p_1, \ldots, p_r) > 1 - \sum_{a \leq r} \frac{2}{p_a} + \sum_{\omega_1}\sum \frac{2^2}{p_a p_b}\left(1 - \sum_{c<b} \frac{2}{p_c}\right)$$

$$+ \sum_{\omega_1'}\sum \sum_{\omega_1}\sum \frac{2^4}{p_a p_b p_c p_d}\left(1 - \sum_{e<d} \frac{2}{p_e}\right) + \ldots + \frac{RD}{x} \;, \qquad (24)$$

where $\omega_1' \leq \omega_1$ etc.

R denotes the number of the terms of the form $\pm \frac{1}{n}$ in the formula, (where $\frac{2}{n} = \frac{1}{n} + \frac{1}{n}$, etc.). We have supposed that $p_1 \geq 3$. Besides the designations, all are the same as in the formula (5).

We can also give the formula (24) the following form, on supposing particularly $p_1 = 3$, $p_2 = 5$, $p_3 = 7$, etc.:

$$P(D, x, 3, 5, \ldots, p_r) > \frac{x}{D}\Bigg[1 - \frac{2}{3} - \frac{2}{5} - \cdots - \frac{2}{p_r}$$

$$+ \frac{4}{5\cdot 3} + \frac{4}{7\cdot 3} + \frac{4}{7\cdot 5}\left(1 - \frac{2}{3}\right) + \cdots + \frac{4}{p_r\cdot 3} + \frac{4}{p_r\cdot 5}\left(1 - \frac{2}{3}\right)$$

$$+ \frac{1}{p_r\cdot 7}\left(1 - \frac{2}{3} - \frac{2}{5} + \frac{4}{5\cdot 3}\right) + \frac{4}{p_r\cdot 7}\left(1 - \frac{2}{3} - \frac{2}{5} - \frac{2}{7} + \frac{4}{5\cdot 3} + \frac{4}{7\cdot 3} + \frac{4}{7\cdot 5}\left(1 - \frac{2}{3}\right)\right) + \cdots\Bigg] - R, \tag{25}$$

where one can set aside every term, (the subsequent parenthesis included), which follows the sign + .

We give an example, one studying the following arithmetical progression extended from 0 to 11,776

1	3	5	7	9	11	13	15	...	11,769	11,771	11,773	11,775	
0	3	6		9	12		15	...	11,769	11,772		11,775	
1	4		7	10		13				11,770	11,773		11,776
	. . .												
0							19	...	11,761				
						15		...	11,757				11,776

The starting points of the effacements are 0 and 11,776 (see §1).

We obtain by means of (25), on observing that $a_i \neq b_i$, since $11{,}776 = 2^9\cdot 23$ is indivisible by 3, 5, 7,...,19 :

$$P(2,\ 11{,}776,\ 3,\ 5,\dots,19) > \frac{11{,}776}{2}\Bigg[1 - \frac{2}{3} - \frac{2}{5} - \frac{2}{7} - \frac{2}{11} - \frac{2}{13} - \frac{2}{17}$$

$$- \frac{2}{19} + \frac{4}{5\cdot 3} + \frac{4}{7\cdot 3} + \frac{4}{7\cdot 5}\left(1 - \frac{2}{3}\right) + \frac{4}{11\cdot 3} + \frac{4}{11\cdot 5}\left(1 - \frac{2}{3}\right)$$

$$+ \frac{4}{11\cdot 7}\begin{pmatrix} 1 - \frac{2}{3} - \frac{2}{5} \\ + \frac{4}{5\cdot 3} \end{pmatrix} + \frac{4}{13\cdot 3} + \frac{4}{13\cdot 5}\left(1 - \frac{2}{3}\right) + \frac{4}{13\cdot 7}\begin{pmatrix} 1 - \frac{2}{3} - \frac{2}{5} \\ + \frac{4}{5\cdot 3} \end{pmatrix}$$

$$+ \frac{4}{17\cdot 3} + \frac{4}{17\cdot 5}\left(1 - \frac{2}{3}\right) + \frac{4}{19\cdot 3} + \frac{4}{19\cdot 5}\left(1 - \frac{2}{3}\right)\Bigg] - R\ ,$$

where

$$R = 1 + 14 + 4 + 16 + 52 + 52 + 32 = 171\ ,$$

whence $P(2,\ 11{,}776,\ 3,\ 5,\dots,19) > 296 - 171 = 125$.

The number (t) not effaced of the first progression, whose number is more than 125, having the following property: t and $11{,}776 - t$ are indivisible by 2, 3, 5,...,19. They cannot composed of three or more prime factors, because otherwise one of these factors would be less than $\sqrt[3]{11{,}776} < 22.9$.

One can then write the number 11,776 as the sum of two numbers, whose number of prime factors do not exceed 2, in 125 or more different ways.

However, I have not succeeded in giving an example of the justness of the theorem of Goldbach by this method.

Nevertheless we see that we can deduce important results by means of the formula (24), the method being completely analogous to that employed above.

One should only replace $\frac{1}{p_i}$ by $\frac{2}{p_i}$ everywhere.

We calculate by means of the same diagram in the form of stairs as in §4 on replacing $\frac{1}{p_i}$ by $\frac{2}{p_i}$. One should then replace the sums and the products considered in §4 by the following:

$$\sigma_1 = \frac{2}{p_t} + \ldots + \frac{2}{p_r} < 2\log\alpha_0 \quad , \quad \text{etc.} \; ,$$

and

$$\Pi_1 = (1 - \frac{2}{p_t}) \ldots (1 - \frac{2}{p_r}) < \frac{1}{\alpha_0^2} \quad , \quad \text{etc.} \quad ,$$

on applying the following formula

$$\prod_3^x (1 - \frac{2}{p}) = \frac{0.8322}{\log^2 x} \cdot e^{c\theta/\log x} \quad .$$

We suppose now $2\log\alpha_0 < 1$.

We deduce the following formula analogous to (18):

$$E_{m+1} > \Pi_{m+1} E_m - (e \log \alpha_0)^{2m+2} \quad ,$$

whence one gets

$$E_n > \Pi_1 \ldots \Pi_n \left(1 - 2\log\alpha_0 - \frac{\alpha_0^2 (e\log\alpha_0)^4}{1 - \alpha_0^2 (e\log\alpha_0)^2} \right) \quad .$$

Choose particularly

$$\alpha = \frac{5}{4} = 1.25 \quad \text{and} \quad \alpha_0 = 1.2501 \quad .$$

We obtain then

$$E_n > 0.05(1 - \frac{2}{p_1}) \ldots (1 - \frac{2}{p_r}) \quad . \tag{26}$$

We study the number (R) of terms in E_n, on forming the following product

$$\left(1 - \frac{2}{p_p} - \ldots - \frac{2}{p_r}\right)\left(1 - \frac{2}{p_1} - \ldots - \frac{2}{p_{t-1}}\right)^2 \ldots \left(1 - \frac{2}{p_1} - \ldots - \frac{2}{p_{w-1}}\right)^2 .$$

This product contains all the terms of E_n and more. The number $(2r+1)$ of terms in the first factor is less than p_r whenever $p_1 > 3$, and in the second less than $p_r^{1/\alpha}$, etc. Hence we conclude

$$R < p_r \, p_r^{2/\alpha} \ldots p_r^{2/\alpha^n} < p_r^{(\alpha+1)/(\alpha-1)} = p_r^9 \quad .$$

We obtain then the formula

$$P(D, x, p_1, \ldots, p_r) > \frac{x}{D} \cdot 0.05(1 - \frac{2}{p_1}) \ldots (1 - \frac{2}{p_r}) - p_r^9 \tag{27}$$

a formula which is valid for all successive prime numbers $p_1, \ldots, p_r$, whenever $p_1 \geq p_e$, where p_e denotes a determinable prime number.

We obtain also a formula analogous to (21):

$$P(D, x, 3, 5, \ldots, p_r) > \frac{x}{D} \cdot 0.05(1 - \frac{2}{3}) \ldots (1 - \frac{2}{p_r}) - 3^3 p_r^9 \tag{28}$$

valid for all $r > e$.

Hence we conclude

$$P(D, x, 3, 5, \ldots, p_r) > \frac{x}{D} \cdot \frac{0.041}{(\log p_r)^2} - e^e p_r^9 \tag{29}$$

for all $r > c$, where $c \geq e$.

Choose particularly $p_r = p(x^{1/10})$. We obtain then

$$P\left(D, x, 3, 5, \ldots, p(x^{1/10})\right) > \frac{0.41\,x}{D(\log x)^2} - 3^e\, x^{9/10} > \frac{0.4\,x}{D(\log x)^2} \tag{30}$$

for all $x > x_0$.

On supposing $D = 1$, we can therefore state the following theorem:

When we efface double among x terms all the multiples of three, five, etc. up to $p(x^{1/10})$, there always remain more than $\frac{0.4\,x}{(\log x)^2}$ terms provided $x > x_0$.

We have supposed that

$$a_i \neq b_i \quad ,$$

that is to say that none of the double effacements are reduced to a single one. When the question is to determine the Goldbachian partitions of the number $x = 2^s p_\alpha^t \ldots p_\gamma^v$, one see yet that

$$a_\alpha = b_\alpha, \ldots, a_\gamma = b_\gamma .$$

But the lower bound for P will not naturally less, when one reduces the effacements (compare §5). One should then replace $\frac{2}{p_\alpha}$ by $\frac{1}{p_\alpha}$ and $\frac{2}{p_\gamma}$ by $\frac{1}{p_\gamma}$. We obtain then the new lower bound for P:

$$\frac{0.4\,x}{D(\log x)^2}\cdot\frac{(1-\frac{1}{p_\alpha})\ \ldots\ (1-\frac{1}{p_\gamma})}{(1-\frac{2}{p_\alpha})\ \ldots\ (1-\frac{2}{p_\gamma})} > \frac{0.4\,x}{D(\log x)^2}\ .$$

Hence we conclude, as in the previous example, on choosing $D=2$, the following theorem, analogous to that of Goldbach:

One can write even number x, greater than x_0, as a sum of two numbers, whose numbers of prime factors do not exceed nine. x_0 denotes a determinable number and the prime factors can be different or not.

We can also deduce the following theorem:

There exists an infinity of the pairs of numbers, having the difference 2, in the class of the numbers whose numbers of prime factors do not exceed nine.

§7. We can also determine an upper bound for the number of numbers, which remain non-effaced on employing the sieves of Eratosthenes and Merlin.

We apply the following inequality

$$N(\Delta,\ D,\ x,\ a_1,\ p_1,\ldots,a_r,\ p_r,\ldots,a_n,\ p_n)$$

$$\leq N(\Delta,\ D,\ x,\ a_1,\ p_1,\ldots,a_r,\ p_r)$$

or more briefly

$$N(D,\ x,\ p_1,\ldots,p_r,\ldots,p_n) \leq N(D,\ x,\ p_1,\ldots,p_r)\ , \qquad (31)$$

where $r<n$.

We apply also the formula

$$N(D, x, p_1,\ldots,p_r) = N(D, x) - \sum_{a \le r} N(Dp_a, x)$$

$$+ \sum_{a \le r} \sum_{b < a} N(Dp_a p_b, p_1,\ldots,p_{b-1}) \,. \tag{3'}$$

To estimate the terms of the last sum, we apply (31) and the same formula (3'). On continuing we obtain the formula analogous to (14):

$$N(D, x, p_1,\ldots,p_r) < \frac{x}{D}\Bigg[1 - \sum_{a \le r} \frac{1}{p_a} + \sum_{a \le r} \sum_{\substack{b < a \\ b < r}} \frac{1}{p_a p_b}$$

$$- \sum_{a \le r} \sum_{\substack{b < a \\ b < r}} \sum_{\substack{c < b \\ c < t}} \frac{1}{p_a p_b p_c}$$

$$+ \sum_{a \le r} \sum_{\substack{b < a \\ b < r}} \sum_{\substack{c < b \\ c < t}} \sum_{\substack{d < c \\ d < t}} \frac{1}{p_a p_b p_c p_d} - \ldots\Bigg] + R \,, \tag{32}$$

or more briefly

$$D(D, x, p_1,\ldots,p_r) < \frac{x}{D}\Big[1 - S_1 + S_2 - \ldots + S_{2n}\Big] + R \;,$$

where the expression

$$E_n = 1 - S_1 + S_2 - \ldots + S_{2n}$$

is calculated by means of the diagram

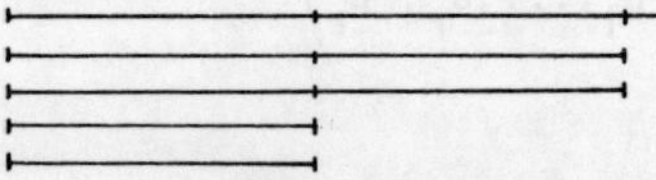

On employing the same method as before, we obtain

$$E_{m+1} < \Pi_{m+1} E_m + \left(\frac{e \log \alpha_0}{2}\right)^{2m+3}$$

and particularly

$$E_1 < \Pi_1 + \left(\frac{e \log \alpha_0}{2}\right)^3$$

whence

$$E_2 < \Pi_1\Pi_2 \left[1 + \alpha_0 \left(\frac{e \log \alpha_0}{2}\right)^3 + \alpha_0^2 \left(\frac{e \log \alpha_0}{2}\right)^5\right] .$$

On continuing we obtain at last

$$E_n < \Pi_1 \ldots \Pi_n \left[1 + \alpha_0 \left(\frac{e \log \alpha_0}{2}\right)^3 + \alpha_0^2 \left(\frac{e \log \alpha_0}{2}\right)^5 + \ldots\right]$$

or

$$E_n < (1 - \frac{1}{p_1}) \ldots (1 - \frac{1}{p_r}) \left(1 + \frac{\alpha_0 \left(\frac{e \log \alpha_0}{2}\right)^3}{1 - \alpha_0 \left(\frac{e \log \alpha_0}{2}\right)^2}\right), \qquad (33)$$

whenever $\alpha_0 \left(\frac{e \log \alpha_0}{2}\right)^2 < 1$.

Choose particularly

$$\alpha = \frac{3}{2} \quad \text{and} \quad \alpha_0 = 1.51 \quad .$$

We obtain then

$$E_n < 1.505 \, (1 - \frac{1}{p_1}) \ldots (1 - \frac{1}{p_r}) \quad .$$

We study the number (R) of terms in E_n on forming the following product

$$\left(1 - \frac{1}{p_1} - \ldots - \frac{1}{p_r}\right)^2 \left(1 - \frac{1}{p_1} - \ldots - \frac{1}{p_{t-1}}\right)^2 \ldots \left(1 - \frac{1}{p_1} - \ldots - \frac{1}{p_{w-1}}\right)^2 \quad .$$

We see, as before, that

$$R < p_r^2\, p_r^{2/\alpha} \ldots p_r^{2/\alpha^n} < p_r^{(2\alpha/\alpha-1)} = p_r^6 .$$

We can give (32) the following form

$$N(D, x, p_1,\ldots,p_r) < \frac{x}{D} \cdot 1.505\left(1-\frac{1}{p_1}\right)\ldots\left(1-\frac{1}{p_r}\right) + p_r^6 .$$

Thence we conclude the formula

$$N(D, x, 2, 3,\ldots,p_r)$$
$$< \frac{x}{D} \cdot 1.505\left(1-\frac{1}{2}\right)\left(1-\frac{1}{3}\right)\ldots\left(1-\frac{1}{p_r}\right) + 2^e p_r^6$$

valid for all $r > e$.

But in virtue of the Mertens' formula we obtain

$$N(D, x, 2, 3,\ldots,p_r) < \frac{0.9\,x}{D \log p_r} + 2^e p_r^6$$

for all $r > c$, where $c \geq e$.

Choose particularly $p_r = p(2\sqrt[7]{x})$. Thence we conclude that

$$\sqrt[7]{x} < p_r \leq 2\sqrt[7]{x}$$

on applying a celebrated theorem of Tchebycheff.

Therefore we obtain

$$N(1, x, 2, 3,\ldots,p(2\sqrt[7]{x})) < \frac{6.5\,x}{\log x} + 2^{e+6}\, x^{6/7} < \frac{7x}{\log x} \tag{34}$$

for all $x > x_0$.

On applying the inequality (31), we obtain

$$N(1, x, 2,\ldots,p(\sqrt{x})) \leq N(1, x, 2,\ldots,p(\sqrt[6]{x}))$$
$$\leq N(1, x, 2,\ldots,p(2\sqrt[7]{x})) < \frac{7x}{\log x}$$

for all $x > x_0$.

Thence we conclude particularly that

$$\pi(x) - \pi(\sqrt{x}) + 1 < \frac{7x}{\log x} .$$

whence

$$\pi(x) < \frac{7x}{\log x} + \sqrt{x} < \frac{8x}{\log x}$$

for all $x > x_0$, $\pi(x)$ denoting the number of the prime numbers not exceeding x.

On comparing the theorem in §4, we obtain also

$$\frac{x}{\log x} < N(1, x, 2, \ldots, p(\sqrt[6]{x})) < \frac{7x}{\log x} . \qquad (35)$$

When we efface among x terms all the multiples of two, three etc. up to $p(\sqrt[6]{x})$, there remain always N terms, where N is a number lying in the interval $\left[\frac{x}{\log x}, \frac{7x}{\log x}\right]$, whenever $x > x_0$.

We study at last the sieve of Merlin. We obtain the formula analogous to (33):

$$E_n < (1 - \frac{2}{p_1}) \ldots (1 - \frac{2}{p_r}) \left(1 + \frac{\alpha_0^2(e \log \alpha_0)^3}{1 - \alpha_0^2(e \log \alpha_0)^2}\right)$$

Choose particularly

$$\alpha = 1.25 \quad \text{and} \quad \alpha_0 = 1.2501 ,$$

whence one gets

$$E_n < 1.82 (1 - \frac{2}{p_1}) \ldots (1 - \frac{2}{p_r}) .$$

Thence we deduce as before

$$P(D, x, 3, 5, \ldots, p_r)$$
$$< \frac{x}{D} \cdot 1.82 (1 - \frac{2}{3})(1 - \frac{2}{5}) \ldots (1 - \frac{2}{p_r}) + 3^e p_r^{10}$$

or

$$P(D, x, 3, 5, \ldots, p_r) < \frac{1.6 x}{D(\log p_r)^2} + 3^e p_r^{10} . \qquad (36)$$

for all $r > c$, where $c \geq e$ (see §6).

Choose now $p_r = p(2x^{1/11})$. We obtain then

$$P(D,\ x,\ 2,\ 3,\ldots,p(2x^{1/11}))$$

$$< \frac{194\,x}{D(\log x)^2} + 3^{e+10}\,x^{10/11} < \frac{195\,x}{D(\log x)^2}$$

for all $x > x_0$.

We apply now the inequality

$$P(D,\ x,\ 2,\ 3,\ldots,p(\sqrt{x})) \leq P(D,\ x,\ 2,\ 3,\ldots,p(2\sqrt[11]{x}))$$

and the equation

$$Z(x) - Z(\sqrt{x} + 2) + 1 = P(2,\ x,\ 2,\ 3,\ldots,p(\sqrt{x})) \ ,$$

where $Z(x)$ denotes the number of the twin prime numbers not exceeding x, and where we have chosen 0 and 2 as starting points of the effacements.

We obtain therefore

$$Z(x) < \frac{195\,x}{2(\log x)^2} + \sqrt{x} + 2$$

or

$$Z(x) < \frac{100\,x}{(\log x)^2}$$

for all $x > x_0$, where x_0 denotes a determinable number. Here $Z(x)$ denotes the number of the twin prime numbers not exceeding x.

(See: Skr. Norske Vid.-Akad; Kristiania, I (1920) no. 3. Some formulas in the text are slightly modified by the Editor).

Translated by Yu Kun Rui

New Improvements in the Method of the Sieve of Eratosthenes

A. A. Buchstab

In 1919, V. Brun [1] gave a method for applying the sieve of Eratosthenes to a series of problems in number theory.

V. Brun proved that there exists infinitely many integer pairs such that 1) each integer of the pair has at most nine prime factors, and 2) the difference of integers in each pair is equal to 2, where 2 can be replaced by any given even number.

V. Brun established also that every large even number is the sum of two numbers each having at most nine prime factors. In 1924, Rademacher [2] improved the number nine to seven in the above results. In 1930, I was able to improve the number seven to six, and it was also established by Estermann in 1932.

In this paper, I give a new approach to these problems in which the number of prime factors is decreased to five. By the use of precise iteration of integrals, the number of prime factors can be decreased further.

We consider the problems of solubility of the equations $2 = n' - n''$ and $2N = n' + n''$, where the number of prime factors of n' and n'' is required to be bounded by a constant. The other problems considered by Brun and his successors can be treated similarly.

At the same time, I obtain a better upper estimation for the number of solutions of the above equations.

The estimations given in the first and second lemmas are obtained by the ordinary Brun's method.

As distinct from the other works, I shall obtain here the sufficiently closed upper and lower estimations. The basic part of our work was introduced in my paper [3].

1. We use $P_\omega(x, y)$ to denote the number of non-negative integers $\le x$ such that they are not contained in any of the $2r+1$ progressions

$$\begin{array}{lll} a_0, & a_0 + p_0, & a_0 + 2p_0, \ldots \\ a_1, & a_1 + p_1, & a_1 + 2p_1, \ldots \\ b_1, & b_1 + p_1, & b_1 + 2p_1, \ldots \\ & \ldots & \\ a_r, & a_r + p_r, & a_r + 2p_r, \ldots \\ b_r, & b_r + p_r, & b_r + 2p_r, \ldots \end{array} \tag{1}$$

where $p_0 = 2$, $0 \le a_0 \le 2$, p_i the odd prime number $\le y$ with the order $3 = p_1 < \ldots < p_r \le y$, $0 \le a_i < p_i$, $0 \le b_i < p_i$, $a_i \ne b_i$, and the index ω denotes the set of integers a_i and b_i in (1).

Lemma 1. If $p_1 = 3$, $p_2, \ldots, p_r$ are all the odd prime numbers $\le \sqrt[10]{x}$, then

$$p_\omega(x, x^{1/10}) > 98 \frac{cx}{\log^2 x}$$

holds uniformly on ω the set of a_i and b_i, where c is a constant.

According to Rademacher's paper cited above, we have

$$P_\omega(x, x^{1/10}) = P_\omega(x, p_r) > \frac{x}{2} E - R \quad ,$$

where

$$E = (1 - 2 \sum_{1 \le a \le r} \frac{1}{p_a}) + \sum_{1 \le a \le r} \sum_{1 \le b \le r_1} \frac{2^2}{p_a p_b} (1 - 2 \sum_{1 \le c \le b} \frac{1}{p_c})$$

$$+ \sum_{1 \le a \le r} \sum_{1 \le b \le r_1} \sum_{1 \le c \le r_1} \sum_{1 \le d \le r_2} \frac{2^4}{p_a p_b p_c p_d}$$

$$\cdot (1 - 2 \sum_{1 \le e \le d} \frac{1}{p_e}) + \ldots$$

and R denotes the number of terms $\frac{1}{p_a p_b \cdots}$ in E.

Let $r = r_1$ and p_r be the greatest prime number $\le x^{1/10}$. Let p_{r_k} be the greatest prime $\le x^{1/(10BH^{k-2})}$ for $2 \le k \le t+1$, where $B = \frac{22}{17} - \varepsilon$ and $h = \sqrt[4]{e} - \varepsilon$ in which ε denotes a pre-assigned positive number and t is the integer such that $p_{r_{t+1}}^{1/h} < \omega_0 \le p_{r_{t+1}}$. When $t+1 < k \le n$, we take $p_{r_k} = p_{r_{t+1}}$ and $p_{r_{n+1}} = p_0 = 2$.

We denote by E_k for $k = 1,2,\ldots,n$ $(E_n = E)$ the sum of those terms in E, where their denominators have only prime factors with indexes greater than r_{k+1}, i.e., the denominators have at most $2k+1$ prime factors. Hence

$$E_k = 1 - E_k^{(1)} + \ldots + E_k^{(2k)} - E_k^{(2k+1)} ,$$

where $E_k^{(i)}$ denotes the sum of those terms in E_k with exactly i prime factors in their denominators.

Let $S_k^{(i)}$ be the i-th elementary symmetric function of the numbers

$$\frac{2}{p_{r_{k+1}+1}} , \frac{2}{p_{r_{k+1}+2}} , \ldots , \frac{2}{p_{r_k}}$$

and

$$\Pi_k = \prod_{i=r_{k+1}+1}^{r_k} \left(1 - \frac{2}{p_i}\right) .$$

Then we have evidently

$$E_{k+1} \ge E_k \, \Pi_{k+1} - \Phi_{k+1} , \tag{2}$$

where

$$\Phi_{k+1} = S_{k+1}^{(2k+4)} + S_{k+1}^{(2k+3)} E_k^{(1)} + \ldots + S_{k+1}^{(3)} E_k^{(2k+1)} ,$$

$$\Phi_{k+1} = 0 \quad \text{if} \quad k+1 > t , \tag{3}$$

and

$$E_1 > \Pi_1 - S_1^{(4)} \quad . \tag{4}$$

By the successive application of the inequalities (2) and (4), we have

$$E = E_n > \Pi_1 \Pi_2 \ldots \Pi_n \left(1 - \frac{1}{\Pi_1} S_1^{(4)} - \frac{1}{\Pi_1 \Pi_2} \Phi_2 - \frac{1}{\Pi_1 \Pi_2 \Pi_3} \Phi_3 - \ldots \right) .$$

Choose ω_0 such that

$$S_1^{(1)} = 2 \sum_{a = r_2+1}^{r_1} \frac{1}{p_a} < 2 \log \frac{22}{17} < 0.516 \ ,$$

$$S_k^{(1)} = 2 \sum_{a = r_{k+1}+1}^{r_k} \frac{1}{p_a} < 2 \log \sqrt[4]{e} = \frac{1}{2} \quad (2 \le k \le t) \ ,$$

$$S_k^{(i)} \le \frac{S_k^{(1)i}}{i!} < \frac{1}{2^i \, i!} \quad (1 \le i \le 2k+1 \quad \text{and} \quad 2 \le k \le t) \ ,$$

and in particular,

$$S_1^{(4)} < \frac{S_1^{(1)4}}{4!} < 0.003 \quad .$$

Therefore

$$\frac{1}{\Pi_1} = \prod_{i = r_2+1}^{r_1} \left(1 - \frac{2}{p_i}\right)^{-1} < \left(\frac{22}{17}\right)^2 < 1.675 \quad ,$$

$$\frac{1}{\Pi_k} = \prod_{i = r_{k+1}+1}^{r_k} \left(1 - \frac{2}{p_i}\right)^{-1} < \sqrt{e} \quad (2 \le k \le t) \quad .$$

Denote $E_k^{(i)}$ by

$$E_k^{(i)} = S_k^{(i)} + S_k^{(i-1)} E_{k-1}^{(1)} + \ldots + S_k^{(1)} E_{k-1}^{(i-1)} + E_{k-1}^{(i)}$$

$$(i = 1,2,\ldots,2k+1, \quad E_{k-1}^{(2k)} = E_{k-1}^{(2k+1)} = 0) \quad .$$

Since

$$E_1^{(i)} = S_1^{(i)} < 2.14 \cdot \frac{1}{4^i} \qquad (i = 1,2,3) \quad ,$$

we have for all $k \le t-1$,

$$E_k^{(i)} < 2.14 \cdot \frac{1}{4^i} e^{2(k-1)} \quad ,$$

and therefore from (3),

$$\Phi_{k+1} < 2.14 \cdot \frac{1}{4^{2k+4}} e^{2(k-1)} (e^2 - 5) \qquad (2 \le k+1 \le t) \quad .$$

Hence

$$\Phi = \frac{1}{\Pi_2} \Phi_2 + \frac{1}{\Pi_2 \Pi_3} \Phi_3 + \ldots < 2.14 (e^2 - 5)$$

$$\cdot \frac{1}{4^6} \left(e^{1/2} + e^{6/2} \frac{1}{4^2} + e^{11/2} \frac{1}{4^4} + \ldots \right)$$

$$= 2.14(e^2 - 5) e^{1/2} 4^{-6} \left(1 - \frac{e^{5/2}}{16} \right)^{-1} < 0.0087$$

and

$$1 - \frac{1}{\Pi_1} (S_1^{(4)} + \Phi) > 0.98 \quad .$$

Denote

$$A = \lim_{x \to \infty} \left(2 \log \log x + \sum_{3 \le p \le x} \log(1 - \frac{2}{p}) \right) \quad .$$

When n is sufficiently large, we have

$$\Pi_1 \ldots \Pi_n = \prod_{3 \le p < x^{1/10}} (1 - \frac{2}{p}) = 100 \cdot \frac{e^A}{\log^2 x} + O(\frac{1}{\log^3 x}) \quad ,$$

i.e.,

$$E > 98 \frac{2c}{\log^2 x} + O(\frac{1}{\log^3 x})$$

where $c = \frac{1}{2} e^A = 0.4161 \ldots$

R does not exceed the number of terms $\frac{1}{p_a p_b \cdots}$ in the expression

$$\left(1-\sum_{a=1}^{r_1}\frac{2}{p_a}\right)\left(1-\sum_{b=1}^{r_1}\frac{2}{p_b}\right)\left(1-\sum_{c=1}^{r_1}\frac{2}{p_c}\right)\left(1-\sum_{d=1}^{r_2}\frac{2}{p_d}\right)\dots ,$$

and thus

$$R \le (2r_1+1)^3(2r_2+1)^2 \dots (2r_n+1)^2 < p_{r_1}^3\, p_{r_2}^2 \dots p_{r_n}^2$$

$$< A_1\, x^{3/10}\, x^{2/10B}\, x^{2/10Bh} \dots = A_1\, x^{(3/10)+2h/(10B(h-1))} .$$

Since $\frac{3}{10}+\frac{2h}{10B(h-1)}$ is less than 0.999 if ε is sufficiently small, we have

$$R < O(x^{0.999}) = O\left(\frac{x}{\log^3 x}\right) .$$

And therefore

$$P_\omega(x, x^{1/10}) > 98\,\frac{cx}{\log^2 x} + O\left(\frac{x}{\log^3 x}\right) .$$

Lemma 2.

$$P_\omega(x, x^{1/10}) < 101.6\,\frac{cx}{\log^2 x} + O\left(\frac{x}{\log^3 x}\right) .$$

By the same designation, we have for $3 = p_1 < \dots < p_r < x^{1/10}$,

$$P_\omega(x, x^{1/10}) < \frac{x}{2}E + R + 1 ,$$

where

$$E = 1 - \sum_{a\le r_1}\frac{2}{p_a}\left(1-\sum_{b\le a}\frac{2}{p_b}\right)$$

$$-\sum_{a\le r_1}\sum_{b\le r_1}\sum_{c\le r_2}\frac{2^3}{p_a p_b p_c}\left(1-\sum_{d\le c}\frac{2}{p_d}\right) - \dots$$

in which $r \ge r_1 \ge r_2 \ge \dots$. Let p_{r_1} be the greatest prime $\le x^{1/10}$, i.e., $r = r_1$. Let p_{r_k} denote the greatest prime $\le x^{1/(10Bh^{k-2})}$ for $2 \le k \le t+1$, where $B = \frac{26}{23} - \varepsilon$ and $h = \sqrt[4]{e} - \varepsilon$ in which t denotes the integer such that $p_{r_{t+1}}^{1/h} < \omega_0 \le p_{r_{t+1}}$.

When $t+1 \le k \le m$, we define $p_{r_k} = p_{r_{t+1}}$ and $p_{r_{m+1}} = 2$. Then

$$E_k = 1 - E_k^{(1)} + E_k^{(2)} - \ldots + E_k^{(2k)} \qquad (1 \le k \le t) , \qquad E_m = E$$

and

$$E_{k+1} \le \Pi_{k+1} E_k + \Phi_{k+1} ,$$

where

$$\Phi_{k+1} = S_{k+1}^{(2k+3)} + S_{k+1}^{(2k+2)} E_k^{(1)} + \ldots + S_{k+1}^{(3)} E_k^{(2k)} ,$$

$$\Phi_{k+1} = 0 \quad \text{if} \quad k \ge t$$

and

$$E_1 < \Pi_1 + S_1^{(3)} .$$

By the successive use of the above inequalities, we have

$$E = E_m < \Pi_1 \ldots \Pi_m \left(1 + \frac{1}{\Pi_1} S_1^{(3)} + \frac{1}{\Pi_1\Pi_2} \Phi_2 + \frac{1}{\Pi_1\Pi_2\Pi_3} \Phi_3 + \ldots\right) .$$

Choose ω_0 such that

$$S_1^{(1)} = 2 \sum_{a=r_2+1}^{r_1} \frac{1}{p_a} < 2 \log \frac{26}{23} < 0.2453 ,$$

$$S_1^{(3)} < \frac{S_1^{(1)3}}{6} < 0.0025 ,$$

$$\frac{1}{\Pi_1} = \prod_{a=r_2+1}^{r_1} \left(1 - \frac{2}{p_a}\right)^{-1} < \left(\frac{26}{23}\right)^2 < 1.28 ,$$

and the estimations of $S_k^{(i)}$ and $\frac{1}{\Pi_k}$ are similar to those given in Lemma 1 for $k \ge 2$. Now we evaluate the Φ_i as follows.

$$\Phi_2 = S_2^{(5)} + S_2^{(4)} E_1^{(1)} + S_2^{(3)} E_1^{(2)} < 0.00154 ,$$

$$E_2^{(1)} = S_1^{(1)} + E_1^{(1)} < 0.746 ,$$

$$E_2^{(2)} = S_2^{(2)} + S_2^{(1)} E_1^{(1)} + E_1^{(2)} < 0.278 ,$$

$$E_2^{(3)} = S_2^{(3)} + S_2^{(2)} E_1^{(1)} + S_2^{(1)} E_1^{(2)} < 0.068 \quad ,$$

$$E_2^{(4)} = S_2^{(4)} + S_2^{(3)} E_1^{(1)} + S_2^{(2)} E_1^{(2)} < 0.012 \quad ,$$

and from $E_2^{(i)} < 4.45 \cdot \frac{1}{4^i}$ $(i = 1,2,3,4)$, we have

$$E_k^{(i)} < 4.45\, e^{2(k-2)} \frac{1}{4^i} \quad (i = 1,2,\ldots,2k)$$

and

$$\Phi_{k+1} < 4.45\, e^{2(k-2)} \frac{1}{4^{2k+3}} (e^2 - 5) \quad .$$

Therefore

$$\Phi = \frac{1}{\Pi_2 \Pi_3} \Phi_3 + \frac{1}{\Pi_2 \Pi_3 \Pi_4} \Phi_4 + \ldots < 4.45\,(e^2 - 5)\, e\left(\frac{1}{4^7} + \frac{\sqrt{e^5}}{4^9} + \frac{\sqrt{e^9}}{4^{11}} + \ldots\right)$$

$$= 4.45(e^2 - 5)e \cdot 4^{-7} \left(1 - \frac{e^{5/2}}{16}\right)^{-1} < 0.0074$$

and

$$1 + \frac{1}{\Pi_1}\left(S_1^{(3)} + \frac{1}{\Pi_2} \Phi_2 + \Phi\right) < 1.016 \quad .$$

By the definition of m, $\Pi_1 \ldots \Pi_m$ is also equal to

$$\prod_{3 \le p \le x^{1/10}} \left(1 - \frac{2}{p}\right) = 100 \frac{e^A}{\log^2 x} + O\left(\frac{1}{\log^3 x}\right) \quad .$$

For sufficiently small ε, the estimation of R is given by

$$R < A_2\, x^{2/10}\, x^{2/10B}\, x^{2/10Bh} \ldots$$

$$= A_2\, x^{1/5(1 + h/B(h-1))} < A_2\, x^{0.9999} = O\left(\frac{x}{\log^3 x}\right) \quad ,$$

and therefore we have

$$P_\omega(x, x^{1/10}) < 101.6 \frac{cx}{\log^2 x} + O\left(\frac{x}{\log^3 x}\right)$$

where c is the constant defined in Lemma 1.

Lemma 3. Let u and v be two constants or variables depending on x such that $2 \leq u \leq v \leq A$, where A is a constant. Then

$$\sum_{x^{1/v} \leq p < x^{1/u}} \frac{1}{p(\log \frac{x}{p})^2}$$

$$= \frac{1}{\log^3 x} \left(\log \frac{v-1}{u-1} + \frac{u}{u-1} - \frac{v}{v-1} \right) + O(\frac{1}{\log^4 x}) \quad .$$

The proof is similar to the proof of a lemma in paper [3].

2. Consider now the function $P_\omega(x, x^{1/\alpha})$ $(\alpha \leq 10)$. It is evident that for $2 \leq \alpha \leq 10$,

$$P_\omega(x, x^{1/\alpha}) \leq P_\omega(x, x^{1/10}) \quad , \tag{5}$$

$$P_\omega(x, x^{1/\alpha}) \geq 0 \quad . \tag{5a}$$

By Lemma 1 and inequality (5), it asserts that there exists a non-decreasing function $\lambda(\alpha)$ which is continuous or has only a discontinuity of the first kind on the interval $2 \leq \alpha \leq 10$ such that

$$P_\omega(x, x^{1/\alpha}) > \lambda(\alpha) \frac{cx}{\log^2 x} + O(\frac{x}{\log^3 x})$$

holds uniformly on ω, where c is defined in Lemmas 1 and 2.

For example, $\lambda(\alpha)$ is defined by

$$\lambda(\alpha) = 0 \ , \quad \text{if} \quad 2 \leq \alpha < 10 \ ,$$

$$\lambda(\alpha) = 98 \ , \quad \text{if} \quad \alpha = 10 \quad .$$

By Lemma 2 and (5), it follows that there exists a continuous non-decreasing function $\Lambda(\alpha)$ on the interval $2 \leq \alpha \leq 10$ such that for any ω, we have

$$P_\omega(x, x^{1/\alpha}) < \Lambda(\alpha) \frac{cx}{\log^2 x} + O(\frac{x}{\log^3 x}) \quad .$$

As an example, we may take

$$\Lambda(\alpha) = 101.6, \quad \text{if} \quad 2 \le \alpha \le 10 \quad .$$

We use $\lambda_i(\alpha)$ and $\Lambda_i(\alpha)$ to denote the functions with the properties as $\lambda(\alpha)$ and $\Lambda(\alpha)$.

Theorem 1. Suppose that $\lambda_i(\alpha)$ and $\Lambda_k(\alpha)$ are two functions satisfying the above conditions. Then the function $\Psi(\alpha)$ defined by

$$\Psi(\alpha) = 0 \ , \quad \text{if} \quad 2 \le \alpha \le \tau \ ,$$

$$\Psi(\alpha) = \lambda_i(\beta) - 2\int_{\alpha-1}^{\beta-1} \Lambda_k(z)\frac{z+1}{z^2}\,dz \ , \quad \text{if} \quad 3 \le \tau \le \alpha \le 10 \quad ,$$

where β is any number satisfying $\alpha \le \beta \le 10$, is also a λ-function i.e., $\Psi(\alpha) = \lambda_{i+1}(\alpha)$.

First, notice that the difference between $P_\omega(x, p_{r+1})$ and $P_\omega(x, p_r)$ is equal to the number of integers $\le x$ in the progressions

$$a_r \ , \quad a_r + p_r \ , \quad a_r + 2p_r, \ldots$$

$$b_r \ , \quad b_r + p_r \ , \quad b_r + 2p_r, \ldots$$

but not in any of the first $2r-1$ progressions of (1). If $a_r + kp_r = a_i + np_i$, then $k \equiv a_i' \pmod{p_i}$, $i \ge 0 \left(0 \le k \le \frac{x-a_r}{p_r}, \ a_i' < p_i\right)$, and if $a_r + kp_r = b_i + np_i$, then $k \equiv b_i' \pmod{p_i}$, $i \ge 1$ $(b_i' < p_i)$. Therefore the number of integers $\le x$ in the progression a_r, $a_r + p_r$, $a_r + 2p_r, \ldots$ but not in any of the first $2r-1$ progressions of (1) equals to the number of non-negative ingegers $\le \frac{x-a_r}{p_r}$ which are not contained in the progressions

$$a_i' \ , \quad a_i' + p_i \ , \quad a_i' + 2p_i, \ldots, \qquad i = 0,1,\ldots,r-1 \ ,$$

$$b_i' \ , \quad b_i' + p_i \ , \quad b_i' + 2p_i, \ldots, \qquad i = 1,2,\ldots,r-1 \ ,$$

i.e., it is equal to $P_{\omega_r'}\left(\frac{x-a_r}{p_r}, p_r\right)$, where ω_r' denotes the set of integers a_i' and b_i'.

Similarly, the number of integers in the progression b_r, $b_r + p_r$, $b_r + 2p_r, \ldots$ but not in any of the first $2r-1$ progressions of (1) is equal to $P_{\omega_r''}\left(\frac{x - b_r}{p_r}, p_r\right)$. $P_{\omega_r'}\left(\frac{x - a_r}{p_r}, p_r\right)$ is coincident with $P_{\omega_r'}\left(\frac{x}{p_r}, p_r\right)$ or they are distinct by 1, and the same situation holds for $P_{\omega_r''}\left(\frac{x - b_r}{p_r}, p_r\right)$ and $P_{\omega_r''}\left(\frac{x}{p_r}, p_r\right)$.

We have

$$P_\omega(x, p_{r+1}) = P_\omega(x, p_r) - P_{\omega_r'}(\frac{x}{p_r}, p_r) - P_{\omega_r''}(\frac{x}{p_r}, p_r) - \mu_r, \tag{6}$$

where $0 \leq \mu_r \leq 2$. Let $p_t, p_{t+1}, \ldots, p_r$ be all the prime numbers between $x^{1/\beta}$ and $x^{1/\alpha}$, i.e.;

$$x^{1/\beta} \leq p_t < p_{t+1} < \ldots < p_r < x^{1/\alpha} \leq p_{r+1} .$$

Then

$$P_\omega(x, x^{1/\alpha}) = P_\omega(x, p_{r+1}) \quad \text{and} \quad P_\omega(x, x^{1/\beta}) = P_\omega(x, p_t) .$$

By the successive use of (6), we have

$$P_\omega(x, x^{1/\alpha}) = P_\omega(x, x^{1/\beta}) - \sum_{x^{1/\beta} \leq p_i < x^{1/\alpha}} P_{\omega_i'}\left(\frac{x}{p_i}, p_i\right)$$

$$- \sum_{x^{1/\beta} \leq p_i < x^{1/\alpha}} P_{\omega_i''}\left(\frac{x}{p_i}, p_i\right) - \sum \mu_i , \tag{7}$$

where $\sum \mu_i = O(\sqrt{x})$.

For simplicity, we omit the index i hereafter. Let

$$u_s = \alpha + \frac{\beta - \alpha}{n} s - 1 \qquad (s = 0, 1, \ldots, n) ,$$

where $c_1 \log x \leq n \leq c_2 \log x$. For given prime number p with

$x^{1/(u_{s+1}+1)} \le p < x^{1/(u_s+1)}$, we have

$$\alpha - 1 \le u_s < \frac{\log \frac{x}{p}}{\log p} \le u_{s+1} \le \beta - 1 ,$$

$$T_s = \sum_{x^{1/(u_{s+1}+1)} \le p < x^{1/(u_s+1)}} \left(P_{\omega_i'}\left(\frac{x}{p}, p\right) + P_{\omega_i''}\left(\frac{x}{p}, p\right) \right)$$

$$= \sum_{x^{1/(u_{s+1}+1)} \le p < x^{1/(u_s+1)}} \left(P_{\omega_i'}\left(\frac{x}{p}, \left(\frac{x}{p}\right)^{\log p/(\log x/p)}\right) + P_{\omega_i''}\left(\frac{x}{p}, \left(\frac{x}{p}\right)^{\log p/(\log x/p)}\right) \right)$$

$$\le 2c \sum_{x^{1/(u_{s+1})} \le p < x^{1/(u_s+1)}} \frac{x}{p \log^2 \frac{x}{p}} \Lambda_k\left(\frac{\log \frac{x}{p}}{\log p} \right) + O\left(\sum_{x^{1/(u_{s+1}+1)} \le p \le x^{1/(u_s+1)}} \frac{x}{p \log^3 \frac{x}{p}} \right),$$

and by Lemma 3,

$$T_s \le 2c\, \Lambda_k(u_{s+1}) \frac{x}{\log^2 x} \left(\log \frac{u_{s+1}}{u_s} + \frac{u_{s+1} - u_s}{u_s u_{s+1}} \right) + O\left(\frac{x}{\log^3 x} \left(\log \frac{u_{s+1}}{u_s} + \frac{u_{s+1} - u_s}{u_s u_{s+1}} \right) \right) .$$

Therefore

$$T = \sum_{x^{1/\beta} \le p < x^{1/\alpha}} \left(P_{\omega_i'}\left(\frac{x}{p}, p\right) + P_{\omega_i''}\left(\frac{x}{p}, p\right) \right)$$

$$= \sum_{s=0}^{n-1} T_s \le 2c \frac{x}{\log^2 x} \sum_{s=0}^{n-1} \Lambda_k(u_{s+1}) \left(\log \frac{u_{s+1}}{u_s} + \frac{u_{s+1} - u_s}{u_s u_{s+1}} \right)$$

$$+ O\left(\frac{x}{\log^3 x}\sum_{s=0}^{n-1}\left(\log\frac{u_{s+1}}{u_s}+\frac{u_{s+1}-u_s}{u_s\,u_{s+1}}\right)\right)$$

Since

$$\sum_{s=0}^{n-1}\Lambda(u_{s+1})\left(\log\frac{u_{s+1}}{u_s}+\frac{u_{s+1}-u_s}{u_s\,u_{s+1}}\right)$$

$$=\int_{\alpha-1}^{\beta-1}\Lambda_k(z)(d\log z+\frac{dz}{z^2})+O(\frac{1}{n})$$

$$=\int_{\alpha-1}^{\beta-1}\Lambda_k(z)\,\frac{z+1}{z^2}\,dz+O(\frac{1}{\log x})$$

and

$$\sum_{s=0}^{n-1}\left(\log\frac{u_{s+1}}{u_s}+\frac{u_{s+1}-u_s}{u_s\,u_{s+1}}\right)=O(1)\quad ,$$

we have

$$T\le 2c\,\frac{x}{\log^2 x}\int_{\alpha-1}^{\beta-1}\Lambda_k(z)\,\frac{z+1}{z^2}\,dz+O(\frac{x}{\log^3 x})\quad ,$$

and from (7),

$$P_\omega(x,x^{1/\alpha})\ge\frac{cx}{\log^2 x}\left(\lambda_i(\beta)-2\int_{\alpha-1}^{\beta-1}\Lambda_k(z)\,\frac{z+1}{z^2}\,dz\right)+O(\frac{x}{\log^3 x})\quad ,$$

i.e.,

$$\lambda_{i+1}(\alpha)=\lambda_i(\beta)-2\int_{\alpha-1}^{\beta-1}\Lambda_k(z)\,\frac{z+1}{z^2}\,dz\quad .$$

The theorem is proved.

<u>Theorem 2</u>. Let $\lambda_i(\alpha)$ and $\Lambda_k(\alpha)$ be two functions satisfying the stated conditions. Then the function $\omega(\alpha)$ defined by

$$\omega(\alpha)=\Lambda_k(\beta)-2\int_{\alpha-1}^{\beta-1}\lambda_i(z)\,\frac{z+1}{z^2}\,dz\qquad(3\le\alpha\le 10)\quad ,$$

where β is any number satisfying $\alpha\le\beta\le 10$, is also a Λ-function, i.e., $\omega(\alpha)=\Lambda_{k+1}(\alpha)$.

The proof of the theorem is completely similar to that of Theorem 1.

Let $\beta \leq 10$. Let $\lambda_0(\alpha)$ and $\Lambda_0(\alpha)$ be two functions on the interval $6 \leq \alpha \leq \beta$ such that

$$\lambda_0(\alpha) = 0, \quad \text{if } \alpha < \beta$$

$$\lambda_0(\beta) \text{ equals to a positive constant },$$

and

$$\Lambda_0(\alpha) = \Lambda_0(\beta), \quad \text{if } 6 \leq \alpha \leq \beta$$

By the successive application of Theorems 1 and 2 and starting from the functions with index $i = 0$, we have

$$\lambda_{i+1}(x) = \lambda_0(\beta) - 2\int_{\alpha-1}^{\beta-1} \Lambda_i(y)\frac{y+1}{y^2}\,dy ,$$

$$\Lambda_{i+1}(\beta-1) = \Lambda_0(\beta) - 2\int_{\beta-1}^{\beta-1} \lambda_{i+1}(x)\frac{x+1}{x^2}\,dx$$

$$= \Lambda_0(\beta) - 2\lambda_0(\beta)\int_{\beta-2}^{\beta-1} \frac{x+1}{x^2}\,dx$$

$$+ 4\Lambda_i(\beta-1)\int_{\beta-2}^{\beta-1}\int_{x-1}^{\beta-1} \frac{x+1}{x^2}\frac{y+1}{y^2}\,dx\,dy \qquad (i = 0,1,\ldots) ,$$

where for all i, $\Lambda_i(\beta) = \Lambda_0(\beta)$ and $\lambda_i(\beta) = \lambda_0(\beta)$, and $\Lambda_i(y) = \Lambda_i(\beta-1)$ if $y < \beta-1$.

The coefficient of $\Lambda_i(\beta-1)$ in the right hand side of the above expression is less than 1 if $8 \leq \beta \leq 10$, and thus by the successive iteration, we may obtain a $\Lambda(\beta-1)$ which is sufficiently close to the root of the corresponding equation, i.e., we obtain a Λ-function $\bar{\Lambda}_0(\alpha)$ defined by

$$\bar{\Lambda}_0(\alpha) = \bar{\Lambda}_0(\beta-1) = \frac{\Lambda_0(\beta) - 2\lambda_0(\beta)\displaystyle\int_{\beta-2}^{\beta-1} \frac{x+1}{x^2}\,dx}{1 - 4\displaystyle\int_{\beta-2}^{\beta-1}\int_{x-1}^{\beta-1} \frac{x+1}{x^2}\cdot\frac{y+1}{y^2}\,dx\,dy} + \varepsilon \quad ,$$

where $7 \leq \alpha \leq \beta - 1$ and ε is a sufficiently small number.

Now we obtain a new λ-function $\bar{\lambda}_0(\alpha)$ defined by

$$\bar{\lambda}_0(\beta-1) = \lambda_0(\beta) - 2\int_{\beta-2}^{\beta-1} \bar{\Lambda}_0(x)\,\frac{x+1}{x^2}\,dx - \varepsilon \quad ,$$

$$= \lambda_0(\beta) - \Lambda_0(\beta-1)\int_{\beta-2}^{\beta-1} \frac{x+1}{x^2}\,dx - \varepsilon_1 \quad ,$$

$$\bar{\lambda}_0(\alpha) = 0 \quad \text{if} \quad \alpha < \beta-1 \quad .$$

By the similar method, we may obtain $\bar{\bar{\lambda}}_0$ and $\bar{\bar{\Lambda}}_0$ from $\bar{\lambda}_0$ and $\bar{\Lambda}_0$, and so on. Starting from $\lambda_0(10) = 98$ and $\Lambda_0(10) = 101.6$, the results are given as follows.

$$\bar{\Lambda}_0(9) = \frac{101.6 - 2\cdot 98\displaystyle\int_8^9 \frac{x+1}{x^2}\,dx}{1 - 4\displaystyle\int_8^9\int_{x-1}^9 \frac{x+1}{x^2}\cdot\frac{y+1}{y^2}\,dx\,dy} + \varepsilon = 85.1 \quad ,$$

$$\bar{\lambda}_0(9) = 98 - 2\cdot 85.1\int_8^9 \frac{x+1}{x^2}\,dx - \varepsilon_1 = 75.58 \quad ,$$

$$\bar{\bar{\Lambda}}_0(8) = \frac{85.1 - 2\cdot 75.58\displaystyle\int_7^8 \frac{x^2+1}{x^2}\,dx}{1 - 4\displaystyle\int_7^8\int_{x-1}^8 \frac{x+1}{x^2}\cdot\frac{y+1}{y^2}\,dx\,dy} + \varepsilon' = 72.86 \quad ,$$

$$\bar{\bar{\lambda}}_0(8) = 75.58 - 2\cdot 72.86\int_7^8 \frac{x+1}{x^2}\,dx - \varepsilon_1' = 53.51 \quad ,$$

$$\bar{\bar{\Lambda}}_0(7) = \frac{72.86 - 2\cdot 53.51\int_6^7 \frac{x+1}{x^2}\,dx}{1 - 4\int_6^7\int_{x-1}^7 \frac{x+1}{x^2}\cdot\frac{y+1}{y^2}\,dx\,dy} + \varepsilon'' = 67.58 \ ,$$

and finally

$$\lambda(6) = \bar{\bar{\lambda}}_0(8) - 2\bar{\bar{\Lambda}}_0(7)\int_5^7 \frac{x+1}{x^2}\,dx - \varepsilon_1'' = 0.03 \ ,$$

i.e.,

$$P_\omega(x, x^{1/6}) > 0.03\,\frac{cx}{\log^2 x} + O(\frac{x}{\log^3 x}) \tag{8}$$

and

$$P_\omega(x, x^{1/6}) \le P_\omega(x, x^{1/7}) < 67.58\,\frac{cx}{\log^2 x} + O(\frac{x}{\log^3 x})$$

hold uniformly on ω.

In particular, if we take $a_i = 0$ and $b_i = p_i - 2$ then $P_\omega(x, x^{1/6})$ is equal to the number of integers $n \le x$ such that n and $n+2$ do not divide by any prime number $\le x^{1/6}$, i.e., there exists a pair of integers n and $n+2$ each having at most 5 prime factors.

The inequality (8) shows that such pairs form an infinite set. That is, we have proved the following result.

There exists infinitely many integer pairs such that each integer of the pair has at most 5 prime factors and the difference of integers in each pair is 2.

Suppose that x is an even integer, $a_i = 0$ and b_i is the least non-negative residue of x modulo p_i. Then $a_i = b_i$ if $p_i | x$. In all the estimations of $P_\omega(x, x^{1/\alpha})$, the factor $\frac{x}{\log^2 x}$ should be replaced by $\frac{x}{\log^2 x}\,v(x)$, where $v(x) = \prod_{\substack{p|x \\ p>2}} \frac{p-1}{p-2}$. Since

$v(\frac{x}{p}) = v(x)\,\frac{p-2}{p-1} = v(x)\left(1 + O\left(\frac{1}{10\sqrt{x}}\right)\right)$ if $x^{1/10} \le p < x^{1/2}$, the results corresponding to Theorems 1 and 2 still hold, and we have.

There exists a constant A_0 such that every even integer greater than A_0 can be represented as the sum of two integers each having at most five prime factors.

Concerning the number of prime pairs $Z(x)$ in the interval $[2, x]$, we have

$$Z(x) < 28.2 \frac{x}{\log^2 x} .$$

for $x > x_0$, here $c = \frac{e^A}{2} < 0.417$ is used.

References

[1]. V. Brun, Skr. Norske Vid.-Akad. Kristiania, I, No. 3 (1920).

[2]. H. Rademacher, Abh. Math. Sem. Univ. Hamburg, 3 (1924) 12-30.

[3]. A. A. Buchstab, Mat. Sbornik, 44 (1937) 1239-1246. (See Mat. Sbornik, 46 (1938) 375-387.

Translated by Wang Yuan

On Prime Divisors of Polynomials

P. Kuhn

We use small Latin letters to denote the natural numbers which are also called numbers for simplicity, and p, q, s, t the prime numbers. Let

$$P_n(x) = a_0x^n + a_1x^{n-1} + \dots + a_n\,, \quad a_0 > 0 \tag{1}$$

be an integral-valued and primitive polynomial which is a product of r $(1 \le r \le n)$ integral-valued, primitive and irreducible polynomials. The fixed divisor of (1) is assumed to be $T = t_1^{b_1} \dots t_e^{b_e}$.

We shall find out a possibly smaller integer k such that there are infinitely many numbers in

$$P_n(1), P_n(2), \dots, P_n(x), \dots \tag{2}$$

which have at most k prime factors besides the fixed prime divisors t_i $(1 \le i \le e)$.

H. Rademacher [1] and G. Ricci [2] have used the Brun's sieve method to treat this problem, and they have found out a smaller number k for the case $r = 1$ only. It needs also to determine a corresponding smaller number k for the case $1 < r \le n$. Here the proof for the case $r = n$ will be given.

Suppose that p runs over all prime numbers satisfying

$$p < x^{1/v}\,, \qquad p \ne t_i \tag{3}$$

where v will be determined in the latter as a function of n.

Let d be an integer satisfying $d \not\equiv 0 \pmod p$ and $d \not\equiv 0 \pmod{t_i}$. Let $N_n(dx, x^{1/v})$ be the number of integers in (2) which are $\le P_n(x)$, $\equiv 0 \pmod d$, but $\not\equiv 0 \pmod p$ and $\not\equiv 0 \pmod{t_i^{b_i+1}}$. By

Brun's method, we may prove that for $r = n$ and $x \to \infty$,

$$N_n(x, x^{1/v}) > C_n \cdot 0.98\, x\, v^n \log^{-n} x + O\left(x^{\chi(n)/v}\, v^{n+1} \log^{-n-1} x\right) ,$$

$$N_n(dx, x^{1/v}) < C_n \cdot 1.016\, \frac{nx}{d}\, v^n \log^{-n} x + O\left(x^{\chi(n)/v}\, v^{n+1} \log^{-n-1} x\right) ,$$

$$\chi(2) \geq 9.99 , \quad \chi(3) \geq 13.67 ,$$

$$\chi(4) \geq 17.50 , \quad \chi(5) \geq 22.02, \ldots \tag{4}$$

where C_n is a positive constant depending on $P_n(x)$.

<u>Theorem</u>. If $r = n$, then it is sufficient to take $k = \omega + n$, where ω is the smallest integer such that

$$\frac{0.98}{1.016} (\omega + 1) > n \log \chi(n) \quad . \tag{5}$$

For examples, $n = 2$, $k = 6$; $n = 3$, $k = 10$; $n = 4$, $k = 15$; $n = 5$, $k = 21, \ldots$.

Suppose that $v = 2\chi(n)$ in (3) and that q runs over all prime numbers satisfying

$$v^{1/v} < q \leq (2a_0 x)^{\frac{1}{2}} + 1, \qquad q \neq t_i \quad . \tag{6}$$

Let m denote the number in (2) satisfying

$$m \leq P_n(x) , \qquad m \not\equiv 0 (\mathrm{mod}\ p) ,$$

$$m \not\equiv 0 (\mathrm{mod}\ t_i^{b_i+1}) , \qquad m \not\equiv 0 (\mathrm{mod}\ q^2) \quad . \tag{7}$$

Let U be a lower estimation for $M_n(x, x^{1/v})$ the number of integers m. Since $M_n(x, x^{1/v}) = N_n(x, x^{1/v}) + O(x^{1 - 1/v})$, we have by (4)

$$U = C_n \cdot 0.98\, x\, v^n \log^{-n} x + O(x^{1/2} \log^{-n-1} x) + O(x^{1 - 1/v}) \quad . \tag{8}$$

Let $M_n(qx, x^{1/v})$ be the number of m which is $\equiv 0 \pmod q$. Let V be an upper estimation of $\sum_q M_n(qx, x^{1/v}) = L_n$, where q runs over (6). Then $L_n \le \sum_q N_n(qx, x^{1/v})$, and therefore by (4), we have

$$V = C_n \cdot 1.016 \sum_q \frac{nx}{q} v^n \log^{-n} x + O(x \log^{-n-1} x) \quad . \tag{9}$$

If m has at least $\omega+1$ prime factors q, then it is counted at least $\omega+1$ times in L_n, and therefore the difference $\Delta = U - \frac{1}{\omega+1} V$ gives a lower estimation for the number of m which has at most ω prime factors q and its other prime factors are $s > (2a_0x)^{\frac{1}{2}}+1$ besides those t_i. The number of such prime factors s is at most n when $x \to \infty$, since each linear factor of $P_n(x)$ has at most one prime factor s. Hence if

$$\frac{0.98}{1.016}(\omega+1) > \sum_q \frac{n}{q} \quad , \tag{10}$$

then $\Delta \to \infty$ when $x \to \infty$. Since $\sum_q \frac{1}{q} \sim \log \chi(n)$, the theorem is proved.

References

[1]. H. Rademacher, Abh. Math. Sem. Univ. Hamburg, 3 (1924) 12-30.

[2]. G. Ricci, I, Ann. Scuola Norm. Sup. Pisa, (2) 6 (1937) 71-90; II, Ibid. 91-116.

[3]. P. Kuhn, Den Skand. 12-th Mat. Kongr; Lund (1953) 160-168.
(See Proc. Intern. Cong. Math.; Amsterdam, 2 (1954) 35-37.)

Translated by Wang Yuan

Noted by the Editor: Let N be an even integer. Let $P_2(x) = x(N-x)$ $(x = 1,2,\ldots,N-1)$. Then by the similar arguments, one can prove (a, b), where $a+b \le 6$.

DET KONGELIGE NORSKE VIDENSKABERS SELSKAB
FORHANDLINGER BD XIX, NR 18

511.287

On an Elementary Method in the Theory of Primes

By

ATLE SELBERG

(Innsendt til Generalsekretæren 18de oktober 1946 av herr S. Selberg)

In the following we shall give a brief sketch of an elementary method which can be applied to the same problems as the "sieve method" which has been developed by BRUN. The new method is very simple and also generally yields better results than Brun's.

Suppose that we have given a finite sequence of integers α the total number of which is N. We shall study the problem of finding an upper bound for the number N_z of α's which are not divisible [1] by any prime $\leqslant z$.

We define a sequence of numbers λ_γ for $1 \leqslant \gamma \leqslant z$ such that $\lambda_1 = 1$ while the other λ's are arbitrary real numbers. Then obviously

$$N_z \leqslant \sum_{\alpha}\Big\{\sum_{\gamma/\alpha} \lambda_\gamma\Big\}^2 = \sum_{\gamma_1, \gamma_2 \leqslant z} \lambda_{\gamma_1}\lambda_{\gamma_2} \sum_{\frac{\gamma_1 \gamma_2}{\chi}/\alpha} 1 \quad ,$$

where χ denotes the greatest common divisor of γ_1 and γ_2.

We now suppose that when ρ is a positive integer it is possible to find an approximate formula for the number of α's which are divisible by ρ, in the form

$$\sum_{\rho/\alpha} 1 = \frac{1}{f(\rho)} N + R_\rho$$

where R_ρ is a remainder term. We further suppose that the function $f(\rho)$

function $f(\rho)$ is multiplicative, that is, that $f(\rho_1\rho_2)=f(\rho_1)f(\rho_2)$ if ρ_1 and ρ_2 are coprime integers. Since $\frac{1}{f(\rho)}$ can be said to represent the 'probability' that α is divisible by ρ, the latter supposition means that the 'event' that ρ_1/α shall be independent of the 'event' that ρ_2/α, if ρ_1 and ρ_2 are coprime. If this is the case we have

$$\sum_{\frac{\gamma_1\gamma_1}{x}/\alpha} = \frac{1}{f\left(\frac{\gamma_1\gamma_2}{x}\right)}N + R_{\frac{\gamma_1\gamma_2}{x}} = \frac{f(\chi)}{f(\gamma_1)f(\gamma_2)}N + R_{\frac{\gamma_1\gamma_2}{\chi}} .$$

Inserting this in the above inequality for N_z we obtain

$$(1)\quad N_z \leqslant N \sum_{\gamma_1,\gamma_2\leqslant z} \frac{\lambda_{\gamma_1}}{f(\gamma_1)}\cdot\frac{\lambda_{\gamma_2}}{f(\gamma_2)} f(\chi) + \sum_{\gamma_1,\gamma_2\leqslant z} \lambda_{\gamma_1}\lambda_{\gamma_2} R_{\frac{\gamma_1\gamma_2}{\chi}}$$

Writing now

$$Q(\lambda) = \sum_{\gamma_1,\gamma_2\leqslant z} \frac{\lambda_{\gamma_1}}{f(\gamma_1)}\cdot\frac{\lambda_{\gamma_2}}{f(\gamma_2)} f(\chi) ,$$

we shall determine the λ_γ's for $2\leqslant\gamma\leqslant z$ such that Q becomes a minimum. We write when ρ is a positive integer,

$$f_1(\rho) = \sum_{d/\rho} \mu(d) f\left(\frac{\rho}{d}\right)$$

where $\mu(d)$ is Möbius' function, in particular if ρ is *quadratfrei*

$$f_1(\rho) = f(\rho)\prod_{p/\rho}\left(1-\frac{1}{f(p)}\right) .$$

According to a well-known formula we then have

$$f(x) = \sum_{\rho/x} f_1(\rho) = \sum_{\substack{\rho/\gamma_1\\ \rho/\gamma_2}} f_1(\rho) ,$$

Inserting this in the expression for Q we get

$$Q = \sum_{\rho \leqslant z} f_1(\rho) \left\{ \sum_{\substack{\rho / \gamma \\ \gamma \leqslant z}} \frac{\lambda_\gamma}{f(\gamma)} \right\}^2 .$$

Writing for $1 \leqslant \rho \leqslant z$,

$$y_\rho = \sum_{\substack{\rho / \gamma \\ \gamma \leqslant z}} \frac{\lambda_\gamma}{f(\gamma)} ,$$

we have that

$$\frac{\lambda_\gamma}{f(\gamma)} = \sum_{\rho \leqslant \frac{z}{\gamma}} \mu(\rho) y_{\rho\gamma} .$$

Now we determine the minimum of the form

$$Q = \sum_{\rho \leqslant z} f_1(\rho) y_\rho^2 ,$$

under the condition

$$\sum_{\rho \leqslant z} \mu(\rho) y_\rho = \frac{\lambda_1}{f(1)} = 1.$$

We easily find that the values of y_ρ which make the form a minimum are

$$y_\rho = \frac{\mu(\rho)}{f_1(\rho)} \cdot \frac{1}{\sum_{\rho' \leqslant z} \frac{\mu^2(\rho')}{f_1(\rho')}} ,$$

and that the minimum value of the form Q is

$$\frac{1}{\sum_{\rho \leqslant z} \frac{\mu^2(\rho)}{f_1(\rho)}}$$

For the corresponding values of the λ_γ's we find for $1 \leqslant \gamma \leqslant z$,

$$\lambda_\gamma = \frac{f(\gamma)}{\sum\limits_{\rho \leqslant z} \frac{\mu^2(\rho)}{f_1(\rho)}} \cdot \sum_{\rho \leqslant \frac{z}{\gamma}} \frac{\mu(\rho)\mu(\rho\gamma)}{f_1(\rho\gamma)}$$

(2)

$$= \mu(\gamma) \prod_{p/N} \left(1 - \frac{1}{f(p)}\right)^{-1} \cdot \frac{1}{\sum\limits_{\rho \leqslant z} \frac{\mu^2(\rho)}{f_2(\rho)}} \cdot \sum_{\substack{\rho \leqslant \frac{z}{\gamma} \\ (\rho,\gamma)=1}} \frac{\mu^2(\rho)}{f_1(\rho)} .$$

Inserting these values of the λ's in (1), we obtain

(3)
$$N_z \leqslant \frac{N}{\sum\limits_{\rho \leqslant z} \frac{\mu^2(\rho)}{f_1(\rho)}} + \sum_{\gamma_1, \gamma_2 \leqslant z} \left| \lambda_{\gamma_1} \lambda_{\gamma_2} R_{\frac{\gamma_1 \gamma_2}{\chi}} \right| ,$$

which, if the last term on the right-hand side is not too great, give us the required upper bound for N_z.

Applying this method to the number $\alpha = n(n+2)$, $1 \leqslant n \leqslant x$ we find, taking $z = x^{\frac{1}{2}-\epsilon}$ where ϵ is a sufficiently small positive fixed number, that the number of prime twins not exceeding x is less than

$$\frac{10.6x}{\log^2 x}, \quad x \geqslant x_0 \quad .$$

This is better than the best upper bound established by BRUN'S methods.

I have also developed a method based on similar principles for dealing with the problem of a lower bound. A full account of these methods, with applications to several problems, will appear later elsewhere.

---

[1] We may replace this condition by $\alpha \not\equiv r_p \pmod p$ for all primes $p \leqslant z$, where the r_p's are integers depending on p only.

Trykt 1ste februar 1947
I kommisjon hos F. Bruns Bokhandel
Aktietrykkeriet i Trondhjem

SCIENCE RECORD
New Ser. Vol. I, No. 5, 1957

MATHEMATICS

ON THE REPRESENTATION OF LARGE EVEN NUMBER AS A SUM OF TWO ALMOST-PRIMES* †

WANG YUAN (王 元)
Institute of Mathematics, Academia Sinica
(Communicated by Prof. Hua, L. K., Member of Academia Sinica)

For the sake of briefness, we write the following proposition by (a, b).

Every sufficiently large even integer can be represented as a sum of two integers > 1, of which one contains at most a and other at most b prime factors.

The aim of the present note is to prove $(3, 3)$ and (a, b) $(a + b \leqslant 5)$ by the method used in previous papers[1, 2]. These results improve the $(3, 4)$[3] of the auther in 1955. Moreover, using Бухштаб's[4] method with more complicated numerical calculations, we have $(2, 3)$. Recently, we have found some mistakes in numerical calculations in the proof of $(3, 3)$ of А. И. Виноградов[5]. We shall state it at the end of this note.

In this paper, p denotes prime number and p_i denotes i-th odd prime.

Let x be an even integer and ξ be a real number. Let

(w) $a;\ a_i,\ b_i\ (1 \leqslant i \leqslant r)$

be a sequence of integers satisfying the following conditions:

(1) $a = 0$ or 1; $0 \leqslant a_i,\ b_i < p_i$, if p_i / x, then $a_i = b_i$, otherwise $a_i \neq b_i$ $(1 \leqslant i \leqslant r)$,

where $p_r \leqslant \xi < p_{r+1}$. Let $P_w(x, \xi)$ be the number of integers n satisfying the following conditions:

(2) $1 \leqslant n \leqslant x$, $n \equiv a \pmod 2$, $n \not\equiv a_i \pmod{p_i}$, $n \not\equiv b_i \pmod{p_i}$ $(1 \leqslant i \leqslant r)$.

Let $v > u > 1$ be two given positive numbers. Let $\mathfrak{N}$ denote the set of integers $n\,(x-n)$ satisfying the following conditions:

(3) $1 \leqslant n \leqslant x$, $n\,(x-n) \not\equiv 0 \pmod 2$, $n\,(x-n) \not\equiv 0 \pmod{p_i}$ $(1 \leqslant i \leqslant s)$,

where $p_s \leqslant x^{\frac{1}{v}} < p_{s+1}$. Let $\mathfrak{M}$ denote the set of integers $n\,(x-n)$

---

* Received June 29, 1957.

† An integer is called almost prime, if the number of its prime factors is not exceeding a fixed constant.

satisfying (3) and the following conditions:

(4) $n(x-n) \not\equiv o \pmod{p_{s+j}^2}$ $\quad 1 \leqslant j \leqslant t-s,$

where $p_t \leqslant x^{\frac{1}{u}} < p_{t+1}$. We denote the number[1] of elements of $\mathfrak{N}$ and $\mathfrak{M}$ by $N(x, x^{\frac{1}{v}})$ and $M(x, x^{\frac{1}{v}}, x^{\frac{1}{u}})$ respectively.

Lemma 1. $M(x, x^{\frac{1}{v}}, x^{\frac{1}{u}}) = N(x, x^{\frac{1}{v}}) + O(x^{1-\frac{1}{v}}) + O(x^{\frac{1}{u}})$.

Proof.
$$N(x, x^{\frac{1}{v}}) - M(x, x^{\frac{1}{v}}, x^{\frac{1}{u}}) \leqslant \sum_{x^{\frac{1}{v}} < p < x^{\frac{1}{u}}} \sum_{\substack{1<n<x \\ n(x-n) \equiv 0 \pmod{p^2}}} 1 = \sum_{x^{\frac{1}{v}} < p \leqslant x^{\frac{1}{u}}} S_p.$$

(i) $p \mid x$: $\quad S_p \leqslant \sum_{\substack{1 \leqslant n \leqslant x \\ n \equiv o \pmod{p}}} 1 = \left[\frac{x}{p}\right] + 1 = O(x^{1-\frac{1}{v}}).$

(ii) $p \nmid x$: $\quad S_p = \sum_{\substack{1 \leqslant n \leqslant x \\ n(x-n) \equiv o \pmod{p^2}}} 1 \leqslant 2\left[\frac{x}{p^2}\right] + 2.$

Hence, we have
$$\sum_{x^{\frac{1}{v}} < p \leqslant x^{\frac{1}{u}}} S_p = O\Big(\sum_{\substack{p \mid x \\ p > x^{\frac{1}{v}}}} x^{1-\frac{1}{v}}\Big) + O\Big(\sum_{m > x^{\frac{1}{v}}} \frac{x}{m^2}\Big) + O\Big(\sum_{m \leqslant x^{\frac{1}{u}}} 1\Big) =$$
$$= O(x^{1-\frac{1}{v}}) + O(x^{\frac{1}{u}}).$$

Thus we have the lemma.

Lemma 2. There exist sequences of integers (w_j) $(1 \leqslant j \leqslant t-s)$ satisfying (1), such that the number of elements in $\mathfrak{M}$ with at least l prime divisors in the interval $x^{\frac{1}{v}} < p \leqslant x^{\frac{1}{u}}$ is not exceeding
$$\frac{2}{l} \sum_{\substack{1 \leqslant j \leqslant t-s \\ p_{s+j} \nmid x}} P_{w_j}\Big(\frac{x}{p_{s+j}}, x^{\frac{1}{v}}\Big) + O\Big(x^{1-\frac{1}{v}}\Big).$$

Proof. For $1 \leqslant j \leqslant t-s$, let Γ_j be the subset of $\mathfrak{M}$ whose elements are divided by p_{s+j}. Indeed, Γ_j is the set of integers $n(x-n)$ satisfying (3), (4) and the following condition:

(5) $n(x-n) \equiv 0 \pmod{p_{s+j}}$.

(i) $p_{s+j} \mid x$: Evidently, the number of elements of Γ_j is not exceeding

1) If $n = x - n'$ and $n(x-n)$ $(= n'(x-n'))$ belongs to $\mathfrak{N}$ or $\mathfrak{M}$, then we agree that $n(x-n)$ be computed twice.

$$\sum_{\substack{1 \leqslant n \leqslant x \\ n \equiv o \pmod{p_{s+j}}}} 1 = O\left(x^{1-\frac{1}{v}}\right).$$

(ii) $p_{s+j} \nmid x$: From condition (5), we deduce that $n \equiv o \pmod{p_{s+j}}$ or $n \equiv x \pmod{p_{s+j}}$ Let

(w_j) $a = 1$; if p_i / x, then $a_i = b_i = 0$, otherwise $a_i \equiv 0$,

$b_i p_{s+j} \equiv x \pmod{p_i}$ $(1 \leqslant i \leqslant s)$.

Evidently, the number of elements of Γ_j is not exceeding

$$2P_{w_j}\left(\frac{x}{p_{s+j}}, x^{\frac{1}{v}}\right).$$

If $n(x-n)$ belongs to $\mathfrak{M}$ and $n(x-n)$ has at least l prime divisors in the interval $x^{\frac{1}{v}} < p \leqslant x^{\frac{1}{u}}$, then $n(x-n)$ belongs to at least l different sets Γ_j. Hence we have the lemma.

Lemma 3. Let $C > 1$ be a given number. Then there exist two non-decreasing and non-negative functions $\lambda(a)$ and $\Lambda(a)$ $(o < a \leqslant C)$ with the properties that each of $\lambda(a)$ and $\Lambda(a)$ has at most finite discontinuities, such that the following inequality holds uniformly in (w) and z

$$\lambda(z)\frac{c_x x}{\log^2 x} + O\left(\frac{c_x x}{\log^2 x \log\log x}\right) \leqslant P_w(x, x^{\frac{1}{z}}) \leqslant \Lambda(z)\frac{c_x x}{\log^2 x} + O\left(\frac{c_x x}{\log^2 x \log\log x}\right) (0 < z \leqslant C), \tag{6}$$

where $c_x = 2e^{2\gamma}\prod_{p>2}\left(1-\frac{1}{(p-1)^2}\right)\prod_{\substack{p \mid x \\ p>2}}\frac{p-1}{p-2}$ and γ is Euler's constant.

The lemma follows immediately by Brun's method.

Fundamental Theorem. Let m be a non-negative integer and $C > v > u > 1$ be three positive numbers. Let $\lambda(a)$ and $\Lambda(a)$ $(0 < a \leqslant C)$ be two functions with the properties as stated in lemma 3. If

$$\lambda(v) - \frac{1}{m+1}\int_{u-1}^{v-1} \Lambda\left(\frac{vz}{z+1}\right)\frac{z+1}{z^2}\,dz > 0, \tag{7}$$

then for all sufficiently large x, there is always an integer n in the interval $1 < n < x-1$, such that $n(x-n)$ has not prime divisor less than or equal to $x^{\frac{1}{v}}$ and has at most m prime divisors in the interval $x^{\frac{1}{v}} < p \leqslant x^{\frac{1}{u}}$.

Proof. Take

(ω) $a = 1$; if p_i/x, then $a_i = b_i = 0$, otherwise $a_i = 0$, $b_i \equiv x \pmod{p_i}$, $i > 1, 2, \cdots$.

Then we have $N(x, x^{\frac{1}{v}}) = P_{\bar{w}}(x, x^{\frac{1}{v}})$. By lemma 1, 2 and 3, for sufficiently large x, the number of elements in $\mathfrak{M}$ with at most m prime divisors in the interval $x^{\frac{1}{v}} < p \leqslant x^{\frac{1}{u}}$ is not less than

$$M(x, x^{\frac{1}{v}}, x^{\frac{1}{u}}) - \frac{1}{m+1} \sum_{\substack{1 \leqslant j \leqslant t-s \\ p_{s+j} \nmid x}} P_{w_j}\left(\frac{x}{p_{s+j}}, x^{\frac{1}{v}}\right) + O(x^{1-\frac{1}{v}})$$

$$= P_{\bar{w}}(x, x^{\frac{1}{v}}) - \frac{1}{m+1} \sum_{\substack{1 \leqslant j \leqslant t-s \\ p_{s+j} \nmid x}} P_{w_j}\left(\frac{x}{p_{s+j}}, x^{\frac{1}{v}}\right) + O(x^{\frac{1}{u}}) + O(x^{1-\frac{1}{v}})$$

$$\geqslant \left(\lambda(\beta) - \frac{1}{m+1}\int_{u-1}^{v-1} \Lambda\left(\frac{vz}{z+1}\right)\frac{z+1}{z^2}\,dz\right)\frac{c_x x}{\log^2 x} + O\left(\frac{c_x x}{\log^2 x \log\log x}\right) > 3.$$

This means that for sufficiently large x, there exists in the interval $1 < n < x-1$ an integer n having not prime divisor $\leqslant x^{\frac{1}{v}}$ and having at most m prime divisors in the interval $x^{\frac{1}{v}} < p \leqslant x^{\frac{1}{u}}$. Thus we have the Theorem.

By Brun – Бухштаб – Selberg's method (*Cf* [3]), we have the following table:

(8)

a	…	8	…	6	…	5	…	4	…
$\Lambda(a)$	…	68.52511	…	43.0082	…	34.89666	…	29.39023	…
$\lambda(a)$	…	60.88817	…	26.70925	…	9.18109	…	0	…

From table (8), we deduce that

$$\lambda(6) - \frac{2}{3}\int_2^5 \Lambda\left(\frac{6z}{z+1}\right)\frac{z+1}{z^2}\,dz > 0.33829$$

and

$$\lambda(8) - \frac{1}{2}\int_1^7 \Lambda\left(\frac{8z}{z+1}\right)\frac{z+1}{z^2}\,dz > 0.56125.$$

Hence, (3, 3) and (a, b) $(a+b \leqslant 5)$ follow from the Fundamental theorem.

By Бухштаб's method[4] with more complicated numerical calculations, we have improved the values in table (8) and obtain the following

(9)

a	…	8	…	7	…	6	…	5
$\Lambda(a)$	…	64.403149	…	50.529826	…	41.01897	…	34.89666
$\lambda(a)$	…	63.59931	…	47.471252	…	31.004145	…	13.61559

From table (9), we have

$$\lambda(8)-\frac{2}{3}\int_{\frac{9}{7}}^{7}\Lambda\left(\frac{8z}{z+1}\right)\frac{z+1}{z^2}\,dz > 0.43$$

Hence, (2, 3) follows from the Fundamental Theorem.

Finally, we indicate some mistakes in the proof of (3, 3) of А. И. Виноградов*. Here, we use his notations and omit the explanations. He has obtained that

(10) $3.2I - 2I_1 < 0.3167.$

Hence for sufficiently large z, we have

(11) $$\int_{1.1}^{\lambda} \varepsilon(u)(2u+1)\,du \leqslant \frac{e^{2w-1.1}}{\pi}(3\cdot 2I - 2I_1) + O\left(\frac{1}{\sqrt{\log z}}\right) < 0.5.$$

On the other hand, we know that $\varepsilon(u)$ is a non-negative and non-increasing function and $1-\varepsilon(2) = (4.5-4\log 2)\,e^{-2\gamma}$. Hence, it follows that

(12) $$\int_{1.1}^{\lambda} \varepsilon(u)(2u+1)\,du \geqslant \int_{1.1}^{2} \varepsilon(u)(2u+1)\,du \geqslant \varepsilon(2)\int_{1.1}^{2}(2u+1)\,du > 1.5,$$

which is a contradiction with (11). Moreover, one can prove

(13) $$(4\cdot 1)^2 - 4\int_{1.55}^{\lambda}\frac{\varepsilon(u)}{1-\varepsilon(u)}(2u+1)\,du < 16\cdot 81 - 4\int_{1.55}^{3}\frac{\varepsilon(u)}{1-\varepsilon(u)}(2u+1)\,du < -1.$$

Corresponding results of twin-primes problems have also been obtained.

References

[1] Wang, Y., 1957. On Sieve Methods and Some of the Related Problems, *Science Record*, Academia Sinica, New Ser. I, 1, 9–12.

[2] Wang, Y., 1957. On Sieve Methods and Their Some Applications, *Science Record*, Academia Sinica, New Ser. I, 3. 1–6.

[3] Wang, Y., 1956. On the Representation of Large Even Integer as a Sum of a Product of at most 3 Primes and a Product of at most 4 Primes, *Acta Math. Sinica*, 3, 500–513.

[4] Бухштаб, А. А., 1940. О Разложении Чётных Чисел на Сумму Двух Слагаемых с Ограниченным Числом Множителей, *ДАН СССР;* 29, 544–548.

[5] Виноградов, А. И., 1957. Применение ζ(s) к Решету Эратосфена, *матем, сб;* 41: 1 pp. 49–80.

* Added 6. Sept. 1957. I have been informed that this mistake has also been discovered and corrected by himself (Cf. Матем. сб. 41 (83): 3, 415, 1957).

$$\lambda(2) - \frac{2}{3}\int_{\frac{1}{2}}^{1} \lambda\left(\frac{3x}{x+1}\right)\frac{x+1}{x^2}\,dx > 0.43$$

Hence, (2; 3) follows from the Fundamental Theorem.

Finally, we indicate some mistakes in the proof of (3, 3) of A. H. Бухштаб*. Here, we use his notations and omit the explanations. He has obtained that

(10) $3.2I - 2I_1 < 0.3167$.

Hence for sufficiently large x, we have

(11) $$\int_{1.1}^{\lambda} \varepsilon(u)\,(2u+1)\,du \leqslant \frac{e^{-\gamma}}{\pi}(3.2I - 2I_1) + O\left(\frac{1}{\sqrt{\log x}}\right) < 0.5.$$

On the other hand, we know that $\varepsilon(u)$ is a non-negative and non-increasing function and $1 - \varepsilon(2) = (4.5 - 4\log 2)e^{-\gamma}$. Hence, it follows that

(12) $$\int_{1.1}^{\lambda} \varepsilon(u)\,(2u+1)\,du \geqslant \int_{1.1}^{2} \varepsilon(u)\,(2u+1)\,du \geqslant \varepsilon(2)\int_{1.1}^{2}(2u+1)\,du > 1.5,$$

which is a contradiction with (11). Moreover, one can prove

(13) $$(4.1)F_{3} - 4\int_{1.85}^{\lambda}\frac{\varepsilon(u)}{1-\varepsilon(u)}(2u-1)\,du < 13.61 -$$

$$- 4\int_{1.85}^{3}\frac{\varepsilon(u)}{1-\varepsilon(u)}(2u+1)\,du < -1.$$

Corresponding results of twin-primes problems have also been obtained.

References

[1] Wang, Y., 1957, On Sieve Methods and Some of the Related Problems. *Science Record, Academia Sinica*, New Ser. 1, 1, 9–12.

[2] Wang, Y., 1957, On Sieve Methods and Their Some Applications. *Science Record, Academia Sinica*, New Ser. 1, 3, 1–5.

[3] Wang, Y., 1956, On the Representation of Large Even Integer as a Sum of a Product of at most 3 Primes and a Product of at most 4 Primes. *Acta Math. Sinica*, 6, 500–513.

[4] Бухштаб, А. А., 1940, О Разложении Четных Чисел на Сумму Двух Слагаемых с Ограниченным Числом Множителей, *ДАН СССР*, 29, 544–548.

[5] Виноградов, А. И., 1957, Применение $\zeta(s)$ к Решету Эратосфена, *Матем. сб.*, 41: 1 pp. 49–80.

* Added 6. Sept. 1957. I have been informed that this mistake has also been discovered and corrected by himself (cf. Матем. сб. 41 (83): 3, 415, 1957).

III. REPRESENTATION OF AN EVEN NUMBER AS THE SUM OF A PRIME AND AN ALMOST PRIME

On the Representation of an Even Number as the Sum of a Prime and an Almost Prime

A. Rényi

The problem concerning the representations of even number as the sum of two primes and of odd number as the sum of three primes was suggested in the correspondence between Euler and Goldbach in 1742.

Using his method on the estimation of trigonometrical sum, academician I. M. Vinogradov [1] has proved the Goldbach theorem for odd number in 1937. In 1938, N. G. Tchudakov [2] has proved, using Vinogradov's method, that almost all even integers are the sums of two primes. The approximate result of other type was obtained by Viggo Brun [3] in 1920, who has proved, using the elementary method of the Eratosthenes sieve, that every even number can be represented as the sum of two almost primes, i.e., $2N = P_1 + P_2$, where P_1 and P_2 have at most 9[a)] prime factors.

A conditional result was proved by T. Estermann in 1932 [6], namely every large even number is the sum of a prime and an almost prime which has at most 6 prime factors. Estermann's result is based on the assumption of the famous unproved Riemann hypothesis for all of Dirichlet L-series. In this paper, I prove the following theorem without any hypothesis.

Theorem 1. Every even number can be represented in the form $2N = p + P$, where p is a prime and P an almost prime, i.e., P has at most K prime factors, where K is an absolute constant.

The detailed proof will be appeared in another place, and we give here only the main steps of the proof.

Riemann hypothesis can be avoided by the use of a new theorem

[a] 9 can be replaced by 4. See Tartakovskii [4] and Buchstab [5].

on the zeros of L-series (Theorem 2) which is established by Ju. V. Linnik's two methods; the method of the large sieve [7] and the method contained in his paper [8].

In order to formulate Theorem 2, we introduce certain definitions. It is known that every character belonging to the $\phi(D)$ characters mod D, where D is a square free number, can be represented uniquely as the product of characters belonging to moduli which are the prime factors of D. Thus if $D = pq$, where p is a prime and $(p,q) = 1$, then every character belonging to the modulus D is of the form $\chi_D(n) = \chi_p(n)\,\chi_q(n)$, where $\chi_p(n)$ and $\chi_q(n)$ are characters belonging to moduli p and q respectively. If $\chi_p(n)$ is not a principal character, then we shall call $\chi_D(n)$ primitive with respective to p. Clearly if $\chi_D(n)$ is primitive with respect to every prime factor of D, then it is primitive in the usual sense.

<u>Theorem 2</u>. Let q be a square free number, $A \geq c_1$[b], $k = \frac{\log q}{\log A} + 1$ and $k \leq \log^3 A$. For all primes p such that $A < p < 2A$ and $(p,q) = 1$, with the possible exception of not more than $A^{3/4}$ such primes, the Dirichlet L-function modulo $D = pq$

$$L(s, \chi) = \sum_{n=1}^{\infty} \frac{\chi(n)}{n^s} \qquad (s = \sigma + it) \quad ,$$

where $\chi(n)$ is primitive with respect to p, has no zero in the domain $\sigma \geq 1 - \frac{\delta}{k+1}$, $|t| \leq \log^3 D$, where $\delta > 0$ is a constant.

It follows, for example, from Theorem 2 that there exist infinitely many primes $p_1, p_2, \ldots, p_n, \ldots$ such that if $\chi(n)$ is not the principal character modulo p_n, then $L(s, \chi) \neq 0$ for $s = \sigma + it$, $\sigma \geq 1 - \frac{\delta}{2}$, $|t| < \log^3 p_n$, where $\delta > 0$ is a constant.

---

b $c_1, c_2, \ldots$ denote the positive absolute constants.

Let

$$H(2N) = \sum_{\substack{p<2N \\ (2N-p,B)=1}} \log p \cdot \exp(-p \frac{\log 2N}{2N}) \quad , \tag{1}$$

where $B = \prod_{c_2 \le p \le (2N)^{1/R}} p$ and R is a given integer. Let

$$P_Q(x) = \sum_{\substack{p<x \\ p \equiv \ell (\mathrm{mod}\ Q)}} \log p \cdot \exp\left(-p \frac{\log x}{x}\right)$$

$$= \frac{x}{\phi(Q) \log x} + R_Q(x) \quad , \tag{2}$$

where $(\ell,Q) = 1$. Then by Viggo Brun's method, it yields easily

$$H(2N) > \frac{c_3 N}{\log^2 N} - \sum_{Q \in E} |R_Q(2N)| \quad , \tag{3}$$

where the set E is defined as follows: E contains square free numbers of the form $Q = p_1 p_2 \cdots p_r$ $(p_1 > p_2 > \ldots > p_r)$, if $c_2 \le p_i \le (2N)^{1/Rh^{[i/2]}}$, $i = 1,\ldots,r$, where $h = 1.25$.

If we can prove that $H(2N) > 0$ for $N \ge c_4$, then Theorem 1 clearly follows with $K = \max(R+c_2, c_4)$. Hence the problem is reduced to the estimation of the sum

$$\sum_{Q \in E} |R_Q(2N)| \quad . \tag{4}$$

We shall prove that

$$\sum_{Q \in E} |R_Q(2N)| < \frac{4N}{\log^3 N} \quad . \tag{5}$$

In order to estimate (4), we derive Theorem 3 from Theorem 2.

Theorem 3. Let q_1 be a square free number, $A \ge c_1$ and

$$\exp((\log x)^{2/5}) < Aq_1 < \sqrt{x} \quad .$$

Let $k_1 = \dfrac{q_1}{\log (p_1/2)} + 1$, where p_1 is a prime, $A \le p_1 < 2A$ and

$(p_1, q_1) = 1$. Suppose that $k_1 \le \log^3 A$. For all primes p_1, with the exception of at most $A^{3/4}$ such primes, we have

$$\left| \sum_{p \le x} \chi(p) \log p \cdot \exp\left(-p \frac{\log x}{x}\right) \right| \le x^{1-(\delta_1/k_1+1)} \qquad (6)$$

for any character $\chi(n)$ modulo $D = p_1 q_1$, where $\chi(n)$ is primitive with respect to p_1 and $\delta_1 > 0$ is a constant.

It can be derived easily from Theorem 2 and the well-known J. E. Littlewood's formula (Cf. [8]) that

$$\sum_1^\infty \Lambda(n)\, \chi(n)\, e^{-n/Y} = -\frac{1}{2\pi i} \int_{2-i\infty}^{2+i\infty} \frac{L'}{L}(s, \chi)\, \Gamma(s)\, Y^s\, ds \ . \qquad (7)$$

From the well-known results of E. C. Titchmarsh [9], A. Page [10], and C. L. Siegel [11], it follows that

$$P_D(x) = \frac{x}{\phi(D) \log x} + O(x \exp(-c_6\sqrt{\log x}\,)\,) \qquad (8)$$

holds for all $D \le \exp(c_5\sqrt{\log x})$ with the possible exception of those values of D which are multiples of a certain integer D_1 which eventually may exist.

For the case D_1/D, we have

$$P_D(x) = \frac{x}{\phi(D) \log x} + O\left(x \exp(-c_6\sqrt{\log x})\right)$$

$$+ O\left(\frac{1}{\phi(D)}\, x^{1-(c_\varepsilon/D_1^\varepsilon)} \right) \ , \qquad (9)$$

where ε is any positive number and c_ε depends on ε only. Furthermore, we need the Brun-Titchmarsh's formula (Cf. [9]):

---

[c] D_1 is the modulus for which the corresponding L-series has the Siegel's zero $\rho = \sigma + it$ in the domain $\sigma > 1 - \dfrac{c_7}{\sqrt{\log x}}$.

$$P_D(x) = O\left(\frac{x}{\phi(D)}\right) \qquad \text{uniformly on} \quad D \le \sqrt{x} \ . \tag{10}$$

Consider the sum (4). Let $2N = x$ and

$$S_\chi(x) = \sum_{p \le x} \chi(p) \log p \cdot \exp\left(-p \frac{\log x}{x}\right) . \tag{11}$$

If $Q \ge \exp((\log x)^{2/5})$ and $Q = p_1 q_1$, where p_1 is the greatest prime divisor of Q and not an exception in the sense of Theorem 3. Then from

$$P_Q(x) = \frac{1}{\phi(Q)} \sum_{(\chi)} \bar{\chi}(\ell)\, S_\chi(x) \ , \tag{12}$$

we have

$$P_Q(x) = \frac{1}{\phi(p_1)} P_{q_1}(x) + O\left(x^{1 - (\delta_1/k_1+1)} \right) . \tag{13}$$

This process may be continued for $q_1 = p_2 p_2$, $q_2 = p_3 q_3$ and so on, until after a certain number of steps, s say, the condition in Theorem 3 is not fulfilled by $q_s = p_{s+1}\, q_{s+1}$. Then if $q_s < \exp(\log x)^{2/5}$, we use (8) or (9), while if $q_s \ge \exp(\log x)^{2/5}$ and p_{s+1} is an exceptional prime, we use (10). Hence the estimation of (4) is reduced to estimate the sums of the following four types:

I. $x \exp(-c_6 \sqrt{\log x})$. II. $\frac{1}{\phi(D)} x^{1 - (c_\varepsilon / D_1^\varepsilon)}$.

III. $\frac{x}{\phi(D)}$. IV. $x^{1 - (\delta_1/k_1+1)}$.

The sum of terms with type I is obviously of $O\left(\frac{N}{\log^4 N}\right)$.

The sum of terms with type II does not exceed

$$N \log^3 N \cdot \exp\left(- \log D_1 - \frac{c_\varepsilon}{D_1^\varepsilon} \log N\right) \ . \tag{14}$$

Although the value of D_1 is an unknown, but we can prove that the maximum of (14) for $1 \le D_1 < \infty$, $N \ge c_4$ and $\varepsilon = \frac{1}{8}$ does not exceed

$\frac{N}{\log^3 N}$.

The sum of terms with type III may be calculated by noting that for any q, the number of exceptional primes p^* in any interval $(A, 2A)$ does not exceed $A^{3/4}$, and thus

$$\sum_{p^* \geq T} \frac{1}{p^*-1} < \frac{\log^2 T}{T^{1/4}}, \qquad T \geq c_8 . \tag{15}$$

Finally, the following elementary property of E is needed for the estimation of the sum of terms of the type IV: the number of integers $Q = pq$, where p is the greatest prime divisor of Q, which belongs to E and satisfies $p < q^{1/k}$ ($k \geq 1$ integer) does not exceed $(2N)^{40k/(Rh^{k/2})}$.

Therefore we have proved that for sufficiently large R, the sum of terms of any type does not exceed $\frac{N}{\log^3 N}$ for $N > c_8$, i.e.,

$$\sum_{Q \in E} |R_Q(2N)| < \frac{4N}{\log^3 N}, \qquad N > c_8 . \tag{16}$$

From (3) and (16), we have $H(2N) > \frac{c_9 N}{\log^2 N}$ for $N > c_4$, and thus Theorem 1 is proved. The number of solutions of $2N = p + P$ is not less than $\frac{c_9 N}{\log^3 N}$.

It is natural to expect that the number of solutions will be of $O\left(\frac{N}{\log^2 N}\right)$. The weakness of our result lies on that the sum $\Sigma \log p \cdot \exp\left(-p \frac{\log x}{x}\right)$ is used instead of $\Sigma \log p$ in order that the length of zero free rectangle in Theorem 2 can be decreased when the Littlewood's formula (7) is applied.

Similar to the proof of Theorem 1, we have

<u>Theorem 4</u>. There exist infinitely many primes p such that $p = p+2$ is an almost prime, i.e., the number of prime factors of P

does not exceed an absolute constant.

Theorem 4 gives an approximation to the well-known hypothesis that there exist infinitely many prime pairs.

References

[1]. I. M. Vinogradov, C. R. Acad. URSS, 15 (1937) 291-294.

[2]. N. G. Tchudakov, Izv. Akad. Nauk SSSR, Ser. Math., 1 (1938) 25-40.

[3]. V. Brun, Skr. Norske Vid. Akad., Kristiania, I, 3 (1920).

[4]. V. A. Tartakovskii, Dokl. Akad. Nauk SSSR, 23 (1939) 126-129.

[5]. A. A. Buchstab, Dokl. Akad. Nauk SSSR, 29 (1940) 544-548.

[6]. T. Estermann, J. Reine Angew. Math., 168 (1932) 106-116.

[7]. Ju. V. Linnik, Dokl. Akad. Nauk SSSR, 30 (1941) 292-294.

[8]. Ju. V. Linnik, Mat. Sbornik, 15 (1944) 3-12.

[9]. E. C. Titchmarsh, Rend. Cir. Mat. Palermo, 54 (1930) 414-429.

[10]. A. Page, Proc. London Math. Soc., 39 (1935) 116-141.

[11]. C. L. Siegel, Acta Arith., 1 (1936) 83-86.

(See Dokl. Akad. Nauk SSSR, 56 (1947) 455-458, also Izv. Akad. Nauk SSSR, Ser. Mat., 12 (1948) 57-78).

Translated by Wang Yuan

SCIENTIA SINICA
Vol. XI, No. 8, 1962

MATHEMATICS

ON THE REPRESENTATION OF LARGE INTEGER AS A SUM OF A PRIME AND AN ALMOST PRIME*

WANG YUAN (王 元)
(Institute of Mathematics, Academia Sinica)

§ 1

In this paper, we shall give the detailed proofs of certain results obtained upon assuming the truth of the grand Riemann hypothesis. (Cf. [1], [2]). First of all, let us state the grand Riemann hypothesis as follows:

(*R*) *The real parts of all zeros of all Dirichlet's L — functions* $L(s,\chi)$ *are* $\leqslant 1/2$.

From (*R*) we derive the following[3]

(R^*) *Let* $(l, k)=1$. *Then*

$$\pi(x; k, l) = \sum_{\substack{p\leqslant x \\ p\equiv l \pmod k}} 1 = \frac{\operatorname{li} x}{\varphi(k)} + O(x^{1/2}\log x),$$

where $\operatorname{li} x = \int_2^x \frac{dt}{\log t}$.

Now we state the results as follows:

Theorem 1. *Under the truth of* (R^*), *every sufficiently large even integer is a sum of a prime and a product of at most 3 primes.*

Theorem 2. *Under the truth of* (R^*), *there exist infinitely many primes* p *such that* $p+2k$ *is a product of at most 3 primes, where* k *is a given positive integer.*

Theorem 3. *Under the truth of* (R^*), *every sufficiently large odd integer* N *can be represented as* $N = p + 2P$, *where* p *is a prime number and* P *is an almost prime of not more than 3 prime divisors.*

* This paper has been published previously in Chinese in *Acta Math. Sinica*, Vol. X, No. 2, pp. 168—181, 1960, but the Appendix is added during translation.

1034

Theorem 4. *Let $Z_k(x)$ be the number of prime pairs of the form $(p, p+2k)$ not exceeding x. Then*

$$Z_k(x) \leqslant 8 \prod_{\substack{p|2k \\ p>2}} \frac{p-1}{p-2} \prod_{p>2} \left(1 - \frac{1}{(p-1)^2}\right) \frac{x}{\log^2 x} + O\left(\frac{x}{\log^3 x} \log\log x\right).$$

Theorems 1, 2, 3 improve the results which were obtained independently and simultaneously by the author[4] and А. И. Виноградов[5]. Our original results were obtained by replacing 3 by 4 in these Theorems.

It is well known that if $\pi(x; k, l)$ is represented by

$$P(x; k, l) = \sum_{\substack{p \leqslant x \\ p \equiv l \pmod k}} e^{-\frac{p \log x}{x}} \log p,$$

then Theorems 1, 2, 3 may be derived from the following weaker hypothesis (R^{**})

(R^{**}) *Let χ be the character* mod D. *Then $L(s, \chi)$ has no zeros in the domain*

$$|t| \leqslant \log^3 D, \quad \sigma > \frac{1}{2} \quad (s = \sigma + it).$$

In this paper, $p, p', p'', \cdots; p_1, p_2, \cdots$ denote primes.

§ 2

Lemma 1. *If $x \geqslant 1$ and $z \geqslant 1$, then*

$$\sum_{\substack{1 \leqslant n \leqslant z \\ (n, x)=1}} \frac{\mu^2(n)}{\varphi(n)} = \frac{\varphi(x)}{x} \log z + O(\log\log 3x).$$

(Cf. [4]).

Lemma 2. *Let $f(k) = \varphi(k) \prod_{p|k} \frac{p-2}{p-1}$. If $1 \leqslant z \leqslant x$, $1 \leqslant y \leqslant x$, then*

$$\sum_{\substack{1 \leqslant k \leqslant z \\ (k, 2y)=1}} \frac{\mu^2(k)}{f(k)} = \frac{1}{2} \prod_{\substack{p|y \\ p>2}} \frac{p-2}{p-1} \prod_{p>2} \left(1 + \frac{1}{p(p-2)}\right) \log z + O(\log\log 3x).$$

Proof. Let $\psi(q) = \prod_{p|q} \frac{p-2}{p-1}$. Then

$$\sum_{\substack{1 \leqslant k \leqslant z \\ (k, 2y)=1}} \frac{\mu^2(k)}{f(k)} = \sum_{\substack{1 \leqslant k \leqslant z \\ (k, 2y)=1}} \frac{\mu^2(k)}{\varphi(k)} \prod_{p|k} \left(1 + \frac{1}{p-2}\right) = \sum_{\substack{1 \leqslant k \leqslant z \\ (k, 2y)=1}} \frac{\mu^2(k)}{\varphi(k)} \sum_{q|k} \frac{1}{\psi(q)} =$$

$$= \sum_{\substack{q \le z \\ (q,2y)=1}} \frac{\mu^2(q)}{\varphi(q)\psi(q)} \sum_{\substack{t \le z/q \\ (t,2qy)=1}} \frac{\mu^2(t)}{\varphi(t)} =$$

$$= \sum_{\substack{q \le z \\ (q,2y)=1}} \frac{\mu^2(q)}{\varphi(q)\psi(q)} \left[\frac{\varphi(2qy)}{2qy} \log \frac{z}{q} + O(\log\log 6qy) \right] =$$

$$= \frac{\varphi(2y)}{2y} \sum_{\substack{q \le z \\ (q,2y)=1}} \frac{\mu^2(q)}{q\psi(q)} \log z + O(\log\log 3x) =$$

$$= \frac{\varphi(2y)}{2y} \prod_{p \nmid 2y} \left(1 + \frac{1}{p(p-2)}\right) \log z + O(\log\log 3x) =$$

$$= \frac{1}{2} \prod_{\substack{p \mid y \\ p>2}} \frac{p-2}{p-1} \prod_{p>2} \left(1 + \frac{1}{p(p-2)}\right) \log z + O(\log\log 3x).$$

Thus we have the Lemma.

§ 3

Let $2 \le y \le x$ be two given integers. Let

$$(\omega) \qquad a, q; a_i \quad (1 \le i \le r)$$

be a sequence of integers satisfying the following conditions:

$$(1) \qquad q \le x, (a, q) = 1; \text{ if } p_i \mid y, \text{ then } a_i \equiv 0 (\text{mod } p_i), \text{ otherwise}$$
$$a_i \not\equiv 0 (\text{mod } p_i) \quad (1 \le i \le r),$$

where $2 < p_1 < \cdots < p_r \le \xi$ are all primes not exceeding ξ and not dividing q.

Let $P_\omega(x, q, \xi)$ be the number of primes p satisfying the following conditions:

$$(2) \qquad p \le x, p \equiv a (\text{mod } q), p \not\equiv a_i (\text{mod } p_i) \quad (1 \le i \le r).$$

It follows from the Chinese Remainder Theorem that the system of congruences

$$y \equiv a_i (\text{mod } p_i) \quad (1 \le i \le r)$$

has a unique solution in the interval $1 \le y \le p_1 \cdots p_r$. Denote this solution by a^*. Hence $P_\omega(x, q, \xi)$ is equal to the number of primes satisfying the following conditions:

$$(3) \qquad p \le x, p \equiv a (\text{mod } q), p \not\equiv a^* (\text{mod } p_i) \quad (1 \le i \le r).$$

1036

Theorem A. *Let* $c>0$; $P=\prod_{i=1}^{r} p_i$. *Then under the truth of* (R^*), *the estimation*

$$P_\omega(x,q,\xi)\leqslant \frac{\operatorname{li} x}{\varphi(q)\sum\limits_{\substack{1\leqslant k\leqslant \xi^c\\ k\mid P\\ (k,y)=1}}\frac{\mu^2(k)}{f(k)}}+O(x^{1/2}\log x\cdot \xi^{2c}\log^2\xi)$$

holds uniformly in (ω), *where* $f(k)=\varphi(k)\prod_{p\mid k}\frac{p-2}{p-1}$.

Proof. Denote $g(k)=\varphi(k)^{-1}$. If $(k,y)=1$ and $k\mid P$, then it follows from (R^*) that

$$\sum_{\substack{p\leqslant x\\ p\equiv a(\bmod q)\\ p\equiv a^*(\bmod k)}} 1=\frac{\operatorname{li} x}{\varphi(q)\varphi(k)}+O(x^{1/2}\log x).$$

Let

$$\lambda_d=\frac{\mu(d)}{f(d)g(d)}\sum_{\substack{1\leqslant k\leqslant \xi^c/d\\ (k,d)=1\\ k\mid P\\ (k,y)=1}}\frac{\mu^2(k)}{f(k)}\Bigg/\sum_{\substack{1\leqslant l\leqslant \xi^c\\ l\mid P\\ (l,y)=1}}\frac{\mu^2(l)}{f(l)},$$

where $d\mid P$. Then

$$P_\omega(x,q,\xi)=\sum_{\substack{p\leqslant x\\ p\equiv a(\bmod q)\\ (p-a^*,P)=1}}1\leqslant \sum_{\substack{p\leqslant x\\ p\equiv a(\bmod q)}}\Bigg(\sum_{\substack{d\mid (p-a^*,P)\\ (d,y)=1}}\lambda_d\Bigg)^2=$$

$$=\sum_{\substack{d_1\leqslant \xi^c\\ d_1\mid P\\ (d_1,y)=1}}\sum_{\substack{d_2\leqslant \xi^c\\ d_2\mid P\\ (d_2,y)=1}}\lambda_{d_1}\lambda_{d_2}\sum_{\substack{p\leqslant x\\ p\equiv a(\bmod q)\\ p\equiv a^*\left(\bmod \frac{d_1d_2}{(d_1,d_2)}\right)}}1=$$

$$=\frac{\operatorname{li} x}{\varphi(q)}\sum_{\substack{d_1\leqslant \xi^c\\ d_1\mid P\\ (d_1,y)=1}}\sum_{\substack{d_2\leqslant \xi^c\\ d_2\mid P\\ (d_2,y)=1}}\lambda_{d_1}\lambda_{d_2}\frac{g(d_1)g(d_2)}{g((d_1,d_2))}+$$

$$+O\Bigg(x^{1/2}\log x\Bigg(\sum_{\substack{d\leqslant \xi^c\\ d\mid P}}|\lambda_d|\Bigg)^2\Bigg)=\frac{\operatorname{li} x}{\varphi(q)}Q+R.$$

Let

$$S=\sum_{\substack{l\leqslant \xi^c\\ l\mid P\\ (l,y)=1}}\frac{\mu^2(l)}{f(l)}.$$

Then

$$\lambda_k g(k) = \frac{1}{S} \sum_{\substack{m \leqslant \xi^c/k \\ (m,k)=1 \\ m|P \\ (m,y)=1}} \frac{\mu(k)}{f(k)} \cdot \frac{\mu^2(m)}{f(m)} = \frac{1}{S} \sum_{\substack{m \leqslant \xi^c/k \\ (m,y)=(m,k)=1 \\ m|P}} \frac{\mu(mk)\mu(m)}{f(mk)}.$$

For $(d, y)=1$, we have

$$\sum_{\substack{d|k|P \\ k \leqslant \xi^c \\ (k,y)=1}} \lambda_k g(k) = \frac{1}{S} \sum_{\substack{d|k|P \\ k \leqslant \xi^c \\ (k,y)=1}} \sum_{\substack{m \leqslant \xi^c/k \\ (m,y)=(m,k)=1 \\ m|P}} \frac{\mu(mk)\mu(m)}{f(mk)} =$$

$$= \frac{1}{S} \sum_{\substack{r \leqslant \xi^c \\ r|P \\ (r,y)=1}} \frac{\mu(r)}{f(r)} \sum_{d|k|r} \mu\left(\frac{r}{k}\right) = \frac{1}{S} \cdot \frac{\mu(d)}{f(d)}.$$

Hence

$$Q = \sum_{\substack{d_1 \leqslant \xi^c \\ d_1|P \\ (d_1,y)=1}} \sum_{\substack{d_2 \leqslant \xi^c \\ d_2|P \\ (d_2,y)=1}} \lambda_{d_1}\lambda_{d_2} g(d_1) g(d_2) \sum_{d|(d_1,d_2)} f(d) =$$

$$= \sum_{\substack{d \leqslant \xi^c \\ d|P \\ (d,y)=1}} f(d) \Bigg(\sum_{\substack{k \leqslant \xi^c \\ d|k|P \\ (k,y)=1}} \lambda_k g(k) \Bigg)^2 = \frac{1}{S}.$$

By Merten's Theorem, we have

$$|\lambda_d| \leqslant \frac{|\mu(d)|}{|f(d)g(d)|} \leqslant \prod_{p|d} \frac{p-1}{p-2} = O(\log \xi),$$

for $d|P$ and $d \leqslant \xi^c$. Hence

$$R = O(x^{1/2} \log x \cdot \xi^{2c} \log^2 \xi).$$

Thus we have the Theorem.

§ 4

Let $\xi > 2$. Let $l < c \leqslant l+1$, where l is a positive integer. Then

$$\sum_{\substack{1 \leqslant n \leqslant \xi^c \\ n|P \\ (n,y)=1}} \frac{\mu^2(n)}{f(n)} = \sum_{\substack{1 \leqslant n \leqslant \xi^c \\ (n,2qy)=1}} \frac{\mu^2(n)}{f(n)} - \sum_{\xi < p \leqslant \xi^c} \sum_{\substack{1 \leqslant n \leqslant \xi^c \\ (n,2qy)=1 \\ p|n}} \frac{\mu^2(n)}{f(n)} + \sum_{\substack{\xi < p < p' \\ pp' \leqslant \xi^c}} \sum_{\substack{n \leqslant \xi^c \\ pp'|n \\ (n,2qy)=1}} \frac{\mu^2(n)}{f(n)} +$$

1038

$$+\cdots+(-1)^l \sum_{\substack{\xi<p'<\cdots<p^{(l)}\\ p'\cdots p^{(l)}\leqslant\xi^c}} \sum_{\substack{n\leqslant\xi^c\\ p'\cdots p^{(l)}\mid n\\ (n,2qy)=1}} \frac{|\mu(n)|}{f(n)} =$$

$$= \sum_{\substack{1\leqslant n\leqslant\xi^c\\ (n,2qy)=1}} \frac{\mu^2(n)}{f(n)} - \sum_{\substack{\xi<p\leqslant\xi^c\\ (p,qy)=1}} \frac{1}{f(p)} \sum_{\substack{n\leqslant\xi^c/p\\ (n,2pyq)=1}} \frac{\mu^2(n)}{f(n)} +$$

(4) $$+\cdots+(-1)^l \sum_{\substack{\xi<p'<\cdots<p^{(l)}\\ p'\cdots p^{(l)}\leqslant\xi^c\\ (p'\cdots p^{(l)},qy)=1}} \frac{1}{f(p')\cdots f(p^{(l)})} \sum_{\substack{n\leqslant\frac{\xi^c}{p'\cdots p^{(l)}}\\ (n,2p'\cdots p^{(l)}qy)=1}} \frac{\mu^2(n)}{f(n)}.$$

1°. If $3\leqslant u\leqslant 6$ and $x^{1/u}<q\leqslant c_0x^{1/u}$, then we take $\xi=\frac{x^{1/u}}{\log^{12}x}$ and $c=\frac{u-2}{4}<1$. It follows from Lemma 2 and (4) that

$$\sum_{\substack{n\leqslant\xi^c\\ n\mid P\\ (n,y)=1}} \frac{\mu^2(n)}{f(n)} = \sum_{\substack{n\leqslant\xi^c\\ (n,2qy)=1}} \frac{\mu^2(n)}{f(n)} = \frac{1}{2}\prod_{\substack{p\mid qy\\ p>2}} \frac{p-2}{p-1} \prod_{p>2}\left(1+\frac{1}{p(p-2)}\right)\log\xi^c +$$

$$+ O(\log\log 3x) =$$

$$= \frac{u-2}{8u}\prod_{\substack{p\mid qy\\ p>2}} \frac{p-2}{p-1} \prod_{p>2}\left(1+\frac{1}{p(p-2)}\right)\log x + O(\log\log 3x).$$

Hence by Theorem A we have

$$P_\omega(x,q,x^{1/u}) \leqslant P_\omega\left(x,q,\frac{x^{1/u}}{\log^{12}x}\right) \leqslant$$

(5) $$\leqslant \Lambda(u)\frac{c_{qy}x}{\varphi(q)\log^2 x} + O\left(\frac{c_{qy}x}{\varphi(q)}\cdot\frac{\log\log x}{\log^3 x}\right),$$

where

$$\Lambda(u) = \frac{8u}{u-2}e^\gamma,$$

(6) $$c_{qy} = e^{-\gamma}\prod_{\substack{p\mid qy\\ p>2}} \frac{p-1}{p-2} \prod_{p>2}\left(1-\frac{1}{(p-1)^2}\right),$$ γ denotes Euler's constant.

2°. If $6\leqslant u\leqslant 13$ and $x^{1/u}<q\leqslant c_0x^{1/u}$, then we take $\xi=\frac{x^{1/u}}{\log^{12}x}$ and $c=\frac{u-2}{4}<3$. Since

$$\sum_{\substack{\xi<p\leqslant\xi^c\\ p\nmid qy}} \frac{1}{f(p)} - \sum_{\xi<p\leqslant\xi^c} \frac{1}{p} = O\left(\sum_{p>\xi}\frac{1}{p^2}\right) + O\left(\sum_{\substack{p>\xi\\ p\mid qy}}\frac{1}{p}\right) = O\left(\frac{1}{\xi}\right),$$

$$\sum_{\substack{\xi<p\leqslant\xi^c \\ p\nmid qy}} \frac{1}{f(p)} \sum_{\substack{n\leqslant\xi^c/p \\ (n,\,2qy)=1}} \frac{\mu^2(n)}{f(n)} - \sum_{\substack{\xi<p\leqslant\xi^c \\ p\nmid qy}} \frac{1}{f(p)} \sum_{\substack{n\leqslant\xi^c/p \\ (n,\,2pqy)=1}} \frac{\mu^2(n)}{f(n)} =$$

$$= o\Bigg(\sum_{\substack{\xi<p\leqslant\xi^c \\ p\nmid qy}} \frac{1}{f(p)} \sum_{\substack{n\leqslant\xi^c/p \\ (n,\,2qy)=1 \\ p\mid n}} \frac{\mu^2(n)}{f(n)}\Bigg) =$$

$$= o\Bigg(\sum_{\substack{\xi<p\leqslant\xi^c \\ p\nmid qy}} \frac{1}{f(p)^2} \sum_{\substack{n\leqslant\xi^c/p^2 \\ (n,\,2qy)=1}} \frac{\mu^2(n)}{f(n)}\Bigg) = o\left(\frac{\log x}{\xi}\right),$$

therefore

$$\sum_{\xi<p\leqslant\xi^c} \frac{1}{p} \sum_{\substack{n\leqslant\xi^c/p \\ (n,\,2qy)=1}} \frac{\mu^2(n)}{f(n)} - \sum_{\substack{\xi<p\leqslant\xi^c \\ p\nmid qy}} \frac{1}{f(p)} \sum_{\substack{n\leqslant\xi^c/p \\ (n,\,2pqy)=1}} \frac{\mu^2(n)}{f(n)} = o\left(\frac{\log x}{\xi}\right).$$

From Lemma 2 and (4) we have

$$\sum_{\substack{n\leqslant\xi^c \\ n\mid P \\ (n,\,y)=1}} \frac{\mu^2(n)}{f(n)} \geqslant \sum_{\substack{n\leqslant\xi^c \\ (n,\,2qy)=1}} \frac{\mu^2(n)}{f(n)} - \sum_{\xi<p\leqslant\xi^c} \frac{1}{p} \sum_{\substack{n\leqslant\xi^c/p \\ (n,\,2qy)=1}} \frac{\mu^2(n)}{f(n)} + o\left(\frac{\log x}{\xi}\right) =$$

$$= \frac{1}{2}(2c-1-c\log c) \prod_{\substack{p\mid qy \\ p>2}} \frac{p-2}{p-1} \prod_{p>2} \frac{(p-1)^2}{p(p-2)} \log\xi + O(\log\log x).$$

Hence it follows from Theorem A that (5) holds for

$$\Lambda(u) = \frac{2u}{\dfrac{u-2}{2} - 1 - \dfrac{u-2}{4}\log\dfrac{u-2}{4}}\, e^{\gamma} \quad (6\leqslant u\leqslant 13). \tag{7}$$

Let U denote the root of the equation

$$\frac{u}{4} - 2 - \frac{1}{2}\log\frac{u-2}{4} = 0.$$

Then

$$\frac{d\Lambda(u)}{du} = \Lambda'(u)\begin{cases} >0, & \text{if } 13\geqslant u>U; \\ <0, & \text{if } U>u\geqslant 3. \end{cases}$$

Hence $\Lambda(u)$ is decreasing in the interval $(3, U)$ and increasing in the interval $(U, 13)$. By numerical calculations, we have

$$7.35 < U < 7.4.$$

1040

§ 5

Let $v>4$.

1°. If $q=x^{1/u}$ and $2<u\leqslant\frac{1}{\frac{1}{2}-\frac{2}{v}}$, then we take $c=\frac{v}{2}\left(\frac{1}{2}-\frac{1}{u}\right)\leqslant 1$ and $\xi=\frac{x^{1/v}}{\log^{3/c}x}$. Since

$$\sum_{\substack{n\leqslant\xi^c\\ n|P\\ (n,y)=1}}\frac{\mu^2(n)}{f(n)}=\sum_{\substack{n\leqslant\xi^c\\ (n,2qy)=1}}\frac{\mu^2(n)}{f(n)}=\frac{u-2}{8u}\prod_{\substack{p|qy\\ p>2}}\frac{p-2}{p-1}\prod_{p>2}\left(1+\frac{1}{p(p-2)}\right)\log x+ + O(\log\log x),$$

therefore from Theorem A we have

$$P_\omega(x,q,x^{1/v})\leqslant P_\omega(x,q,\xi)\leqslant$$
$$\leqslant\frac{8u}{u-2}\prod_{\substack{p|qy\\ p>2}}\frac{p-1}{p-2}\prod_{p>2}\left(1-\frac{1}{(p-1)^2}\right)\frac{x}{\varphi(q)\log^2 x}+$$
$$+O\left(\frac{xc_{qy}\log\log x}{\log^3 x}\right)=A_1(u)\frac{c_{qy}x}{\varphi(q)\log^2 x}+O\left(\frac{xc_{qy}\log\log x}{\varphi(q)\log^3 x}\right), \tag{8}$$

where

$$A_1(u)=\frac{8u}{u-2}e^{\gamma}. \tag{9}$$

2°. If $q=x^{1/u}$ and

$$\frac{1}{\frac{1}{2}-\frac{2}{v}}<u<\begin{cases}\frac{1}{\frac{1}{2}-\frac{4}{v}} & (v>8);\\ \infty & (v\leqslant 8),\end{cases}$$

then we take $\xi=\frac{x^{1/u}}{\log^3 x}$ and $c=\frac{v}{2}\left(\frac{1}{2}-\frac{1}{u}\right)$. Since

$$\sum_{\substack{n\leqslant\xi^c\\ n|P\\ (n,y)=1}}\frac{\mu^2(n)}{f(n)}=\sum_{\substack{n\leqslant\xi^c\\ (n,2qy)=1}}\frac{\mu^2(n)}{f(n)}-\sum_{\xi<p\leqslant\xi^c}\frac{1}{p}\sum_{\substack{n\leqslant\xi^c/p\\ (n,2qy)=1}}\frac{\mu^2(n)}{f(n)}+O\left(\frac{\log x}{\xi}\right)=$$
$$=\frac{1}{2v}\left[v\left(\frac{1}{2}-\frac{1}{u}\right)-1-\frac{v}{2}\left(\frac{1}{2}-\frac{1}{u}\right)\log\frac{v}{2}\left(\frac{1}{2}-\frac{1}{u}\right)\right]\times$$
$$\times\prod_{\substack{p|qy\\ p>2}}\frac{p-2}{p-1}\prod_{p>2}\frac{(p-1)^2}{p(p-2)}\log x+O(\log\log x),$$

therefore it follows from Theorem A that (8) also holds with

$$(10)\qquad \Lambda_1(u) = \frac{2ve^{\gamma}}{v\left(\frac{1}{2}-\frac{1}{u}\right) - 1 - \frac{v}{2}\left(\frac{1}{2}-\frac{1}{u}\right)\log\frac{v}{2}\left(\frac{1}{2}-\frac{1}{u}\right)}.$$

Since

$$\Lambda_1'(u) = \frac{d}{du}\Lambda_1(u) = \begin{cases} \dfrac{-16}{(u-2)^2} < 0 & (\text{if } 0 < c \leqslant 1), \\ \dfrac{-\frac{v^2}{u^2}(1-\log c)}{(2c-1-c\log c)^2} < 0 & (\text{if } 1 < c \leqslant 2) \end{cases}$$

for given $4 < v < 8$, hence $\Lambda_1(u)$ is a decreasing function for $u \leqslant \dfrac{1}{\frac{1}{2}-\frac{4}{v}}$.

§ 6

Theorem B. *Under the truth of* (R^*), *the estimation*

$$P_\omega(x, q, x^{1/13}) > 25.8096 e^{-\gamma} \prod_{\substack{p>2 \\ p|qy}} \frac{p-1}{p-2} \cdot \prod_{p>2}\left(1 - \frac{1}{(p-1)^2}\right)\frac{x}{\varphi(q)\log^2 x} + O\left(\frac{xc_{qy}}{\log^3 x}\right)$$

holds uniformly in (ω), *where* q *is a given integer.*

Lemma 3. *Let* $r \geqslant r_1 \geqslant \cdots \geqslant r_n \geqslant 1$ *be a given set of integers. Then under the truth of* (R^*), *the estimation*

$$P_\omega(x, q, p_r) > \frac{E \operatorname{li} x}{\varphi(q)} - |R|$$

holds uniformly in (ω), *where*

$$E = 1 - \sum_{\substack{\alpha \leqslant r \\ (p_\alpha, y)=1}} \frac{1}{\varphi(p_\alpha)} + \sum_{\alpha \leqslant r} \sum_{\substack{\beta \leqslant r_1 \\ (p_\alpha p_\beta, y)=1 \\ \alpha > \beta}} \frac{1}{\varphi(p_\alpha)\varphi(p_\beta)} - \cdots - \overbrace{\sum_{\alpha \leqslant r}\sum_{\beta \leqslant r_1}\sum_{\gamma \leqslant r_1}\sum_{\delta \leqslant r_2}\cdots\sum_{\mu \leqslant r_n}}^{2n+1}_{\substack{\alpha > \beta > \cdots > \mu \\ (p_\alpha p_\beta \cdots p_\mu, y)=1}} \frac{1}{\varphi(p_\alpha)\cdots\varphi(p_\mu)},$$

$$R = O((1+r)(1+r_1)^2 \cdots (1+r_n)^2 x^{1/2}\log x).$$

1042

Proof. Let $P_\omega(q; p_1, \cdots, p_r) = P_\omega(x, q, p_r)$. Especially, we have $P_\omega(q) = \pi(x, q, a)$. The difference between $P_\omega(q; p_1, \cdots, p_{r-1})$ and $P_\omega(q; p_1, \cdots, p_r)$ is equal to the number of primes p satisfying the following conditions:

$$p \leqslant x, p \equiv a(\mathrm{mod}\, q), p \not\equiv a_i(\mathrm{mod}\, p_i)(1 \leqslant i \leqslant r-1), p \equiv a_r(\mathrm{mod}\, p_r).$$

It follows from the Chinese Remainder Theorem that the system of congruences

$$\begin{cases} y \equiv a_r(\mathrm{mod}\, p_r), \\ y \equiv a(\mathrm{mod}\, q) \end{cases}$$

has a unique solution a^* in the interval $1 \leqslant a^* \leqslant qp_r$. If $p_r \nmid y$, then $(a^*, qp_r) = 1$; otherwise $(a^*, qp_r) > 1$. For the sake of brevity, we write all the (ω_r) as (ω). Hence

$$P_\omega(q; p_1, \cdots, p_{r-1}) - P_\omega(x; p_1, \cdots, p_r) =$$
$$= \begin{cases} = P_\omega(qp_r; p_1, \cdots, p_{r-1}), \text{ if } p_r \nmid y; \\ \leqslant 1, \text{ if } p_r | y, \end{cases}$$

$$P_\omega(q; p_1, \cdots, p_r) = P_\omega(q) - \sum_{\substack{a=1 \\ p_a \nmid y}}^{r} P_\omega(qp_a; p_1, \cdots, p_{a-1}) - \theta r,$$
$$0 \leqslant \theta \leqslant 1.$$

Using this formula r times and with the restriction $\beta \leqslant r_1$, we have

$$P_\omega(q; p_1, \cdots, p_r) \geqslant P_\omega(q) - \sum_{\substack{a=1 \\ p_a \nmid y}} P_\omega(qp_a) +$$
$$+ \sum_{\substack{a \leqslant r \\ a > \beta \\ (p_a p_\beta, y)=1}} \sum_{\beta \leqslant r_1} P_\omega(qp_a p_\beta; p_1, \cdots, p_{\beta-1}) - \theta(r + rr_1), 0 \leqslant \theta \leqslant 1.$$

Let $r \geqslant r_1 \geqslant \cdots \geqslant r_n \geqslant 1$ be a given sequence of integers. Since

$$P_\omega(qp_a \cdots p_\mu; p_1, \cdots, p_{\mu-1}) \leqslant P_\omega(qp_a \cdots p_\mu),$$

therefore we have

$$P_\omega(q; p_1, \cdots, p_r) \geqslant P_\omega(q) - \sum_{\substack{a \leqslant r \\ (p_a, y)=1}} P_\omega(qp_a) + \sum_{\substack{a \leqslant r \\ a > \beta \\ (p_a p_\beta, y)=1}} \sum_{\beta \leqslant r_1} P_\omega(qp_a p_\beta) -$$
$$- \cdots - \overbrace{\sum_{\substack{a \leqslant r \\ a > \beta > \cdots > \mu \\ (p_a p_\beta \cdots p_\mu, y)=1}} \sum_{\beta \leqslant r_1} \cdots \sum_{\mu \leqslant r_n}}^{2n+1} P_\omega(qp_a \cdots p_\mu) - (1+r)(1+r_1)^2 \cdots (1+r_n)^2.$$

Since we assume the truth of (R^*), hence

$$P_\omega(q; p_1, \cdots, p_r) \geqslant \frac{E \operatorname{li} x}{\varphi(q)} - |R|.$$

Thus we have the Lemma.

The proof of Theorem B. Let ε be a given sufficiently small positive number. Let $h = \frac{55}{35} + \varepsilon$. Then there exists δ_0 such that

$$\begin{cases} \sum\limits_{\substack{\delta < p \leqslant \delta^h \\ p \nmid qy}} \frac{1}{\varphi(p)} < \log(h + \varepsilon) < 0.452 = \tau, \\ \prod\limits_{\substack{\delta < p \leqslant \delta^h \\ p \nmid qy}} \left(1 - \frac{1}{\varphi(p)}\right)^{-1} < h + \varepsilon < 1.572 = \lambda \end{cases}$$

for $\delta > \delta_0$.

Let $p_r = p_{r_1}$ be the greatest prime not exceeding $x^{1/13}$. If $2 \leqslant k \leqslant t+1$, then we denote the greatest prime not exceeding $x^{\frac{1}{13h^{k-1}}}$ by p_{r_k}, where $p_{r_{t+1}}$ is the least prime with the property that $p_{r_{t+1}}^{1/h} < \delta_0 \leqslant p_{r_{t+1}}$. Let n be an integer such that $2n > 2t + r_{t+1}$. Let $r_k = r_{t+1} (t + 1 \leqslant k \leqslant n)$. Then we have (cf. [4])

$$P_\omega(x, q, x^{1/13}) > \frac{E \operatorname{li} x}{\varphi(q)} - |R|,$$

where

$$E > (1 - 0.0073193) \prod_{\substack{2 < p \leqslant x^{1/13} \\ p \nmid qy}} \left(1 - \frac{1}{\varphi(p)}\right) >$$

$$> 25.8096 e^{-\gamma} \prod_{\substack{p \mid qy \\ p > 2}} \frac{p-1}{p-2} \prod_{p > 2} \left(1 - \frac{1}{(p-1)^2}\right) \frac{1}{\log x} + O\left(\frac{c_{qy}}{\log^2 x}\right),$$

$$R = O\left(x^{\frac{1}{2} + \frac{3}{13} + \frac{2}{13h} + \frac{2}{13h^2} + \cdots} \log x\right) = O\left(x^{\frac{1}{2} + \frac{3}{13} + \frac{2}{13(h-1)}} \log x\right) = O\left(\frac{x}{\log^3 x}\right).$$

Thus we have the Theorem.

§ 7

Theorem C$_1$. *Let α, β be two positive numbers satisfying $8 > \beta > 4$ and $\beta \geqslant \alpha > 2$. Then*

1044

$$\sum_{\substack{x^{1/\beta}<p\leqslant x^{1/\alpha}\\ p\nmid qy}} P_\omega(x, pq, x^{1/\beta}) \leqslant \left(\frac{c_{qy}}{\varphi(q)}\int_\alpha^\beta \frac{\Lambda_1(u)}{u}\,du\right)\frac{x}{\log^2 x} + O\left(\frac{c_{qy}x}{\log^3 x}\log\log x\right),$$

where q is a given positive integer.

Proof. Let $n=[\log x]$, $u_l=\alpha+\frac{\beta-\alpha}{n}l(0\leqslant l\leqslant n)$. Then

$$\sum_{\substack{x^{1/\beta}<p\leqslant x^{1/\alpha}\\ p\nmid qy}} P_\omega(x, pq, x^{1/\beta}) = \sum_{l=0}^{n-1}\sum_{\substack{x^{\frac{1}{u_{l+1}}}<p\leqslant x^{\frac{1}{u_l}}\\ p\nmid qy}} P_\omega\left(x, x^{\frac{\frac{1}{\log x}}{\log pq}}, x^{1/\beta}\right) = \sum_{l=0}^{n-1} T_l,$$

$$T_l = \sum_{\substack{x^{\frac{1}{u_{l+1}}}<p\leqslant x^{\frac{1}{u_l}}\\ p\nmid qy}} P_\omega\left(x, x^{\frac{\frac{1}{\log x}}{\log pq}}, x^{1/\beta}\right) \leqslant$$

$$\leqslant \sum_{\substack{x^{\frac{1}{u_{l+1}}}<p\leqslant x^{\frac{1}{u_l}}\\ p\nmid qy}} \Lambda_1\left(\frac{\log x}{\log qp}\right)\frac{c_{qy}x}{\varphi(p)\varphi(q)\log^2 x} + O\left(\frac{c_{qy}x}{\log^3 x}\log\log x\log\frac{u_{l+1}}{u_l}\right).$$

Since $\Lambda_1\left(u+O\left(\frac{1}{\log x}\right)\right)=\Lambda_1(u)+O\left(\frac{1}{\log x}\right)$ and $\Lambda_1(u)$ is a decreasing function, therefore

$$T_l \leqslant \Lambda_1(u_l)\frac{c_{qy}x}{\varphi(q)\log^2 x}\log\frac{u_{l+1}}{u_l} + O\left(\frac{c_{qy}x}{\log^3 x}\log\log x\log\frac{u_{l+1}}{u_l}\right).$$

Since

$$\sum_{l=0}^{n-1}\Lambda_1(u_l)\log\frac{u_{l+1}}{u_l} - \int_\alpha^\beta\frac{\Lambda_1(u)}{u}\,du \leqslant \sum_{l=0}^{n-1}(\Lambda_1(u_{l+1})-\Lambda_1(u_l))\max_{0\leqslant l\leqslant n-1}\log\frac{u_{l+1}}{u_l} =$$

$$= O\left(\frac{1}{n}\right) = O\left(\frac{1}{\log x}\right),$$

hence

$$\sum_{l=0}^{n-1} T_l \leqslant \left(\frac{c_{qy}}{\varphi(q)}\int_\alpha^\beta\frac{\Lambda_1(u)}{u}\,du\right)\frac{x}{\log^2 x} + O\left(\frac{c_{qy}x}{\log^3 x}\log\log x\right).$$

This proves the Theorem.

Theorem C_2. *Let $3 \leqslant \alpha < \beta \leqslant 13$ be two given numbers. Then*

$$P_\omega(x, q, x^{1/\alpha}) \geqslant P_\omega(x, q, x^{1/\beta}) - \frac{c_{qy} x}{\varphi(q) \log^2 x} \int_\alpha^\beta \frac{\Lambda(u)}{u} du + + O\left(\frac{c_{qy} x}{\log^3 x} \log \log x\right),$$

where q is a given positive integer.

Proof. It is evident that we may assume $\alpha < U < \beta$. We estimate the differences $P_\omega(x, q, x^{1/\beta}) - P_\omega(x, q, x^{1/U})$ and $P_\omega(x, q, x^{1/U}) - P_\omega(x, q, x^{1/\alpha})$.

The difference between $P_\omega(x, q, p_m)$ and $P_\omega(x, q, p_{m+1})$ is equal to the number of primes satisfying the following conditions:

$$p \leqslant x,\ p \equiv a(\operatorname{mod} q),\ p \not\equiv a_i(\operatorname{mod} p_i)(i \leqslant m),\ p \equiv a_{m+1}(\operatorname{mod} p_{m+1}).$$

If $p_{m+1} \nmid y$, then by the definition we know that it is equal to $P_\omega(x, qp_{m+1}, p_m)$; otherwise it is equal to 0 or 1. Hence

$$P_\omega(x, q, p_m) - P_\omega(x, q, p_{m+1}) \begin{cases} = P_\omega(x, qp_{m+1}, p_m), \text{ if } p_{m+1} \nmid y; \\ \leqslant 1, \text{ if } p_{m+1} \mid y. \end{cases}$$

Arrange the primes between $x^{1/U}$ and $x^{1/\alpha}$ as follows:

$$p_t \leqslant x^{1/U} < p_{t+1} < \cdots < p_s \leqslant x^{1/\alpha} < p_{s+1}.$$

Then

$$P_\omega(x, q, x^{1/U}) = P_\omega(x, q, x^{1/\alpha}) + \sum_{\substack{t<i<s \\ p_{i+1} \nmid qy}} P_\omega(x, p_{i+1}, q, p_i) + O(1).$$

Let $n = [\log x]$. $u_m = \alpha + \dfrac{U - \alpha}{n} m (0 \leqslant m \leqslant n)$. And put

$$T = \sum_{\substack{t<i<s \\ p_{i+1} \nmid qy}} P_\omega(x, qp_{i+1}, p_i) = \sum_{m=0}^{n-1} T_m.$$

Since $p_i < qp_{i+1} < 4qp_i$ and $\Lambda(u)$ is decreasing in the interval (α, U), hence

$$T_m = \sum_{\substack{x^{\frac{1}{u_{m+1}}} < p_{i+1} \leqslant x^{\frac{1}{u_m}} \\ p_{i+1} \nmid qy}} P_\omega(x, qp_{i+1}, p_i) = \sum_{\substack{x^{\frac{1}{u_{m+1}}} < p_{i+1} \leqslant x^{\frac{1}{u_m}} \\ p_{i+1} \nmid qy}} P_\omega\left(x, qp_{i+1}, x^{\frac{\log p_i}{\log x}}\right) \leqslant$$

$$\leqslant \Lambda(u_m) \frac{c_{qy} x}{\varphi(q) \log^2 x} \log \frac{u_{m+1}}{u_m} + O\left(\frac{c_{qy} x}{\log^3 x} \log \log x \log \frac{u_{m+1}}{u_m}\right).$$

1046

Since

$$\sum_{m=0}^{n-1} \Lambda(u_m) \log \frac{u_{m+1}}{u_m} - \int_a^U \frac{\Lambda(u)}{u}\, du = O\left(\frac{1}{\log x}\right),$$

therefore

$$T \leqslant \left(\frac{c_{qy}}{\varphi(q)}\int_a^U \frac{\Lambda(u)}{u}\, du\right)\frac{x}{\log^2 x} + O\left(\frac{c_{qy}x}{\log^3 x}\log\log x\right).$$

Hence

$$P_\omega(x, q, x^{1/U}) \leqslant P_\omega(x, q, x^{1/\alpha}) + \left(\frac{c_{qy}}{\varphi(q)}\int_\alpha^U \frac{\Lambda(u)}{u}\, du\right)\frac{x}{\log^2 x} + \\ + O\left(\frac{c_{qy}x}{\log^3 x}\log\log x\right).$$

Similarly, we have

$$P_\omega(x, q, x^{1/\beta}) \leqslant P_\omega(x, q, x^{1/U}) + \left(\frac{c_{qy}}{\varphi(q)}\int_U^\beta \frac{\Lambda(u)}{u}\, du\right)\frac{x}{\log^2 x} + \\ + O\left(\frac{c_{qy}x}{\log^3 x}\log\log x\right).$$

Thus we have the Theorem.

§ 8

Let $4<v<8$, $2<u\leqslant v$ be two given numbers. Let $\mathfrak{M}$ denote the set of primes satisfying the following conditions:

$$(11) \qquad \begin{gathered} p \leqslant x,\ p \equiv a(\operatorname{mod} q),\ p \not\equiv a_i(\operatorname{mod} p_i)(i \leqslant s), \\ p \not\equiv a_{s+j}(\operatorname{mod} p_{s+j}^2)(j \leqslant t-s), \end{gathered}$$

where $p_s \leqslant x^{1/v} < p_{s+1}$, $p_t \leqslant x^{1/u} < p_{t+1}$ and q is a given positive integer.

The number of elements of $\mathfrak{M}$ is denoted by $M_\omega(x, x^{1/v}, x^{1/u})$.

Lemma 4. *There exist sequences of integers (ω_j) such that the number of elements of $\mathfrak{M}$ satisfying at least l congruences of*

$$(12) \qquad p \equiv a_{s+j}(\operatorname{mod} p_{s+j})(1 \leqslant j \leqslant t-s)$$

is at most

$$\frac{1}{l}\sum_{\substack{j\leqslant t-s \\ p_{s+j}\nmid y}} P_{\omega_j}(x, qp_{s+j}, x^{1/v}).$$

Proof. Let Γ_j be the subset of $\mathfrak{M}$ whose elements satisfy the congruence

$$p \equiv a_{s+j} (\mathrm{mod}\ p_{s+j}).$$

Now, we estimate the number of elements of Γ_j. If $p_{s+j} | y$, then the number elements of Γ_j is equal to 0 or 1. Assume $p_{s+j} \nmid y$. Denote the solution of the system of congruences

$$\begin{cases} n \equiv a_{s+j} (\mathrm{mod}\ p_{s+j}), \\ n \equiv a (\mathrm{mod}\ q) \end{cases}$$

by $\tilde{a}_{s+j}$. Let

$$(\omega_j) \qquad \tilde{a}_{s+j},\ qp_{s+j};\ a_i (1 \leqslant i \leqslant t).$$

Then the number of elements of Γ_j is not more than $P_{\omega_j}(x, qp_{s+j}, x^{1/v})$.

If the element of $\mathfrak{M}$ satisfies at least l congruences of (12), then it belongs to at least l different sets Γ_j. Hence the number of elements of $\mathfrak{M}$ satisfying at least l congruences of (12) does not exceed

$$\frac{1}{l} \sum_{\substack{j \leqslant t-s \\ p_{s+j} \nmid y}} P_{\omega_j}(x, qp_{s+j}, x^{1/v}).$$

Thus we have the Lemma.

Theorem D. *The number of elements of* $\mathfrak{M}$ *satisfying at most* m *congruences of* (12) *is not less than*

$$P_\omega(x, q, x^{1/v}) - \frac{1}{m+1} \left(\int_u^v \Lambda_1(t) \frac{dz}{z} \right) \frac{c_{qy} x}{\varphi(q) \log^2 x} + O\left(\frac{c_{qy} x}{\log^3 x} \log \log x \right).$$

Proof. Since

$$P_\omega(x, q, x^{1/v}) - M_\omega(x, x^{1/v}, x^{1/u}) = \sum_{j \leqslant t-s} \sum_{\substack{p \equiv a_{s+j} (\mathrm{mod}\ p_{s+j}^2) \\ p \leqslant x}} 1 \leqslant$$

$$\leqslant \sum_{1 \leqslant j \leqslant t-s} \left(\frac{x}{p_{s+j}^2} + 1 \right) = O(x^{1/u}) + O(x^{1-\frac{1}{v}}),$$

therefore it follows from Lemma 4 and Theorem C_1 that the number of elements of $\mathfrak{M}$ satisfying at most m congruences of (12) is not less than

$$M_\omega(x, x^{1/v}, x^{1/u}) - \frac{1}{m+1} \sum_{\substack{j \leqslant t-s \\ p_{s+j} \nmid y}} P_{\omega_j}(x, qp_{s+j}, x^{1/v}) + O(1) \geqslant$$

1048

$$\geqslant P_\omega(x, q, x^{1/v}) - \frac{1}{m+1}\left(\int_u^v \Lambda_1(z)\frac{dz}{z}\right)\frac{c_q y x}{\varphi(q)\log^2 x} + O\left(\frac{c_q y x}{\log^3 x}\log\log x\right).$$

Thus we have the Theorem.

§ 9

It follows from Theorem B and Theorem C_2 that

$$P_\omega(x, q, x^{1/6}) > \left(25.8096 - \int_6^{13}\frac{\Lambda(u)}{u}du\right)\frac{c_q y x}{\varphi(q)\log^2 x} +$$
$$+ O\left(\frac{c_q y x}{\log^3 x}\log\log x\right) > 8.4\frac{c_q y x}{\varphi(q)\log^2 x} + O\left(\frac{c_q y x}{\log^3 x}\log\log x\right).$$

(i) Let $x=y$ be an even integer. Let

(ω_1) $$a = 1, q = 2; a_i = x (i = 1, 2, \cdots).$$

From (9) we know that there exists a positive constant x_1 such that

$$P_{\omega_1}(x, 2, x^{1/6}) - \frac{1}{3}\left(\int_3^6\frac{\Lambda_1(u)}{u}du\right)\frac{c_{2x}x}{\log^2 x} + O\left(\frac{c_{2x}x}{\log^3 x}\log\log x\right) >$$
$$> (8.4 - 6.588)\frac{c_{2x}x}{\log^2 x} + O\left(\frac{c_{2x}x}{\log^3 x}\log\log x\right) > \frac{c_{2x}x}{\log^2 x} > 1$$

for $x > x_1$. Hence it follows from Theorem D that for $x > x_1$ there exists a prime p such that $1 < p < x-1$ and $x-p$ has no prime divisors $\leqslant x^{1/6}$ and has at most 2 prime divisors in the interval $x^{1/6} < p' \leqslant x^{1/3}$. Hence $x-p$ is a product of at most 3 primes. Since $x = p + x - p$, we obtain Theorem 1.

(ii) Let $x=y$ be an odd integer. Let

(ω_2) $$a = x - 2, q = 4; a_i = x (i = 1, 2, \cdots).$$

From (9) we know that there exists a positive constant x_2 such that

$$P_{\omega_2}(x, 4, x^{1/6}) - \frac{1}{3}\left(\int_3^6\frac{\Lambda_1(u)}{u}du\right)\frac{c_{4x}x}{2\log^2 x} + O\left(\frac{c_{4x}x}{\log^3 x}\log\log x\right) > \frac{c_{4x}x}{2\log^2 x} > 2$$

for $x > x_2$. Hence it follows from Theorem D that for $x > x_2$ there exists a prime number p such that $p < x-3$ and $\frac{x-p}{2}$ has no prime divisors $\leqslant x^{1/6}$ and has at most 2 prime divisors in the intervals $x^{1/6} < p' \leqslant x^{1/3}$. Hence $\frac{x-p}{2}$ is a product of at most 3 primes. Thus we have Theorem 3.

(iii) Let k be a given integer. Let

$$(\omega_3) \qquad a = 1, q = 2; a_i = -2k \quad (i = 1, 2, \cdots).$$

It follows from (9) that there exists a positive constant x_3 such that

$$P_{\omega_3}(x, 2, x^{1/6}) - \frac{1}{3}\left(\int_3^6 \frac{\Lambda_1(u)}{u}\, du\right)\frac{c_{4k}x}{\log^2 x} + O\left(\frac{x}{\log^3 x}\log\log x\right) > \frac{c_{4k}x}{\log^2 x}$$

for $x > x_3$. Hence from (9) we know that for $x > x_3$ there exist not less than $\frac{c_{4k}x}{\log^2 x}$ prime numbers p in the interval $1 < p \leqslant x$ such that $p + 2k$ is a product of at most 3 primes. Thus we have Theorem 2.

From Lemma 2 and Theorem A with $c = 1$, we have

$$P_{\omega_3}\left(x, 2, \frac{x^{1/4}}{\log^3 x}\right) \leqslant 8 \prod_{\substack{p|2k \\ p>2}} \frac{p-1}{p-2} \prod_{p>2}\left(1 - \frac{1}{(p-1)^2}\right)\frac{x}{\log^2 x} + O\left(\frac{x}{\log^3 x}\log\log x\right).$$

Since

$$Z_k(x) = \sum_{\substack{p < \frac{x^{1/4}}{\log^3 x} \\ p+2k=p'}} 1 + \sum_{\substack{\frac{x^{1/4}}{\log^3 x} < p \leqslant x \\ p+2k=p'}} 1 \leqslant O(x^{1/4}) + P_{\omega_3}\left(x, 2, \frac{x^{1/4}}{\log^3 x}\right) \leqslant$$

$$\leqslant 8 \prod_{\substack{p|2k \\ p>2}} \frac{p-1}{p-2} \prod_{p>2}\left(1 - \frac{1}{(p-1)^2}\right)\frac{x}{\log^2 x} + O\left(\frac{x}{\log^3 x}\log\log x\right),$$

we have Theorem 4.

References

[1] Wang Yuan 1957 On Sieve Methods and Some of the Related Problems, *Science Record*, Vol. I, No. 1, 9—11.

[2] Wang Yuan 1959 On Sieve Methods and Some of Their Applications, *Scientia Sinica*, **8**, 375—381.

[3] Нудаков, Н. Г. 1948 О конечной разности для функций $\Psi(x, k, l)$, *ИАН СССР, серия матем.*, **12**, 31—46.

[4] Wang Yuan 1956 On the representation of large integer as a sum of a prime and a product of at most 4 primes, *Acta Mathematica Sinica*, **6** (4), 565—582.

[5] Виноградов, А. И. 1957 Применение $\zeta(s)$ к решету Эратосфена, *Мат. Сб*; **41**, 49—80.

1050

APPENDIX

1°. We state the generalized weak Riemann hypothesis as follows: (R_δ) *The real parts of all zeros of all Dirichlet's L-functions* $L(s, \chi)$ *are* $\leqslant \delta^{-1}$, *where* $1 < \delta \leqslant 2$.

Especially, (R_2) *is the well-known grand Riemann hypothesis.*

For the sake of brevity, we denote the following proposition by (1, A):

Every sufficiently large even integer is a sum of a prime and an almost prime of at most A *prime divisors.*

Here, we state the refined result:

Theorem I. (1, 3) *may be derived from* (R_{δ_1}), *where* $\delta_1 \geqslant \frac{2.475}{1.475}$ *and* (1, 4) *is the consequence of* (R_{δ_2}), *where* $\delta_2 \geqslant \frac{3.237}{2.237}$.

All the following results are obtained under the truth of (R_δ).

2°. Let $\eta = \frac{\delta}{\delta - 1}$. Let $x^{1/u} \leqslant q \leqslant c_0 x^{1/u}$, where c_0 is a given constant. Then the estimation

$$P_\omega(x, q, x^{1/u}) \leqslant \Lambda(u) \frac{c_{qy}x}{\varphi(q)\log^2 x} + O\left(\frac{c_{qy}x \log\log x}{\varphi(q)\log^3 x}\right) \tag{1}$$

holds uniformly in (ω), where

$$\Lambda(u) = \frac{4\eta u}{u - \eta} e^\gamma \quad (\text{if} \quad \eta < u \leqslant 3\eta) \tag{2}$$

and

$$\Lambda(u) = \frac{2ue^\gamma}{\frac{u-\eta}{\eta} - 1 - \frac{u-\eta}{2\eta}\log\frac{u-\eta}{2\eta}} \quad (\text{if} \quad 3\eta < u \leqslant 7\eta). \tag{3}$$

3°. Let $v > 2\eta$ be a given number and $q = x^{1/u}$. Then

$$P_\omega(x, q, x^{1/v}) \leqslant \Lambda_1(u) \frac{c_{qy}x}{\varphi(q)\log^2 x} + O\left(\frac{x c_{qy} \log\log x}{\varphi(q)\log^3 x}\right) \tag{4}$$

holds uniformly in (ω), where

$$\Lambda_1(u) = \frac{4\eta u}{u - \eta} e^\gamma \tag{5}$$

for $\eta < u \leqslant \dfrac{1}{\dfrac{1}{\eta} - \dfrac{2}{v}}$, and

$$\Lambda_1(u) = \frac{2ve^{\gamma}}{v\left(\frac{1}{\eta} - \frac{1}{u}\right) - 1 - \frac{v}{2}\left(\frac{1}{\eta} - \frac{1}{u}\right)\log\frac{v}{2}\left(\frac{1}{\eta} - \frac{1}{u}\right)} \tag{6}$$

for

$$\frac{1}{\frac{1}{\eta} - \frac{2}{v}} < v < \begin{cases} \dfrac{1}{\frac{1}{\eta} - \frac{4}{v}} & (\text{if } v > 4\eta); \\ \infty & (\text{if } v \leqslant 4\eta). \end{cases}$$

4°. Let q be a given integer. Then

$$P_\omega(x, q, x^{1/6.5\eta}) > \lambda(6.5\eta)\frac{c_{qy}x}{\varphi(q)\log^2 x} + O\left(\frac{xc_{qy}}{\log^3 x}\right), \tag{7}$$

where

$$\lambda(6.5\eta) \geqslant 2\eta \times 6.453306. \tag{8}$$

The proof is similar to that of Theorem B with the essential difference that here we put $\tau = 0.452$ and $\lambda = 1.5715$ so as to obtain the more exact estimation

$$\sum_{k=0}^{\infty} \frac{\lambda^{k+1}[(k+1)\tau]^{2k+4}}{(2k+4)!} < \sum_{k=0}^{6} \frac{\lambda^{k+1}[(k+1)\tau]^{2k+4}}{(2k+4)!} +$$
$$+ \frac{\lambda^8(8\tau)^{18}}{18!} \sum_{k=0}^{\infty} \left(\frac{\lambda\tau^2 e^2}{4} \times \frac{6561}{6080}\right)^k < 0.007183682.$$

5°. Let $\eta < \alpha < \beta \leqslant 6.5\eta$ be two given numbers. Let q denote a given positive integer. Then

$$P_\omega(x, q, x^{1/\alpha}) \geqslant P_\omega(x, q, x^{1/\beta}) - \frac{c_{qy}x}{\varphi(q)\log^2 x}\int_\alpha^\beta \frac{\Lambda(u)}{u}\,du +$$
$$+ O\left(\frac{c_{qy}x}{\log^3 x}\log\log x\right). \tag{9}$$

6°. Let u, v be two given numbers satisfying $2\eta < v < 10\eta$ and $\eta < u < v$. Let $\mathfrak{M}$ denote the set of primes p satisfying the following conditions:

$$p \leqslant x,\ p \equiv a \pmod q,\ p \not\equiv a_i \pmod{p_i}\ (i \leqslant s),$$
$$p \not\equiv a_{s+j} \pmod{p_{s+j}^2}\ (j \leqslant t - s), \tag{10}$$

1052

where $p_s \leqslant x^{1/v} < p_{s+1}$, $p_t \leqslant x^{1/u} < p_{t+1}$ and q is a given integer. Then the number of elements of $\mathfrak{M}$ satisfying at most m congruences of

(11) $$p \equiv a_{s+j} (\operatorname{mod} p_{s+j})(1 \leqslant j \leqslant t - s)$$

is not less than

(12) $$P_\omega(x, q, x^{1/v}) - \frac{1}{m+1}\left(\int_u^v \Lambda_1(z)\,\frac{dz}{z}\right)\frac{c_{qy}x}{\varphi(q)\log^2 x} + O\left(\frac{c_{qy}x}{\log^3 x}\log\log x\right).$$

7°. Computation of integrals.

(i) $$\Delta_1 = \int_{5\eta}^{6.5\eta} \frac{\Lambda(u)}{u}\,du = 2e^\gamma \int_{5\eta}^{6.5\eta} \frac{du}{\dfrac{u-\eta}{\eta} - 1 - \dfrac{u-\eta}{2\eta}\log\dfrac{u-\eta}{2\eta}}$$

$$= 2\eta e^\gamma \int_4^{5.5} \frac{dw}{w - 1 - \dfrac{w}{2}\log\dfrac{w}{2}} = 2\eta e^\gamma \int_4^{5.5} f(w)dw$$

$$< 2\eta e^\gamma\left(\sum_{i=0}^{71} f(4 + 0.02i) + \sum_{j=0}^{2} f(5.46 + 0.02j)\right)$$

$$< 2\eta e^\gamma \times 0.89050652.$$

(ii) Let $v = 5\eta$ in 3°. Then

$$\Delta_2 = \int_{\frac{5\eta}{3}}^{5\eta} \frac{\Lambda_1(u)}{u}\,du = \int_{\frac{5\eta}{3}}^{5\eta} \frac{2ve^\gamma}{v\left(\dfrac{1}{\eta} - \dfrac{1}{u}\right) - 1 - \dfrac{v}{2}\left(\dfrac{1}{\eta} - \dfrac{1}{u}\right)\log\dfrac{v}{2}\left(\dfrac{1}{\eta} - \dfrac{1}{u}\right)} \cdot \frac{du}{u}$$

$$= 20\eta e^\gamma \int_1^2 \frac{dz}{(5 - 2z)(2z - 1 - z\log z)} = 20\eta e^\gamma \int_1^2 g(z)dz$$

$$< 20\eta e^\gamma\left({\sum_{i=0}^{7}}' g(1 + 0.02i) + \sum_{j=0}^{41} g(1.18 + 0.02j)\right)$$

$$< 20\eta e^\gamma \times 0.3972371.$$

8°. The proof of Theorem I. Let $x = y$ be an even integer. Let

(ω) $$a = 1, q = 2;\ a_i = x \quad (i = 1, 2, \cdots).$$

(i) Let $\eta = 2.475$. Then from 2°—7°, we know that there exists a constant x_1 such that

$$P_\omega(x, 2, x^{1/5\eta}) - \frac{1}{2}\left(\int_{\frac{15\eta}{5\eta-1}}^{5\eta} \frac{\Lambda_1(u)}{u}\,du\right)\frac{c_{2x}x}{\log^2 x} + O\left(\frac{c_{2x}x}{\log^3 x}\log\log x\right) >$$

$$> P_\omega(x, 2, x^{1/6.5\eta}) - \left(\int_{5\eta}^{6.5\eta} \frac{\Lambda(u)}{u} du + \frac{1}{2}\int_{\frac{15\eta}{5\eta-1}}^{5\eta} \frac{\Lambda_1(u)}{u} du\right) \frac{c_{2x}x}{\log^2 x} +$$

$$+ O\left(\frac{c_{2x}x}{\log^2 x} \log\log x\right) > 2\eta[6.453306 - e^\gamma(0.89050652 +$$

$$+ 1.9861855 + 0.738218)] \frac{c_{2x}x}{\log^2 x} + O\left(\frac{c_{2x}x}{\log^3 x}\log\log x\right) >$$

$$> 0.05 \frac{c_{2x}x}{\log^2 x} + O\left(\frac{c_{2x}x}{\log^3 x}\log\log x\right) > 1,$$

for $x > x_1$. Hence it follows from 6° that for $x > x_1$ there exists a prime p such that $p < x-1$ and $x-p$ has no prime divisors $\leqslant x^{1/5\eta}$ and has at most one prime divisor in the interval $x^{1/5\eta} < p' \leqslant x^{\frac{5\eta-1}{15\eta}}$. Hence $x-p$ is a product of at most 3 primes. Thus we have (1, 3).

(ii) Let $\eta = 3.237$. Then from 2°—7°, we know that there exists a constant x_2 such that

$$P_\omega(x, 2, x^{1/5\eta}) - \frac{1}{2}\left(\int_{\frac{20\eta}{5\eta-1}}^{5\eta} \frac{\Lambda_1(u)}{u} du\right)\frac{c_{2x}x}{\log^2 x} + O\left(\frac{c_{2x}x}{\log^3 x}\log\log x\right) >$$

$$> 0.01 \frac{c_{2x}x}{\log^2 x} + O\left(\frac{c_{2x}x}{\log^3 x}\log\log x\right) > 1$$

for $x > x_2$. Hence it follows from 6° that for $x > x_2$ there exists a prime number p such that $p < x-1$ and $x-p$ has no prime divisor $\leqslant x^{1/5\eta}$ and has at most one prime divisor in the interval $x^{1/5\eta} < p' \leqslant x^{\frac{5\eta-1}{20\eta}}$. Hence $x-p$ is a product of at most 4 primes. Thus we have (1, 4).

9°. It is well known that in the proof of Theorem I, the hypothesis (R_δ) may be replaced by

$$(\tilde{R}_\delta) \qquad \sum_{D \leqslant x^{1/\eta}} \mu^2(D) \max_{\substack{l \pmod D \\ (l, D)=1}} \left| \pi(x, D, l) - \frac{\operatorname{li} x}{\varphi(D)} \right| = O\left(\frac{x}{\log^A x}\right),$$

where A is any given positive constant and the constant implied by the symbol "O" depends only on δ and A.

Similarly, (R_δ) may also be replaced by

$$(\tilde{\tilde{R}}_\delta) \qquad \sum_{D \leqslant x^{1/\eta}} \mu^2(D) \max_{\substack{l \pmod D \\ (l, D)=1}} \left| P(x, D, l) - \frac{x}{\varphi(D)\log x} \right| = O\left(\frac{x}{\log^A x}\right),$$

where $P(x, D, l) = \sum_{\substack{p < x \\ p \equiv l \ (\mathrm{mod}\ D)}} \log p \cdot e^{-\frac{\log x}{x} p}$ (cf. [1], [2]).

Барбан[3, 4] first proved $(\tilde{R}_{1.2})$. Later, Pan Chin Tong[2] obtained $(\tilde{\tilde{R}}_{1.5})$ independently, from which he deduced (1, 5). From Theorem I, it can be easily seen that $(\tilde{\tilde{R}}_{1.5})$ implies (1, 4). In other words, we have proved

Theorem II. *Every sufficiently large even integer is a sum of a prime and a product of at most* 4 *primes.*

Remark. (1, 4) has also been proved by Pan and Барбан independently, but their proofs are more complicated than that given here, in fact, their proofs are based on $(\tilde{R}_{1.6})$ and $(\tilde{\tilde{R}}_{1.6})$ respectively (cf. [5]). I am grateful to Messrs. Pan and Барбан for their kindly informing me of their results.

References

[1] Реньи, А. 1948 О представлении четных чисел в виде суммы простого и почти простого числа, *ИАН СССР*, **2**, 57—78.

[2] Pan Chin Tong, 1962 On the representation of large even integer as a sum of a prime and an almost prime, *Acta Math. Sinica*, Vol. 12, No. 1, 95—106.

[3] Барбан, М. Б. 1961 Арифметические функции на редких множествах, *Доклады Академии Наук УзССР*, **8**, 9—11.

[4] Барбан, М. Б. 1961 Новые применении большого решета Ю. В. Линника, *Труды Института Математики, им. В. И. Романовского*, вып. 22.

[5] Линник, Ю. В. 1960 Асимптотическая формула в аддитивной проблеме Гарди Литтльвуда, *ИАН СССР*, Том 24, № 5, 629—706.

On Representation of Even Number as the Sum of a Prime and an Almost Prime

Pan Cheng Dong

§1. Let N be a large even number and $V(m)$ the number of prime divisors of m. In 1948, Hungarian mathematician A. Rényi [1] has proved that $N = a+b$, where $V(a) = 1$ and $V(b) \leq K$ in which K is an absolute constant. Under the assmuption of the Riemann hypothesis, Wang Yuan [2] has established that $K \leq 3$. We shall prove, in this paper, $K \leq 5$, namely

Theorem. Every large even number N can be represented as the sum $p + P$, where p is a prime and P has at most 5 prime factors.

The proof of the theorem is based on the following

Fundamental Theorem. Let $(\ell, D) = 1$ and

$$P_1(N,D,\ell) = \sum_{\substack{p \leq N \\ p \equiv \ell \pmod D}} \log p \cdot e^{-p(\log N/N)}$$

$$= \frac{N}{\phi(D)\log N} + R_D(N) \quad . \tag{1.1}$$

Then

$$\sum_{d \leq N^{1/3-\varepsilon}} |\mu(d)\ \tau(d)\ R_d(N)| = O\left(\frac{N}{\log^5 N}\right) \quad , \tag{1.2}$$

where ε is any given positive number, $\tau(d)$ the divisor function and $\mu(d)$ the Möbius function.

The proof of Fundamental theorem is based on the estimation for the density of zeros of Dirichlet L-series.

We introduce the following notations: $C_1, C_2, \ldots$ positive absolute constants; $\varepsilon, \varepsilon_1, \varepsilon_2, \ldots$ arbitrary small positive numbers; B a bounded number but not always equal in different occurrences; $p, p_1, p_2, \ldots$ odd prime numbers; $\chi_D(n)$ a character modulo D;

$\chi_D^0(n)$ the principal character modulo D; $\rho_{\chi_D} = \beta_{\chi_D} + i\tau_{\chi_D}$ a zero of L-function $L(s, \chi_D)$.

§2. Theorem 2.1. Let $\Delta \geq \frac{1}{2}$. Let $N(\Delta, T, D)$ denote the number of zeros of $L(s, \chi_D)$ in the rectangle $\Delta \leq \sigma \leq 1$, $|t| \leq D$. Then the inequality

$$N(\Delta, T, D) < C_{15} D^{(2+4C)(1-\Delta)} T^3 \log^6 DT$$

holds, where C is defined by

$$|L(\tfrac{1}{2}+it, \chi_D)| \leq 3D^C(|t|+1) , \qquad (\chi_D \neq \chi_D^0) .$$

For the rectangle with length not too large compared with the modulus of the character, the result is better than those of Tatuzawa (Cf. [3]). We need the following lemmas.

Lemma 2.1. Let α and β satisfy $0 < \alpha < \beta < 2$. Let $f(s)$ be an analytic function which is real for real s and is regular for $\sigma \geq \alpha$ except $s = 1$. Further let $|\mathrm{Re}\, f(2+it)| \geq m > 0$ and $|f(\sigma' + it')| \leq M_{\sigma,t}$ $(\sigma' \geq \sigma,\ 1 \leq t' \leq t)$. Then if T is not the ordinate of a zero of $f(s)$, we have

$$|\arg f(\sigma + iT)| \leq \frac{\pi}{\log(\frac{\pi-\alpha}{\pi-\beta})} (\log M_{\alpha,T+2} + \log \frac{1}{m}) + \frac{3\pi}{2}$$

for $\sigma \geq \beta$ (Cf. [4]).

Lemma 2.2. Let $C \leq \frac{1}{4} + \varepsilon_1$. Then

$$|L(\tfrac{1}{2}+it, \chi_D)| \leq 3D^C(|t|+1) , \qquad (\chi_D \neq \chi_D^0) .$$

Proof. It is known that every character $\chi_D(n)$ can be represented as $\chi_D(n) = \chi_{D_1}^0(n)\, \chi_{D_2}(n)$, where $\chi_{D_2}(n)$ is a primitive character modulo D_2, $(D_1, D_2) = 1$ and $D_1 D_2 \leq D_1$.

Let $s = \frac{1}{2} + it$. Since

$$\sum_{n \geq z} \frac{\chi_D(n)}{n^s} = \sum_{\substack{n \geq z \\ (n,D_1)=1}} \frac{\chi_D(n)}{n^s} = \sum_{d|D_1} \frac{\chi_{D_2}(d)\,\mu(d)}{d^s} \sum_{nd \geq t} \frac{\chi_{D_2}(n)}{n^s} \tag{2.1}$$

and

$$\left| \sum_{nd \geq t} \frac{\chi_{D_2}(n)}{n^s} \right| \leq \int_{\frac{z}{d}}^{\infty} \left| \sum_{z/d \leq n < u} \chi_{D_2}(n) \right| \cdot \left| du^{-s} \right|$$

$$< 2|s|\sqrt{D}_2 \log D_2 \left(\frac{z}{d}\right)^{-\frac{1}{2}} \leq 2(|t|+1)\sqrt{D} \log D \left(\frac{z}{d}\right)^{-\frac{1}{2}} , \tag{2.2}$$

we have

$$\left| \sum_{n \geq z} \frac{\chi_D(n)}{n^s} \right| \leq 2(|t|+1)\sqrt{D} \log D \cdot \tau(D_1) z^{-\frac{1}{2}} . \tag{2.3}$$

Set $z = \sqrt{D}$. Then

$$|L(s, \chi_D)| \leq \left| \sum_{n \leq z} \frac{\chi_D(n)}{n^s} \right| + \left| \sum_{n \geq z} \frac{\chi_D(n)}{n^s} \right| \leq 3(|t|+1) D^{1/4+\varepsilon_1} . \tag{2.4}$$

Lemma 2.3. Let

$$\rho_{\chi_D}(s, z) = \rho_{\chi_D}(s) = \sum_{n \leq z} \frac{\mu(n)\,\chi_D(n)}{n^s} ,$$

where $z \geq D \log D$. Then

$$\sum_{\chi_D} \left| \rho_{\chi_D}\left(\frac{1}{2} + it\right) \right|^2 \leq C_1 z + \phi(D) \log z .$$

Proof.

$$\sum_{\chi_D} \left| \rho_{\chi_D}\left(\frac{1}{2} + it\right) \right|^2 = \sum_{\chi_D} \sum_{n \leq z} \frac{\mu(n)\,\chi_D(n)}{n^{\frac{1}{2}+it}} \sum_{m \leq z} \frac{\mu(m)\,\chi_D(m)}{m^{\frac{1}{2}-it}}$$

$$\leq \phi(D) \sum_{n \leq z} \frac{\mu^2(n)}{n} + 2\phi(D) \sum_{\substack{m < n \leq z \\ n \equiv m \pmod D}} \frac{1}{(nm)^{\frac{1}{2}}} \leq \phi(D) \log z + C_1 z .$$

Lemma 2.4. Let $0<\delta<1$ and

$$f_{\chi_D}(s,z) = f_{\chi_D}(s) = L(s, \chi_D)\, \rho_{\chi_D}(s) - 1 .$$

Then

$$\sum_{\chi_D} |f_{\chi_D}(1+\delta+it)|^2 \le C_4\left(\frac{D}{z}\delta^{-1}\log^3 z + \delta^{-2}\log^2 z\right) .$$

Proof.

$$f_{\chi_D}(s) = \sum_{n\ge z} \frac{a_n\, \chi_D(n)}{n^s} ,$$

where $a_n = \sum_{\substack{d|n \\ d<z}} \mu(d)$. Therefore

$$\sum_{\chi_D} |f_{\chi_D}(1+\delta+it)|^2 = \sum_{\chi_D}\sum_{n\ge z} \frac{a_n\, \chi_D(n)}{n^{1+\delta+it}} \sum_{m\ge z} \frac{a_m\, \bar{\chi}_D(m)}{m^{1+\delta-it}}$$

$$\le \phi(D) \sum_{n\ge z} \frac{a_n^2}{n^{2+2\delta}} + 2\phi(D) \sum_{\substack{z\le m<n \\ n\equiv m(\mathrm{mod}\ D)}} \frac{|a_m a_n|}{(nm)^{1+\delta}}$$

$$\le \phi(D) \sum_{n\ge z} \frac{\tau^2(n)}{n^{2+2\delta}} + 2\phi(D) \sum_{\substack{z\le m<n \\ n\equiv m(\mathrm{mod}\ D)}} \frac{\tau(n)\ \tau(m)}{(nm)^{1+\delta}}$$

$$\le \phi(D)\left(\sum{}^1 + \sum{}^2\right) , \tag{2.5}$$

where

$$\sum{}^1 = \sum_{n\ge z} \frac{\tau^2(n)}{n^{2+2\delta}} \le 4\int_z^\infty \sum_{z\le n<u} \tau^2(n)\, u^{-3-2\delta}\, du$$

$$\le C_2\, z^{-1}\, \delta^{-1} \log^3 z , \tag{2.6}$$

$$\sum{}^2 \le 2 \sum_{\substack{z\le m<n \\ n\equiv m(\mathrm{mod}\ D)}} \frac{\tau(n)\ \tau(m)}{(nm)^{1+\delta}} \le C_3\, D^{-1}\, \delta^{-2} \log^2 z . \tag{2.7}$$

From (2.5), (2.6) and (2.7), we have

$$\sum_{\chi_D} |f_{\chi_D}(1+\delta+it)| \le C_4(Dz^{-1}\delta^{-1}\log^3 z + \delta^{-2}\log^2 z) \quad .$$

<u>Lemma 2.5</u>. Let $G(s, z) = G(s) = \prod_{\chi_D} g_{\chi_D}(s)$, where $g_{\chi_D}(s, z) = g_{\chi_D}(s) = 1 - f^2_{\chi_D}(s)$. Then $G(s)$ has the following properties: 1) $G(s)$ is real for real s, and 2) $\mathrm{Re}\, G(2+it) \ge \frac{1}{2}$.

<u>Proof</u>. For the proof of 1), we may refer to [3]. Now we proceed to prove 2). Since

$$|f_{\chi_D}(2+it)| \le \left| \sum_{n \ge z} \frac{a_n \chi_D(n)}{n^{2+it}} \right| \le \sum_{n \ge z} \frac{\tau(n)}{n^2} \le \frac{3 \log z}{z} \quad ,$$

we have

$$\mathrm{Re}\, G(2+it) = \mathrm{Re} \prod_{\chi_D} (1 - f^2_{\chi_D}(2+it)) \ge 1 - \left(\prod_{\chi_D} (1 + |f_{\chi_D}|^2) - 1 \right)$$

$$\ge 2 - (1 + \frac{10}{D^2})^D > \frac{1}{2} \quad .$$

<u>Lemma 2.6</u>. Let $f_1(s), \ldots, f_n(s)$ be an analytic and bounded functions in the stripe $\alpha \le \sigma \le \beta$. Let

$$F(s) = \sum_{i=1}^{n} |f_1(s)|^2 \quad \text{and} \quad M(\sigma) = \sup_{\mathrm{Re}\, s = \sigma} F(s) \quad .$$

Then

$$M(\sigma) < M(\alpha)^{(\beta-\sigma)/(\beta-\alpha)} \, M(\beta)^{(\sigma-\alpha)/(\beta-\alpha)} \quad .$$

(Cf. [3]).

From the well-known Littlewood's theorem (Cf. [4]) and Lemma 2.1, we have

$$N(\Delta, T, D) \le C_5 \, \delta^{-1} \int_{-T}^{T} \sum_{\chi_D} |f_{\chi_D}(\Delta - \delta + it)|^2 dt$$

$$+ \max_{\substack{\sigma \ge \Delta - \delta \\ |t| \le T+2}} \sum_{\chi_D} |f_{\chi_D}(s)|^2 \quad . \tag{2.8}$$

In order to use Lemma 2.6, we introduce the function

$$h_{\chi_D}(s,z) = h_{\chi_D}(s) = \frac{s-1}{s} \cos^{-1}\left(\frac{s}{2T}\right) f_{\chi_D}(s) \quad .$$

We have

$$C_6 |f_{\chi_D}(s)| e^{-(t/2T)} \le |h_{\chi_D}(s)| \le C_7 |f_{\chi_D}(s)| e^{-(t/2T)} \quad .$$

Let

$$H(s) = \sum_{\chi_D} |h_{\chi_D}(s)|^2 \quad \text{and} \quad M(\sigma) = \sup_{\mathrm{Re}\, s=\sigma} H(s) \quad .$$

Then from Lemmas 2.2 and 2.3, we have

$$\begin{aligned} H(\tfrac{1}{2}+it) &\le C_8 e^{-(|t|/T)} \sum_{\chi_D} |f_{\chi_D}(\tfrac{1}{2}+it)|^2 \\ &\le C_8 e^{-(|t|/T)} (|t|+1)^2 D^{2c} \left(\sum_{\chi_D} |\rho_{\chi_D}(\tfrac{1}{2}+it)|^2 + C_8 D \right) \\ &\le C_8 e^{-(|t|/T)} (|t|+1)^2 D^{2c} (z + D \log z) \quad , \end{aligned}$$

and therefore

$$M(\tfrac{1}{2}) = C_9 D^{2c} T^2 (z + D \log z) \quad . \tag{2.9}$$

By Lemma 2.4, we have

$$\begin{aligned} H(1+\delta+it) &\le C_{10}\, e^{-(|t|/T)} \sum_{\chi_D} |f_{\chi_D}(1+\delta+it)|^2 \\ &\le C_{11} \left(\delta^{-2} \log^2 z + \frac{D}{z} \delta^{-1} \log^3 z \right) \quad . \end{aligned}$$

Take $\delta = \dfrac{1}{\log DT}$ and $z = D \log D$. Then

$$M(1+\delta) = C_{12} \log^4 DT$$

and

$$M(\tfrac{1}{2}) = C_9\, D^{1+2c}\, T^2 \log DT \quad .$$

Set $H(s) = F(s)$, $\alpha = \dfrac{1}{2}$ and $\beta = 1+\delta$ in Lemma 2.6. Then we have

$$M(\sigma) \le M(\tfrac{1}{2})^{(1+\delta-\sigma)/(\frac{1}{2}+\delta)} M(1+\delta)^{(\sigma-\frac{1}{2})/(\frac{1}{2}+\delta)}$$

$$\le C_{13} D^{(2+4c)(1-\sigma)} T^{4(1-\sigma)} \log^6 DT$$

for $\frac{1}{2} \le \sigma \le 1+\delta$. Therefore

$$M(\Delta-\delta) \le C_{14} D^{(2+4c)(1-\Delta)} T^{4(1-\Delta)} \log^6 DT \quad , \qquad (2.10)$$

and by (2.8), we have

$$N(\Delta,T,D) \le C_{15} D^{(2+4c)(1-\Delta)} T^3 \log^6 DT \quad .$$

The theorem is proved.

Theorem 2.2. Let $D \le z^{(1/3)-\varepsilon_2}$. If $L(s, \chi_D)$ has no zero in the domain

$$1 - \frac{C_{16}}{\log^{4/5} D} \le \sigma \le 1 \ , \quad |t| \le \log^3 D \quad . \qquad (R_1)$$

Then

$$\sum_{\chi_D}{}' \Big| \sum_{n=1}^{\infty} \chi_D(n)\, \Lambda(n)\, e^{-(n/z)} \Big| \le C_{17}\, z\, e^{-\varepsilon_3 (\log z)^{1/5}} \ ,$$

where $\sum_{\chi_D}{}'$ denotes a sum over all characters $\chi_D(n)$ in which $L(s, \chi_D) \ne 0$ in (R_1).

Proof. Since

$$\sum_{n=1}^{\infty} \chi_D(n)\, \Lambda(n)\, e^{-(n/z)} = - \frac{1}{2\pi i} \int_{2-i\infty}^{2+i\infty} \frac{L'}{L}(s, \chi_D)\, \Gamma(s)\, z^s\, ds$$

$$= - \frac{1}{2\pi i} \int_{\frac{1}{2}-i\infty}^{\frac{1}{2}+i\infty} \frac{L'}{L}(s, \chi_D)\, \Gamma(s)\, z^s\, ds + \sum_{\rho_{\chi_D}} \Gamma(\rho_{\chi_D})\, z^{\rho_{\chi_D}}$$

$$= \sum_{\rho_{\chi_D}} \Gamma(\rho_{\chi_D})\, z^{\rho_{\chi_D}} + B \log D$$

and

$$\sum_{\chi_D}{}' \sum_{\rho_{\chi_D}} |\Gamma(\rho_{\chi_D})| z^{\rho_{\chi_D}} \le \sum_{0 \le \beta \le 1 - [(C_{16})/\log^{4/5} D]} |\Gamma(\rho)| z^{\beta}$$

$$\le \sum_{\substack{0 \le \beta \le 1 - [(C_{16})/\log^{4/5} D] \\ |\tau| \le \log^3 D}} |\Gamma(\beta + i\tau)| z^{\beta}$$

$$+ \sum_{\substack{0 \le \beta \le 1 - [(C_{16})/\log^{4/5} D] \\ |\tau| > \log^3 D}} |\Gamma(\beta + i\tau)| z^{\beta}$$

$$\le \sum_{\substack{\frac{1}{2} \le \beta \le 1 - [(C_{16})/\log^{4/5} D] \\ |\tau| \le \log^3 D}} |\Gamma(\beta + i\tau)| z^{\beta} + z\, e^{-\varepsilon_3 (\log z)^{1/5}}$$

$$\le C_{18} \log^2 z \sum_{\frac{1}{2} \le \Delta \le 1 - [(C_{16})/\log^{4/5} D]} N(\Delta, \log^3 D, D) z^{\Delta}$$

$$+ z\, e^{-\varepsilon_3 (\log z)^{1/5}}$$

$$\le C_{19} \log^{20} z \sum_{\frac{1}{2} \le \Delta \le 1 - [(C_{16})/\log^{4/5} D]} \left(\frac{D^{2+4c}}{z} \right)^{1-\Delta}$$

$$+ z\, e^{-\varepsilon_3 (\log z)^{1/5}} ,$$

we have

$$\sum_{\chi_D}{}' \left| \sum_{n=1}^{\infty} \chi_D(n)\, \Lambda(n)\, e^{-(n/z)} \right| \le \sum_{\chi_D}{}' \sum_{\rho_{\chi_D}} |\Gamma(\rho_{\chi_D})| z^{\beta_{\chi_D}} + B\, D \log D , \tag{2.11}$$

and thus the theorem follows.

§3. If

$$D = p_1 p_2 \dots p_s \ , \quad p_1 > p_2 > \dots > p_s , \quad s \le 10 \log\log N \ ,$$

then we put

$$D = p_1 q_1 \ , \quad q_1 = p_2 p_2, \dots, q_{s-2} = p_{s-1} q_{s-1}, \quad q_{s-1} = p_s \ .$$

The numbers $q_1, q_2, \dots, q_{s-1}$ are called the "diagonal divisors" of D. It is known that every character modulo D, where D is square free, can be represented uniquely as a product of characters such that their moduli are prime divisors of D. For example, if $D = p_1 q_1$, then $\chi_D(n) = \chi_{p_1}(n)\chi_{q_1}(n)$. If $\chi_{p_1}(n) \ne \chi^0_{p_1}(n)$, then $\chi_D(n)$ is called to be primitive with respect to p_1.

Theorem 3.1. (A. Rényi) [1]. Let q be a square free number, $A \ge C_{20}$ and put $k = \frac{\log q}{\log A} + 1$. Suppose that $k \le \log^3 A$. Then for all primes p satisfying $(p,q) = 1$ and $A < p \le 2A$, with the possible exception of at most $A^{3/4}$ such primes, no L-series formed with a character, which belongs to the modulus $D = pq$ and is primitive with respect to p, has a zero in the domain

$$1 - \frac{C_{21}}{\log^{4/5} D} \le \sigma \le 1 \ , \qquad |t| \le \log^3 D \ .$$

We need the following lemmas.

Lemma 3.1.

$$\sum_{\substack{d \le z \\ V(d) > 10\log\log z}} \frac{|\mu(d)|\tau(d)}{\phi(d)} \le \frac{C_{22}}{\log^5 z} \ .$$

Proof.

$$\sum_{\substack{d \le z \\ V(d) > 10\log\log z}} \frac{|\mu(d)|\tau(d)}{\phi(d)} \le 2^{-10\log\log z} \sum_{d \le z} \frac{\tau^2(d)}{\phi(d)} \le \frac{C_{22}}{\log^5 z} \ .$$

Lemma 3.2. Let $\{p^*\}$ be a sequence of prime numbers with the property that there exist not more than $A^{3/4}$ numbers belonging to $\{p^*\}$ in any interval $(A, 2A)$. Then

$$\sum_{p^* > M} \frac{1}{p^* - 1} \leq C_{23} M^{-1/4} .$$

Lemma 3.3.

$$\sum_{p > N} \chi_D(p) \log p \cdot e^{-(p \log N/N)} \leq C_{24} N^{1/2} .$$

Lemma 3.4.

$$\sum_{p \leq N} \chi_D(p) \log p \; e^{-(p \log N/N)}$$

$$= \sum_{n=1}^{\infty} \chi_D(n) \Lambda(n) \; e^{-(n \log N/N)} + BN^{1/2} .$$

Lemma 3.5. For all $D \leq \exp(C_{25} \sqrt{\log x}\,)$ with the possible exception of those values of D which are multiples of a certain number $\tilde{D}$ which eventually may exist, we have

$$\sum_{\substack{p \leq N \\ p \equiv \ell (\mathrm{mod}\ D)}} \log p \cdot e^{-(p \log N/N)}$$

$$= \frac{N}{\phi(D) \log N} + BN e^{-C_{26}\sqrt{\log N}} \tag{3.1}$$

for $(\ell, D) = 1$. For the case $\tilde{D}|D$, the term

$$\frac{BN^{1 - C(\varepsilon)/D^{\varepsilon}}}{\phi(D)}$$

should be added on the right hand side of (3.1), where $C(\varepsilon)$ depends on ε only.

Lemma 3.6.

$$P_1(N, D, \ell) < \frac{C_{27}N}{\phi(D)}$$

holds uniformly on $D < \sqrt{N}$.

Consider any $D = p_1 p_2 \ldots p_s \le N^{1/3 - \varepsilon_2}$, where $p_1 > p_2 > \ldots > p_s$ and $s \le 10 \log\log N$. If $D > \exp(\log N)^{2/5}$, then

$$p_1 > D^{1/V(D)} > \exp(\log N)^{1/3} \tag{3.2}$$

and

$$q_1 < p_1^{V(D)} < p_1^{10 \log\log N} .$$

Therefore

$$k_1 = \frac{\log q_1}{\log \frac{p_1}{2}} + 1 < 11 \log\log N . \tag{3.3}$$

When Theorem 3.1 is used to apply to (3.2) for fixed q_1, we may consider only the interval $(A, 2A)$, where $A = 2^k \ell$, $k = 0,1,2\ldots.$ and $\ell = \exp(\log N)^{1/3}$. We call $D > \exp(\log N)^{2/5}$ to be the "condition 1". Further, we suppose that if p_1 is the greatest prime divisor of D and $D = p_1 q_1$, then p_1 is not an exceptional prime in the sense of Theorem 3.1 with respect to q_1, which is called to be the "condition 2". If these two conditions are all satisfied, then from Theorems 2.2 and 3.1, and from Lemmas 3.3 and 3.4, we have

$$P_1(N,D,\ell) = \frac{1}{\phi(p_1)} P_1(N, q_1, \ell) + \frac{BN}{\phi(D)} \exp(-\varepsilon_3 (\log N)^{1/5}) . \tag{3.4}$$

If $q_1 = p_2 q_2$ still satisfies the conditions 1 and 2, then

$$P_1(N,D,\ell) = \frac{1}{\phi(p_1 p_2)} P_1(N, q_2, \ell) + \frac{BN}{\phi(D)} \exp(-\varepsilon_3 (\log N)^{1/5}) . \tag{3.5}$$

If for any integer m, the condition 1 is not satisfied, i.e., $q_m < \exp(\log N)^{2/5}$, then from Lemma 3.5, we have

$$P_1(N,D,\ell) = \frac{1}{\phi(D)} \cdot \frac{N}{\log N} + \frac{BN}{\phi(D)} \exp(-\varepsilon_3(\log N)^{1/5})$$

$$+ E_1(q_m) \frac{BN^{1 - C(\varepsilon)/D^{\varepsilon}}}{\phi(D)} , \tag{3.6}$$

where

$$E_1(q_m) = \begin{cases} 1 , & \text{if } \tilde{D} | q_m , \\ 0 , & \text{if } \tilde{D} \nmid q_m . \end{cases}$$

If for a prime p_{m+1}, the condition 2 is not satisfied, i.e., p_{m+1} is an exceptional prime with respect to q_{m+1}, then from Lemma 3.6, we have

$$P_1(N, D, \ell) = \frac{BN}{\phi(D)} . \tag{3.7}$$

From Lemma 3.1, it yields

$$\sum_{d \le N^{1/3 - \varepsilon_2}} |\mu(d)\ \tau(d)\ R_d(N)|$$

$$\le \sum_{\substack{d \le N^{1/3 - \varepsilon_2} \\ V(d) \le 10 \log\log N}} |\mu(d)\ \tau(d)\ R_d(N)|$$

$$+ \sum_{\substack{d \le N^{1/3 - \varepsilon_2} \\ V(d) > 10 \log\log N}} |\mu(d)\ \tau(d)\ R_d(N)|$$

$$\le \sum_{\substack{d \le N^{1/3 - \varepsilon_2} \\ V(d) \le 10 \log\log N}} |\mu(d)\ \tau(d)\ R_d(N)| + \frac{BN}{\log^5 N} . \tag{3.8}$$

From (3.6), (3.7) and Lemma 3.2, we have

$$\sum_{\substack{d \leq N^{1/3-\varepsilon_2} \\ V(d) \leq 10 \log\log N}} |\mu(d)\ \tau(d)\ R_d(N)|$$

$$\leq \left(\sum_{d \leq N^{1/3-\varepsilon_2}} \frac{|\mu(d)|\ \tau(d)}{\phi(d)} \right) N e^{-\varepsilon_3 (\log N)^{1/5}}$$

$$+ \frac{\tau(\tilde{d})}{\phi(\tilde{d})} N^{1 - C(\varepsilon)/\tilde{d}^{\varepsilon}} \left(\sum_{d \leq N} \frac{\tau(d)}{\phi(d)} \right)^2$$

$$+ N \sum_{d \leq N} \frac{\tau(d)}{\phi(d)} \sum_{p^* > e^{(\log N)^{1/3}}} \frac{1}{p^* - 1} \leq \frac{N}{\log^5 N}, \qquad (3.9)$$

and therefore the fundamental theorem follows.

References

[1]. A. Rényi, Izv. Akad. Nauk SSSR, Ser. Mat., 12 (1948) 57-78.

[2]. Wang Yuan, Acta Math. Sinica, 10 (1960) 168-181.

[3]. K. Prachar, Primzahlverteilung, Springer-Verlag, 1957.

[4]. E. C. Titchmarsh, The theory of the Riemann zeta function, Oxford Univ. Press (1951).

(See Acta Math. Sinica, 12 (1962) 95-106.)

Translated by Wang Yuan

Noted by the Editor: We omit the remaining part of the paper, since from the fundamental theorem, it can derive that (1,4) by the arguments of the Appendix in the preceding paper by Wang Yuan.

The "Density" of the Zeros of Dirichlet *L*-Series and the Problem of the Sum of Primes and "Near Primes"

M. B. Barban

Let $\pi(x, D, \ell)$ denote the number of primes in $(1, x)$ which are $\equiv \ell (\text{mod } D)$. In this paper, a mean value theorem on $\pi(x, D, \ell)$ for $(\ell, D) = 1$ and "almost" all $D \leq x^{3/8-\varepsilon}$ is proved, where ε is any pre-assigned positive number.

Theorem 1. For any given large number A, the inequality

$$\sum_{D \leq x^{3/8-\varepsilon}} \mu^2(D) \max_{\substack{\ell (\text{mod } D) \\ (\ell, D) = 1}} \left| \pi(x, D, \ell) - \frac{\text{li}\, x}{\phi(D)} \right| = O\left(\frac{x}{\log^A x} \right) \tag{1}$$

holds.

By the combination of Theorem 1 and the Selberg's sieve method, we have

Theorem 2. Every sufficiently large even integer is the sum of a prime and a product of at most 4 primes.

We sketch the history of this problem as follows.

In 1947, A. Rényi [1,2] proved the following theorem which gives an important approach to the unsolved binary Goldbach problem:

There exists an absolute constant R such that every large even integer is the sum of a prime and a number which has at most R prime factors.

The constant R in Rényi's theorem depends on a lot of constants contained in the analytic lemmas of Linnik [3]. It needs complicated computation for evaluating the R, and its value will be very large.

By the use of A. Rényi's method and some contemporary theorems on the "density" of the zeros of Dirichlet L-series, the author proved in [4] that the conclusion of Theorem 1 holds if the sum is over $D \leq x^{1/6-\varepsilon}$, and it can derive already $R = 9$. Notice that $R = 3$ has established by the assumption of grand Riemann hypothesis. (Cf. [5]).

The further progress is connected with the refinement of the "density" theorems of L-series.

Let $N(\alpha, T)$ denote the number of zeros of all the L-functions mod D in the domain

$$\alpha < \sigma < 1, \quad |t| \leq T \quad , \tag{2}$$

where the repeated zero is counted by its repetition.

The argument introduced in [4] shows that the relation (1) with a sum of $D \leq x^{1/a-\varepsilon}$ can be derived by the estimation

$$N(\alpha, T) \ll T^{c_1} D^{a(1-\alpha)} \log^{c_2} DT \quad , \tag{3}$$

where a, c_1, c_2 are absolute constants.

In spite of the solutions of Titchmarsh's divisor problem [6] and Hardy-Littlewood's problem [7] by Ju. V. Linnik's new "dispersion method", it is not without interest to notice that in the famous conditional solutions of these problems [8,9], the Riemann hypothesis may be changed by the "density" hypothesis, i.e., (3) holds for $a = 2$.

In [4], we have used the "density" theorem of T. Tatuzawa [10] which corresponds to (3) with $a = 6$.

Out Theorem 1 is obtained based on a refined Tatuzawa's theorem and also a deep theorem of Ju. V. Linnik [7] concerning the estimation of sixth moment of the L-series on a half line.

We start from the following auxiliary lemma.

<u>Lemma 1</u>. Let $0 \leq \alpha < \beta < 2$. Let $f(s)$ be an analytic function which is real if s is real, and regular in $\sigma \geq \alpha$ besides $s = 1$.

Further let $|\mathrm{Re}\, f(2+it)| \geq m > 0$ and

$$|f(\sigma' + it')| \leq M_{\sigma,t} \qquad (\sigma' \geq \sigma, \quad 1 \leq t' \leq t) \quad .$$

Then if T is not the ordinate of a zero of $f(s)$, we have for $\sigma \geq \beta$,

$$|\arg f(\sigma + iT)| \leq \frac{\pi}{\log\left\{\frac{2-\alpha}{2-\beta}\right\}} \left(\log M_{\alpha,T+2} + \log \frac{1}{m}\right) + \frac{3\pi}{2} \quad .$$

For the proof, we refer, for example, [11], 210-211.

We introduce the following notations:

$$Q_z(s,\chi) = \sum_{n<z} \mu(n)\, \chi(n)\, n^{-s}, \qquad f_z(s,\chi) = L(s,\chi)\, Q_z(s,\chi) - 1 \ ,$$

$$h_z(s,\chi) = 1 - f_z^2(s,\chi) \ , \qquad K_z(\sigma,T) = \max_{|t| \leq T} \sum_{\chi} |f_z(\sigma + it, \chi)|^2 \ .$$

All zeros of $L(s, \chi)$ are also zeros of $h_z(s, \chi)$. Hence $N(\alpha, T) \leq N_1(\alpha, T)$, where $N_1(\alpha, T)$ denotes the number of zeros of $H_z(s) = \prod_{\chi} h_z(s, \chi)$ in the domain (2). Apply the well-known Littlewood's theorem to this function. Since $N_1(\alpha, T)$ is non-decreasing if α increases, we have

$$N_1(\alpha, T) \leq \delta^{-1} \int_{\alpha-\delta}^{\alpha} N_1(\sigma, T)\, d\sigma \leq \delta^{-1} \int_{\alpha-\delta}^{2} N_1(\sigma, T)\, d\sigma$$

$$= \frac{\delta^{-1}}{2\pi} \int_{-T}^{T} \left\{\log|H_z(\alpha-\delta + it)| - \log|H_z(2 + it)| \right\} dt$$

$$+ \frac{\delta^{-1}}{2\pi} \int_{\alpha-\delta}^{2} \left\{H_z(\sigma + iT) - \arg H_z(\sigma - iT) \right\} d\sigma + O(\delta^{-1}) \ , \qquad (4)$$

here the parameter δ will be determined in the latter.

In the following, D is assumed to be sufficiently large and $z \geq D$.

When $\sigma > 1$, we have

$$f_z(s, \chi) = \sum_{n=1}^{\infty} n^{-s} \sum_{\substack{d|n \\ d<z}} \mu(d)\, \chi(d)\, \chi(\tfrac{n}{d}) - 1$$

$$= \sum_{n \geq z} \chi(n)\, n^{-s} \sum_{\substack{d|n \\ d<z}} \mu(d) = \sum_{n \geq z} \chi(n)\, a_n\, n^{-s} , \quad |a_n| \leq \tau(n),$$

where $\tau(n)$ denotes the number of divisors of n.

Since $\tau(n) = O(n^{\varepsilon})$ holds for any given ε, we have

$$|f_z(2+it, \chi)| \leq \sum_{n \geq z} \tau(n)\, n^{-2} \leq \sum_{n \geq D} n^{0.1}\, n^{-2} < D^{-0.8} .$$

Now we apply Lemma 1 to (4) with

$$f(s) \to H_z(s), \qquad \alpha \to (\alpha - 2\delta), \qquad \beta \to (\alpha - \delta) .$$

Since the Dirichlet series of $H_z(s)$ has positive coefficients, $H_z(s)$ is real if s is real. (See [10], 301). Next,

$$\mathrm{Re}\, H_z(2+it) = \mathrm{Re} \prod_{\chi} \left\{ 1 - f_z^2(2+it, \chi) \right\} = 1 + \mathrm{Re} \left\{ \prod_{\chi} (1 - f_z^2) - 1 \right\}$$

$$\geq 1 - \left| \prod_{\chi} (1 - f_z^2) - 1 \right| \geq 1 - \left\{ \prod_{\chi} (1 + |f_z|^2) - 1 \right\}$$

$$\geq 1 - \left\{ \prod_{\chi} (1 + D^{-1.6}) - 1 \right\} \geq 2 - (1 + D^{-1.6})^D \geq \frac{1}{2} .$$

Therefore m may be chosen to be $\frac{1}{2}$. Finally,

$$|H_z(s)| \leq \prod_{\chi} (1 + |f_z(s, \chi)|^2) \leq \exp \sum_{\chi} |f_z(s, \chi)|^2 .$$

Therefore $M_{\sigma,t}$ may be taken to be $\exp \max_{\sigma < \sigma' \leq 2} K_z(\sigma', t)$.

We have still $|H_z(2+it)| \geq \mathrm{Re}\, H_z(2+it) \geq \frac{1}{2}$, and thus by the combination of all the above estimations, we have the following lemma.

<u>Lemma 2</u>. If $z \geq D$, then

$$N(\alpha, T) \ll \delta^{-2} T \max_{\alpha-3\delta < \sigma < z} K_z(\sigma, T+2) .$$

In order to estimate $K_z(\sigma, T)$, we shall use the classical method on the convexity theorem of analytic function. We start from the estimation of $K_z(1+\delta, T)$.

<u>Lemma 3</u>. If $z \geq D$ and $0 < \delta \leq 3$, then

$$K_z(1+\delta, T) \ll \delta^{-5} .$$

<u>Proof</u>. We have

$$\sum_{\chi} |f_z(1+\delta+it, \chi)|^2$$

$$= \sum_{m,n > z} \sum_{\substack{(m,D)=1 \\ n \equiv m (\mathrm{mod}\ D)}} \frac{\phi(D)}{(mn)^{1+\delta}} \sum_{\substack{d|m \\ d<z}} \mu(d) \sum_{\substack{d|n \\ d<z}} \mu(d) \left(\frac{m}{n}\right)^{it}$$

$$\leq \phi(D) \sum_{\substack{m \geq z \\ (m,D)=1}} \frac{\tau(m)}{m^{1+\delta}} \sum_{\substack{n \equiv m (\mathrm{mod}\ D) \\ n \geq z}} \frac{b_z(n)}{n^{1+\delta}} ,$$

where $b_z(n) = \sum_{\substack{d|n \\ d \leq n/z}} 1$.

Since $(m,D) = 1$, we have

$$\sum_{n \leq x} b_z(n) = \sum_{\substack{n \leq x \\ n \equiv m (\mathrm{mod}\ D)}} \sum_{\substack{d|n \\ d \leq n/z}} 1 = \sum_{d < x/z} \sum_{\substack{n \leq x \\ n \equiv m (\mathrm{mod}\ D) \\ n \equiv 0 (\mathrm{mod}\ d)}} 1$$

$$\ll \sum_{d < x/z} \left(\frac{x}{Dd} + 1\right) \ll \frac{x}{D} \log x + \frac{x}{z} \ll \frac{x \log x}{D} ,$$

and thus

$$K_z(1+\delta, T) \ll \frac{\log z}{z^\delta \delta^2} \sum_{m \geq z} \frac{\tau(m)}{m^{1+\delta}} \ll \frac{\log z}{z^\delta \delta^2} \zeta^2(1+\delta) \ll \frac{\log z}{z^\delta \delta^4} .$$

Since $\delta \log z \ll z^\delta$, the lemma follows.

Lemma 4. Let $z = D$ and $\max_{|t| \le T} |L(\frac{1}{2} + it, \chi)| \le MT^{c_0}$ for all $\chi(\bmod D)$. Then

$$K_z(\frac{1}{2}, T) \ll M^2 T^{2c_0} \phi(D) \log D \ .$$

Proof. It is evident that

$$K_z(\frac{1}{2}, T) \ll M^2 T^{2c_0} \max_{|t| \le T} \sum_{\chi} \left\{ |Q_2(\frac{1}{2} + it, \chi)|^2 + 1 \right\}$$

$$\ll M^2 T^{2c_0} \max_{|T| \le T} \phi(D) \sum_{\substack{m,n < z \\ n \equiv m (\bmod D)}} \sum_{(m,D)=1} \frac{\mu(m)\,\mu(n)}{(mn)^{\frac{1}{2}}} \left(\frac{m}{n}\right)^{it}$$

Since $z = D$, the lemma follows by converting the congruence to the equality.

Lemma 5. Let $z = D$ and $T \ge 2$. Then under the assumption of Lemma 4, we have

$$K_z(\sigma, T) \ll \begin{cases} T^{2c_0} \{M^2 D^2\}^{2(1-\sigma)} \log^5 D \ (\frac{1}{2} \le \sigma \le 1) \ , \\ \log^5 D \quad (1 \le \sigma \le 4) \ . \end{cases}$$

Proof. By the convexity theorem of analytic function (Cf. [10], 309-310) and Lemmas 3 and 4, we have for $\frac{1}{2} \le \sigma \le 1+\delta$,

$$K_z(\sigma, T) \ll \{M^2 T^{2c_0} \phi(D) \log D\}^{(1+\delta-\sigma)/(\frac{1}{2}+\delta)} \delta^{-5(\sigma-\frac{1}{2})/(\frac{1}{2}+\delta)} \ .$$

Let $\delta = \frac{1}{\log D}$. Then the first part of the lemma follows by the well-known estimation of L-series, namely $M \ll D^{1/2}$. The second part follows by Lemma 3.

Basic Lemma. Suppose that $\max_{|t| \le T} |L(\frac{1}{2} + it, \chi)| \le MT^{c_0}$ for all $\chi(\bmod D)$. Then

$$N(\alpha, T) \ll T^{1+2c_0} \{M^2 D\}^{2(1-\sigma)} \log^7 D \ .$$

If $\alpha > \frac{1}{2} + \frac{3}{\log D}$, the lemma follows by Lemmas 2 and 5.

If $0 \leq \alpha \leq \frac{1}{2} + \frac{3}{\log D}$, the lemma follows by the rough estimation $N(\alpha, T) \ll DT \log DT$.

In particular, set $M = D^{\frac{1}{4}} \log D$. The possibility of such choice on M follows by the "approximate functional equation" of L-series, cf., for example [12]. We have (3) with $a = 3$.

For "almost all" D, a considerably precise result is given by the Linnik's estimation on the sixth moment of L-series, and it will be used in the latter.

According to my previous work, we know that Theorem 1 follows by (3) with $a = \frac{8}{3} - \varepsilon$.

By Linnik's estimation on the sixth moment of L-series (Cf. [7]):

$$\sum_{D_1 \leq D \leq D_1(1 + \frac{1}{\log^{20} D})} \sum_{\chi_D} |L(\tfrac{1}{2} + it, \chi_D)|^6$$

$$\ll D_1^2(|t| + 1)^{c_0} \exp(\log D_1)^{\varepsilon} ,$$

we have immediately

<u>Lemma 6</u>. Besides at most $D_1^{1-\varepsilon}$ of D in the interval $D_1 \leq D \leq D_1(1 + \frac{1}{\log^{20} D_1})$, we have

$$\max_{\chi (\mathrm{mod}\ D)} |L(\tfrac{1}{2} + it, \chi)| \ll D^{1/6 + \varepsilon} (|t| + 1)^{c_0} .$$

Hence if D is not an "exception" in the sense of Lemma 6, the Basic lemma gives the estimation (3) with $a = \frac{8}{3} + \varepsilon$. The result given in [4] admits to consider only the case of $D > x^{1/7}$.

Let Σ' denote a sum of D, where D denotes the "exception" in the sense of Lemma 6. Then

$$\sum_{x^{1/7} \le D \le x^{3/8-\varepsilon}}' \mu^2(D) \max_{\substack{\ell (\mathrm{mod}\ D) \\ (\ell,D)=1}} \left|\pi(x, D, \ell) - \frac{\mathrm{li}\, x}{\phi(D)}\right|$$

$$<< \sum_{x^{1/7} \le D \le x^{3/8-\varepsilon}}' \frac{x}{D}$$

$$<< x \sum_{n \le \log^{22} x} \sum_{x^{1/7}(1+\frac{1}{\log^{20} x})^n \le D \le x^{1/7}(1+\frac{1}{\log^{20} x})^{n+1}} \frac{1}{D}$$

$$<< x \sum_{n \le \log^{22} x} \frac{1}{x^{1/7}(1+\frac{1}{\log^{20} x})^n}$$

$$\cdot \sum_{x^{1/7}(1+\frac{1}{\log^{20} x})^n \le D \le x^{1/7}(1+\frac{1}{\log^{20} x})^{n+1}}' 1 << \frac{x}{\log^A x} .$$

Theorem 1 is proved.

Theorem 2 follows by Theorem 1 and Selberg's sieve method in the forms of Wang Yuan [5] or B. V. Levin [16].

Theorem 3. The number of prime pairs, i.e., p and $p+2$ are all primes, in the interval $(2, N)$ does not exceed

$$(\frac{16}{3} + \varepsilon)\ 2 \prod_{p>2} (1 - \frac{1}{(p-1)^2}) \frac{N}{\log^2 N} , \tag{5}$$

where $N \ge N(\varepsilon)$.

The previous best record on this problem is due to A. Selberg [13] with 8 instead of $\frac{16}{3}$ in (5). It is not without interest to notice that Selberg asserted that his result is the limit that may be attained by the "pure" sieve method.

Here we may use A. I. Vinogradov's argument [15] to derive that either Theorem 3 holds with $4-2\varepsilon$ instead of $\frac{16}{3}$ or there exist infinitely many prime numbers p such that $p+2$ has at most 2 prime factors.

Now we give the Selberg's sieve method by the form of the following lemma.

Lemma 7. Let $a_1,\ldots,a_N$ be a set of integers such that

$$\sum_{a_n \equiv 0 (\mathrm{mod}\ d)} 1 = \frac{N}{f(d)} + R_d ,$$

where $f(d)$ is multiplicative and $\frac{p}{f(p)} = O(1)$. If we use N_z to denote the number of a_n's which do not divide by any prime number $\leq z$, then

$$N_z \leq \frac{N}{\sum_{m \leq z} \frac{\mu^2(m)}{f_1(m)}} + O\left\{ (\log\log z)^c \sum_{d \leq z^2} \mu^2(d)|R_d|\ \tau(d) \right\} ,$$

where $f_1(m)$ denotes the Möbius transform of $f(m)$, and $\tau(m)$ the number of divisors of m.

The full exposition of Selberg's sieve method may refer to [10] for example. In order to derive Theorem 3 from Lemma 7, we take $\{a_n\}$ to be the sequence $\{p-2\}$, where p runs over all prime numbers $\leq N$, and $z = N^{3/16-\varepsilon}$.

The principal term can be evaluated by many well-known methods, cf. [14], for example.

The remainder term is the sum

$$\sum_{\substack{d \leq N^{3/8-\varepsilon} \\ d \equiv 1 (\mathrm{mod}\ 2)}} \mu^2(d) \left| \pi(n,d,z) - \frac{\mathrm{li}\, N}{\phi(d)} \right| \tau(d) .$$

Theorem 1 implies that the part of the sum of d satisfying the inequality $\tau(d) \le \log^{A/2} N$, is $<< \frac{N}{\log^{A/2} N}$. And the remaining part is

$$<< \sum_{\substack{d \le N^{3/8-\varepsilon} \\ \tau(d) \ge \log^{A/2} N}} \frac{N}{d} \mu^2(d)\, \tau(d)$$

$$\le N \sum_{d \le N^{3/8-\varepsilon}} \frac{\mu^2(d)}{d} \tau(d) \frac{\tau(d)}{\log^{A/2} N} << \frac{N}{\log^{A/2-5} N} .$$

Since A can be chosen arbitrarily large, the theorem follows.

Added in Proof. Theorem 1 was proved by the author in August 1961. To estimate the Rényi's constant R with the aid of this theorem, we refer to Wang Yuan's paper [5] which gives the known best result on Selberg's "linear" sieve. It was published in Chinese and it needs complicated computation in its applications. B. V. Levin kindly informed me that the conclusion $R \le 4$ can be derived by his new work on Selberg's sieve and Theorem 1 [16,17]. And then Wang Yuan confirmed that the same conclusion can be followed by Theorem 1 and his work [5], and the full exposition was published in an Appendix of the English translation of [5]. It was noted that a similar result to Theorem 1 was also proved by Pan Cheng Dong independently, but it is not in the terminology of $\pi(x, D, \ell)$, but in a "weight" sum, from which the Theorem 2 can be derived, but not the Theorem 3.

The author is grateful to Wang Yuan and B. V. Levin for their systematically and kindly informing me of their results.

References

[1]. A. Rényi, Izv. Akad. Nauk SSSR, Ser. Mat., 12 (1948) 57-78.

[2]. A. Rényi, Dokl. Akad. Nauk SSSR, 56 (1947) 455-458.

[3]. Ju. V. Linnik, Mat. Sbornik, 57 (1944) 3-12.

[4]. M. B. Barban, Trudy Inst. Mat. Akad. Nauk UzSSR, 22 (1961) 1-20.

[5]. Wang Yuan, Acta Math. Sinica, 10 (1960) 168-181.

[6]. Ju. V. Linnik, Dokl. Akad. Nauk SSSR, 137 (1961) 1299-1302.

[7]. Ju. V. Linnik, Izv. Akad. Nauk SSSR, Ser. Math., 24 (1960) 629-706.

[8]. E. Titchmarsh, Rend. Cir. Mat. Palermo, 54 (1930) 414-429.

[9]. C. Hooley, Acta Math., 97 (1957) 189-210.

[10]. K. Prachar, Primzahlverteilung, Springer Verlag (1957).

[11]. E. Titchmarsh, The theory of the Riemann zeta function, Clarendon Press, Oxford (1951).

[12]. Ju. V. Linnik, Mat. Sbornik, 53 (1961) 3-83.

[13]. A. Selberg, Den 11-te Skan. Mat. Kong, (1949) 13-22.

[14]. N. E. Klimov, Usp. Mat. Nauk, 3 (1958) 145-164.

[15]. A. I. Vinogradov, Vest. Leningrad Univ., 7 (1959) 26-31.

[16]. B. V. Levin, Dokl. Akad. Nauk UzSSR, 11 (1962) 7-9.

[17]. B. V. Levin, Mat. Sbornik, 61 (1963) 389-407.

[18]. Wang Yuan, Sci. Sinica, 11 (1962) 1033-1054.
(See Mat. Sbornik, 61 (1963) 418-425.)

Translated by Wang Yuan

New Results in the Investigation of the Goldbach-Euler Problem and the Problem of Prime Pairs

A. A. Buchstab

Goldbach-Euler problem concerning the representation of even number as the sum of two primes has not been solved up to date. With the aid of Eratosthenes sieve method and the theory of Dirichlet L-series developed by Ju. V. Linnik and his successors, one can prove that there exists an integer k such that every large number $2N$ can be represented as $2N = p+n$, where p is a prime number and n has at most k prime factors. A. Rényi [1] first established the existence of such k. $k = 4$ was obtained by B. V. Levin, M. B. Barban, Wang Yuan and Pan Cheng Dong [2,3,4]. The corresponding results are also obtained on the problem of prime pairs, i.e., there exist infinitely many prime numbers p such that $p+2$ has at most k prime factors. In this paper, I shall prove $k = 3$.

Theorem 1. There exists N_0 such that every even number, greater than N_0, can be represented as the sum of a prime and a number which has at most 3 prime factors.

Theorem 2. There exist infinitely many prime numbers p such that $p+2$ is a product of at most k primes.

The proofs are based on the following theorem of M. B. Barban.

Theorem A. Let ν be a number less than $\frac{3}{8}$ and A be a given positive constant. Then

$$\sum_{D \le x^{\nu}} \mu^2(D) \max_{\substack{a(\bmod D)\\(a,D)=1}} \left| \pi_a(x, D) - \frac{\mathrm{li}(x)}{\phi(D)} \right| = O\left(\frac{x}{\ln^A x}\right) .$$

where $\pi_a(x, D)$ denotes the number of primes satisfying $p \le x$ and $p \equiv a (\bmod D)$, $\phi(D)$ the Euler function, and $\mu(D)$ the Möbius function.

The proof of Theorem 2. Notice that it is well-known that the Theorem 1 may be proved in a similar arguments.

Let q be an integer and $2 < p_1 < \ldots < p_r$ be prime numbers, where $p_i | q$ and $p_r \le z < p_{r+1}$. Let $a, a_1, \ldots, a_r$ be a set of integers such that $(a,q) = 1$ and $p_i \nmid a_i$, which is denoted by ω. We use $P_\omega(x,q,z)$ to denote the number of prime numbers p satisfying $p \equiv a (\mathrm{mod}\ q)$, $p \not\equiv a_i (\mathrm{mod}\ p_i)$ $(1 \le i \le r)$. By Brun's method, we have

<u>Theorem B</u>. There exist non-decreasing functions $\lambda(\alpha)$ and $\Lambda(\alpha)$ such that for $\alpha > 0$ and $q < x^\nu$,

$$P_\omega\left(x,q,\left(\frac{x^\nu}{q}\right)^{1/\alpha}\right) > \left\{B_0\lambda(\alpha) + o\left(\frac{1}{(\nu \ln x - \ln q)^{\frac{1}{2}}}\right)\right\}\frac{c(q)\ \mathrm{li}(x)}{\nu \ln x - \ln q}$$

$$- r_\omega\left(x,q,\left(\frac{x^\nu}{q}\right)^{1/\alpha}\right) ,$$

$$P_\omega\left(x,q,\left(\frac{x^\nu}{q}\right)^{1/\alpha}\right) < \left\{B_0\Lambda(\alpha) + o\left(\frac{1}{(\nu \ln x - \ln q)^{\frac{1}{2}}}\right)\right\}\frac{c(q)\ \mathrm{li}(x)}{\ln x - \ln q}$$

$$+ r_\omega\left(x,q,\left(\frac{x^\nu}{q}\right)^{1/\alpha}\right) , \qquad (1)$$

where B_0 is a constant which is independent on the choice of ω, $\lambda(\alpha) > 0$ if $\alpha \ge 10$, $c(q) = \frac{1}{\phi(q)} \prod_{\substack{p|q \\ p \ne 2}} \frac{p-1}{p-2}$, and

$$r_\omega\left(x,q,\left(\frac{x^\nu}{q}\right)^{1/\alpha}\right) < \sum_{D \in \Omega} \mu^2(D) \max_{\substack{a (\mathrm{mod}\ D) \\ (a,D)=1}} \left|\pi_a(x,D) - \frac{\mathrm{li}(x)}{\phi(D)}\right| , \qquad (2)$$

in which the domain $\Omega = \Omega\left(x,q,\left(\frac{x^\nu}{q}\right)^{1/\alpha}\right)$ consists of the numbers D such that $D = qm$, $m < \frac{x^\nu}{q}$, and the greatest prime divisor of m is less than $\left(\frac{x^\nu}{q}\right)^{1/\alpha}$.

We obtain the usual formulas for $\lambda(\alpha)$ and $\Lambda(\alpha)$. The values of $\Lambda(\alpha)$ with step size 0.01 when $\alpha \le 10$, and $\lambda(\alpha) = 9.999942$ are evaluated by the computer "Minsk-1" in the Moskow Pedagogical Institute named Lenin. Two step functions $\Lambda_0(\alpha)$ and $\lambda_0(\alpha)$ are defined by the so-obtained values, where $\lambda_0(\alpha) = 0$ if $\alpha < 10$. It is shown by Wang Yuan's work that one can prove the following theorem by Buchstab's method.

Theorem C. Let $\beta > 1$. If $\lambda(\alpha)$ and $\Lambda(\alpha)$ are changed by

$$\bar{\lambda}(\alpha) = \begin{cases} \max\left(\lambda(\alpha),\ \lambda(\beta) - \displaystyle\int_{\alpha-1}^{\beta-1} \frac{\Lambda(z)}{z}\, dz \right), & \text{if } 1 < \alpha \le \beta \\ \lambda(\alpha), & \text{if } 0 < \alpha \le 1 \text{ or } \alpha > \beta, \end{cases}$$

and

$$\bar{\Lambda}(\alpha) = \begin{cases} \min\left(\Lambda(\alpha),\ \Lambda(\beta) - \displaystyle\int_{\alpha-1}^{\beta-1} \frac{\lambda(z)}{z}\, dz \right), & \text{if } 1 < \alpha \le \beta \\ \Lambda(\alpha), & \text{if } 0 < \alpha \le 1 \text{ or } \alpha > \beta, \end{cases}$$

then the inequalities (1) still hold, where the remainder term also satisfies (2) with the same Ω.

Starting from $\lambda_0(\alpha)$ and $\Lambda_0(\alpha)$, we have from (3) the following functions on the interval $0 < \alpha \le 10$:

$$\lambda_0(\alpha) \le \lambda_1(\alpha) \le \lambda_2(\alpha) \le \dots \le \Lambda_2(\alpha) \le \Lambda_1(\alpha) \le \Lambda_0(\alpha) \quad .$$

By the successive iterations on the same computer, we obtain a table with abundant values of certain functions $\lambda(\alpha)$ and $\Lambda(\alpha)$, where we omit the index for simplicity. In particular, we have the following

α	3	3.1	3.2	3.3	3.4	3.5
$\Lambda(\alpha)$	3.580161	3.58619	3.60711	3.64053	3.68437	3.73696
α	3.6	3.7	3.8	3.9	4.0	4.1
$\Lambda(\alpha)$	3.79694	3.86318	3.93473	4.01079	4.09072	4.17392
α	4.2	4.3	4.4	4.5	4.6	4.7
$\Lambda(\alpha)$	4.25994	4.34834	4.43877	4.53094	4.62455	4.71940
α	4.8	4.9	5.0			
$\Lambda(\alpha)$	4.81526	4.91197	5.00938 .			

The following theorem may be proved by the similar method used for the proof of Theorem C.

<u>Theorem D</u>. Let $\frac{3}{8\nu} < \alpha \leq \beta$ and $\nu_1 < \nu$. Then

$$\sum_{x^{3/8\beta} \leq p < x^{3/8\alpha}} P_\omega(x,p,p) < \frac{B_0}{\nu_1} \cdot \frac{\mathrm{li}\,(x)}{\ln x} \int_{\alpha-1}^{\beta-1} \frac{\Lambda(z)}{z}\,dz + O\left(\frac{x}{\ln^{5/2} x}\right). \tag{4}$$

<u>Theorem E</u>. Let $\frac{3}{8\nu} < \alpha \leq \beta \leq \delta$ and $\nu_1 < \nu$. Then

$$\sum_{x^{3/8\beta} \leq p < x^{3/8\alpha}} P_\omega(x,p,x^{3/8\delta}) < \frac{B_0}{\nu_1} \cdot \frac{\mathrm{li}\,(x)}{\ln x} \int_{\alpha-1}^{\beta-1} \Lambda\left(\frac{z}{z+1}\right) \frac{dz}{z} + O\left(\frac{x}{\ln^{5/2} x}\right) . \tag{5}$$

Consider the intervals $I_n = [x^{n/64}, x^{(22-n)/64}]$ if $4 \leq n \leq 10$; $I_n = [x^{n/64}, x^{(n+1)/64}]$ if $18 \leq n \leq 20$; and $L_n = [x^{n/64}, x^{(n+1)/64}]$ if $4 \leq n \leq 10$. Suppose that c_n and d_n are corresponded to I_n and L_n, where $c_4 = \frac{4}{21}$; $c_n = \frac{1}{21}$ if $5 \leq n \leq 10$; $c_n = \frac{(21-n)}{n}$ if $18 \leq n \leq 20$; and $d_n = \frac{(21-2n)}{21}$. Consider the function $P(x,q,z) = P_\omega(x,q,z)$, where a and a_i are taken to be -2.

Theorem F. Let Ⓢ(x) denote the number of primes $p < x-2$ such that 1) $p+2 \not\equiv 0 \pmod{p_i}$ for all $p_i < x^{1/16}$; and 2) $p+2$ contains at least four distinct prime factors. The set of such p is denoted by Ⓢ. Let

$$S(x) = \sum_{4 \le n \le 10} c_n \sum_{p_i \in I_n} P(x, p_i, x^{n/64})$$

$$+ \sum_{18 \le n \le 20} c_n \sum_{p_i \in I_n} P(x, p_i, x^{1/16})$$

$$+ \sum_{4 \le n \le 10} d_n \sum_{p_i \in L_n} P(x, p_i, p_i) \quad . \tag{6}$$

Then Ⓢ$(x) \le S(x)$.

Let M denote the prime numbers $p < x-2$ such that $p+2 \not\equiv 0 \pmod{p_i}$ for all $p_i < x^{1/16}$. For each $p+2$, where $p \in$ Ⓢ (Ⓢ $\subset M$), it can be represented in the form $p+2 = p_\alpha^{(k_1)} p_\beta^{(k_2)} p_\gamma^{(k_3)} p_\delta^{(k_4)} m$, where $p_\alpha^{(k_1)} < p_\beta^{(k_2)} < p_\gamma^{(k_3)} < p_\delta^{(k_4)}$ are four smallest distinct prime divisors of $p+2$. Denote $p^{(t)}$ by $x^{t/64} \le p^{(t)} < x^{(t+1)/64}$ if $4 \le t \le 20$; and $x^{21/64} \le p^{(21)} < x$. Then $S(x) = \sum_{p \in M} T(p)$, where

$$T(p) = \sum_{p_i/(p+2)} \sum_{\substack{4 \le n \le 10 \\ p_i \in I_n,\ p \in M_n}} c_n$$

$$+ \sum_{p_i/(p+2)} \sum_{\substack{18 \le n \le 20 \\ p_i \in I_n}} c_n + d(p) \quad ,$$

$p \in M_n$ means that $p+2 \not\equiv 0 \pmod{p_i}$ for all $p_i \in x^{n/64}$; $d(p) = d_n$ if $p_\alpha^{(k_1)} \in L_n$ $(4 \le n \le 10)$, and $d(p) = 0$ if $p_\alpha^{(k_1)} \notin L_n$ for all such n.

For $p \in$ Ⓢ, pick out the c_n and $d_n = d(p)$ in the sum $T(p)$, where p_i is the prime divisor of $p_\alpha^{(k_1)} p_\beta^{(k_2)} p_\gamma^{(k_3)} p_\delta^{(k_4)}$. We obtain then its value $U(p) \le T(p)$. In order to prove the theorem, it is sufficient to prove that $U(p) \ge 1$ for all $p \in \circledS$. In fact,

$$S(x) \ge \sum_{p \in \circledS} T(p) \ge \sum_{p \in \circledS} U(p) \ge \sum_{p \in \circledS} 1 = \circledS(x) .$$

In order to prove that $U(p) \ge 1$ for all $p \in \circledS$, we consider all the possible values of k_1, k_2, k_3, k_4. After 108 times of evaluations on this function, we have $U(p) \ge 1$ for all cases.

The problem of optimum selection for the values of c_n and d_n is essentially a problem of linear programming, i.e., to minimize the linear form (6) under the condition $U(p) \ge 1$.

In (6), $S(x)$ is represented as the sum of ten terms of the form $c_n \sum_{p_i \in I_n} P(x, p_i, x^{s/64})$ and seven terms of the form $d_n \sum_{p_i \in L_n} P(x, p_i, p_i)$. These sums can be evaluated by the Theorems D and E, and the table on $\Lambda(\alpha)$. Take $\nu_1 = \frac{3}{8} - \frac{1}{10^7}$. We have $\circledS(x) \le S(x) < 15.0607\, B_0 \frac{x}{\ln^2 x}$ for $x > x_0$. Denote by $P(x)$ the number of primes $p \le x$ such that $p+2$ does not divide by any prime number $\le x^{1/16}$. Let $a = a_1 = \dots = a_r = -2$. Then

$$P(x) = P_\omega(x, 1, x^{1/16}) > \frac{8}{3} B_0\, \lambda(6) \frac{x}{\ln^2 x} > 15.9979\, B_0 \frac{x}{\ln^2 x}$$

for $x > x_0$. Let $K(x)$ denote the number of primes $p \le x$ such that $p+2$ is square free and has no prime factor $\le x^{1/16}$. Then $K(x) < 0.0001\, B_0 \frac{x}{\ln^2 x}$ for $x > x_0$.

Let $F(x)$ be the number of primes $p \le x$ such that 1) $p+2$ has no prime factor $\le x^{1/16}$; 2) $p+2$ is square free; and 3) $p+2$ has at most three prime factors. Then

222

$$F(x) \geq P(x) - \text{⑤}(x) - K(x) - 2 > 0.937\, B_0 \frac{x}{\ln^2 x}$$

for $x > x_0$. Since $F(x) \to \infty$ when $x \to \infty$, Theorem 2 is proved. In order to prove Theorem 1, the $p+2$ in the definition of $\text{⑤}(x)$, M, $P(x)$, $K(x)$, $F(x)$ should be changed by $2N-p$ and we take $a_i = 2N$ for p_i $(1 \leq i \leq r)$ in the definitions of $P(x, p_i, x^{n/64})$ and $P(x, p_i, p_i)$.

References

[1]. A. Rényi, Izv. Akad. Nauk SSSR, Ser. Mat., 12 (1948) 57-78.

[2]. Wang Yuan, Sci. Sinica, 11 (1962) 1033-1054.

[3]. B. V. Levin, Dokl. Akad. Nauk UzSSR, 11 (1962) 7-9, Mat. Sbornik, 61 (1963) 389-407.

[4]. M. B. Barban, Mat. Sbornik, 61 (1963) 418-425.

(See Dokl. Akad. Nauk SSSR, 162 (1965) 735-738.)

Translated by Wang Yuan

The Density Hypothesis for Dirichlet *L*-Series

A. I. Vinogradov

§1. The basic aim of the paper is to prove the following theorem.

Theorem 1. Let $N_d(\sigma, t)$ be the number of zeros ρ of all the Dirichlet L-series modulo d in the domain $\mathrm{Re}\,\rho \geq \sigma$, $|\mathrm{Im}\,\rho| \leq t$. Then besides at most $D^{1-0.5\varepsilon}$ integers in the interval $D \leq d \leq 2D$, we have

$$N_d(\sigma, t) < (t \cdot \ln D)^{c_0 \cdot \varepsilon^{-4}} \cdot D^{2(1+\varepsilon)(1-\sigma)}, \quad \frac{1}{2} \leq \sigma \leq 1, \quad t \geq 1,$$

where ε is any given small number.

This theorem is usually regarded as the density hypothesis for the average of Dirichlet L-series.

It yields from Theorem 1 and M. B. Barban's work [1] the following

Theorem 2. The mean asymptotic law on the distribution of prime numbers in arithmetic progressions:

$$\sum_{d \leq x^{\frac{1}{2}-\varepsilon}} \max_{(\ell,d)=1} \left| \pi(x,d,\ell) - \frac{1}{\phi(d)} \mathrm{Li}(x) \right| \ll \frac{x}{(\ln x)^c}$$

holds, where c is any given large constant and $\varepsilon > 0$ any small fixed number.

For many problems in number theory, Theorem 2 may be used instead of the grand Riemann hypothesis, in particular, it follows by Wang Yuan's work [3] or B. V. Levin's work [4] that

Theorem 3. Every large even integer m can be represented by $m = p + P_3$, where p denotes a prime number and P_3 is an almost prime which contains at most 3 prime factors. More precisely, the number of solutions of this equation is greater than $C_0 \cdot \mathfrak{S}(m) \cdot \frac{m}{\ln^2 m}$, where $C_0 > 0$ is an absolute positive constant and $\mathfrak{S}(m)$ the singular series.

The similar results hold for the difference problems:

$$2k = p - P_3 , \quad k = 1, 2, \ldots .$$

Concerning the upper estimation for the binary problem, we have the following

<u>Theorem 4</u>. Let m be an even integer. Then the number of prime solutions p, q of the equation $m = p + q$ does not exceed $(4 + \varepsilon) \cdot \mathfrak{S}(m) \cdot \frac{m}{\ln^2 m}$, where $\varepsilon > 0$ is any given small number and $\mathfrak{S}(m)$ the singular series.

There exist some well-known relations between the modulus of L-series and the bound of its zeros. The number of zeros of $L(s, \chi)$ satisfies $O(\ln Dt)$ in a certain domain, and thus similar to Theorem 2, by the argument of [1], we may prove a mean value theorem for the power of divisor function $\tau_k^n(m)$, namely

$$\sum_{d \leq x^{\frac{1}{2}-\varepsilon}} \max_{(\ell,d)=1} \left| \sum_{\substack{m \equiv \ell(d) \\ m \leq x}} \tau_k^n(m) - A_k^n(x,d) \right| < \frac{x}{(\ln x)^c} ,$$

where k and n are two given positive integers and $A_k^n(x,d)$ denotes the expected principal term of the sum on $\tau_k^n(m)$.

This mean value theorem may be used to establish a generalized formula of Linnik [6], namely

<u>Theorem 5</u>. The asymptotic relation

$$\sum_{m \leq x} \tau_k^n(m + \ell) \cdot \tau(m) \sim C_{k,n}(\ell)\, x \ln^{k^n} x$$

holds.

Notice that according to E. C. Titchmarsh's argument [11], it gives easily from Theorem 2 a new proof of the Ju. V. Linnik's [7] theorem which is the solution of Titchmarsh's divisor problem, i.e.,

$$\sum_{p \leq x} \tau(p-\ell) \sim E(\ell) \cdot x \quad .$$

The arguments of the proof of Theorem 1 are as follows. First, the main difficulty of the proof lies on the establishment of the following estimation, i.e., for any integer $n \geq 2$ and any Z in the interval $D^{1/n} \leq Z \leq D^{1/n-1}$, the inequality

$$\sum_{d=D}^{2D} \sum_{\chi_d \neq \chi_0} \left| \sum_{m \leq Z} \chi_d(m) \right|^{2n} \leq D^2 Z^n \exp[(\ln D^{\varepsilon})] \qquad (1)$$

holds.

It means that the mean sum for the values of a non-principal character does not exceed the square root of the length of the interval for summation.

The second step is to prove (1) for $n \geq 2$. The method suggested in the present paper can be well used to treat the case of high moments of $n \geq 4$, but not for the cases of $n = 2,3$. Notice that for $n = 3$, the estimation (1) has been established by Ju. V. Linnik, and it will be useful for us essentially.

In a first glance, if we analyse the argument in §5 of the present paper, we may get some strange phenomena.

For $n = 2$, (1) follows easily by the method given by §5.

References

[1]. M. B. Barban, Mat. Sbornik, 61 (1963) 418-425.

[2]. A. I. Vinogradov, Dokl. Akad. Nauk SSSR, 158 (1964) 1014-1017.

[3]. Wang Yuan, Acta Math. Sinica, 10 (1960) 168-181.

[4]. B. V. Levin, Mat. Sbornik, 61 (1963) 389-407.

[5]. Ju. V. Linnik, Izv. Akad. Nauk SSSR, 24 (1960) 629-706.

[6]. Ju. V. Linnik, *Abstract on Intern. Math. Conf.*, Edinburgh, (1958).

[7]. Ju. V. Linnik, *The dispersion method in binary additive problems*, Leningrad Univ. Press (1961), Providence, R.I., (1963).

[8]. Ju. V. Linnik, Mat. Sbornik, 53 (1961) 3-38.

[9]. C. Hooley, Acta Math., 97 (1957) 189-210.

[10]. I. M. Vinogradov, Selected papers, Akad. Nauk SSSR Press (1952).

[11]. E. C. Titchmarsh, Rend. Circ. Mat. Palermo; 54 (1930) 414-429.

(See Izv. Akad. Nauk SSSR, Ser. Mat., 27 (1965) 903-934, *ibid.* 30 (1966) 719-720.)

Translated by Wang Yuan

Noted by the Editor: We omit the remaining part of the paper, since the more elegant proofs of Theorem 2 may be found in the following papers of Bombieri and Pan Cheng Dong in this book.

ON THE LARGE SIEVE

E. Bombieri

1. The purpose of this paper is to give a new and improved version of Linnik's large sieve, with some applications. The large sieve has its roots in the Hardy–Littlewood method, and in its most general form it may be considered as an inequality which relates a singular series arising from an integral $\int_0^1 |S(\alpha)|^2 d\alpha$, where $S(\alpha)$ is any exponential sum, to the integral itself.

Very recently Roth [1] made important progress on this problem by proving the following results:

Theorem A. (Roth [1].) *Let n_j $(1 \leqslant j \leqslant Z)$ be distinct natural numbers not exceeding N, and let $Z(N; q, a)$ denote the number of those n_j that are congruent to a $(\bmod q)$. Let $X \geqslant 2$, and let $\mathscr{P}$ be a set of distinct primes $p \leqslant X$. Then, for any $R \geqslant 2$,*

$$\sum_{p \in \mathscr{P}} p \sum_{a=1}^{p} \left(Z(N; p, a) - Z/p\right)^2 \ll ZN + ZX^2 \log R + Z^2 |\mathscr{P}| R^{-2},$$

where $|\mathscr{P}|$ denotes the number of elements of $\mathscr{P}$.

In particular, if $X \geqslant N^{\frac{1}{2}}(\log N)^{-\frac{1}{2}}$, then

$$\sum_{p \leqslant X} p \sum_{a=1}^{p} \left(Z(N; p, a) - Z/p\right)^2 \ll ZX^2 \log X.$$

We shall improve a little upon this result by proving the following

Theorem 1. *With the notation of Theorem A, we have*

$$\sum_{p \leqslant X} p \sum_{a=1}^{p} \left(Z(N; p, a) - Z/p\right)^2 \leqslant 7 \max(N, X^2)\, Z.$$

The general version of the large sieve which we shall consider here, and which contains Theorem 1 as a special case, will take the form of the following theorem, where now any reference to prime numbers and sequences of integers has disappeared:

Theorem 2. *Let the a_n be any complex numbers, and put*

$$S(\alpha) = \sum_{Y < n \leqslant Z} a_n e(n\alpha), \tag{1.1}$$

where as usual $e(t) = e^{2\pi i t}$. Then we have

$$\sum_{q \leqslant X} \sum_{\substack{a=1 \\ (a,q)=1}}^{q} |S(a/q)|^2 \leqslant 7 \max(Z - Y, X^2) \sum_{Y < n \leqslant Z} |a_n|^2. \tag{1.2}$$

In order to deduce Theorem 1, take $Y=0$ and $Z=N$ in Theorem 2, and take $a_n=1$ if $n=n_j$ and $a_n=0$ otherwise. Then $\Sigma|a_n|^2=Z$ (in the notation of Theorem A), and (1.2) gives

$$\sum_{p\leqslant X}\sum_{a=1}^{p-1}|S(a/p)|^2\leqslant 7\max(N,X^2)Z.$$

A simple computation shows that

$$\sum_{a=1}^{p-1}|S(a/p)|^2=p\sum_{a=1}^{p}\left(Z(N;p,a)-Z/p\right)^2,$$

and Theorem 1 follows immediately.

It may be of interest to remark that Theorem 2 is not far from best possible. Take first $Z-Y\geqslant X^2$ and $a_n=1$. Then $|S(1)|^2=(Z-Y)^2$, and (1.2) gives the upper bound $7(Z-Y)^2$; this shows that for $Z-Y\geqslant X^2$ we cannot replace the factor $7\max(Z-Y,X^2)$ by $\max(Z-Y,X^2)$. Now take $Y=0$, $Z=1$, $a_1=1$. Then $|S(a/q)|=1$, so that the left-hand side of (1.2) is

$$\left(\sum_{q\leqslant X}\phi(q)\right)\left(\sum_{Y<n\leqslant Z}|a_n|^2\right)\sim\frac{3X^2}{\pi^2}\sum_{Y<n\leqslant Z}|a_n|^2.$$

This shows that for $Z-Y<X^2$ we cannot replace the factor 7 by any number less than $3/\pi^2$.

We may look upon (1.2) as an inequality involving additive characters, and we may ask whether there exists a similar inequality but with multiplicative characters instead. This is in fact the case, though the final result takes a different shape.

Let Q denote a finite set of positive integers, and put

$$M=M(Q)=\max_{q\in Q}q, \tag{1.3}$$

$$D=D(Q)=\max_{q\in Q}d(q), \tag{1.4}$$

where $d(q)$ denotes the number of divisors of q. Also, for any character χ to the modulus q, let $\tau(\chi)$ denote the Gaussian sum

$$\tau(\chi)=\sum_{a=1}^{q}\chi(a)e(a/q). \tag{1.5}$$

We have

$$|\tau(\chi)|^2=\begin{cases}\mu^2(q/q^*)q^* & \text{if } (q^*,q/q^*)=1,\\ 0 & \text{otherwise,}\end{cases} \tag{1.6}$$

where q^* is the conductor of the character χ (so that χ is the extension to the modulus q of a primitive character to the modulus q^*). Note that $|\tau(\chi)|^2=q$ if χ is a primitive character (mod q), and $|\tau(\chi_0)|^2=\mu^2(q)$ for the principal character χ_0, and $|\tau(\chi)|^2\leqslant q$ always.

The multiplicative analogue of Theorem 2 is:

THEOREM 3. *Let the a_n be any complex numbers, and let Q be any finite set of positive integers. Then*

$$\sum_{q \in Q} \frac{1}{\phi(q)} \sum_{\chi} |\tau(\chi)|^2 \left| \sum_{Y<n\leq Z} \chi(n) a_n \right|^2$$
$$\leqslant 7D \max(Z-Y, M^2) \sum_{Y<n\leq Z} d(n)|a_n|^2, \tag{1.7}$$

where $\sum_{\chi}$ denotes a summation over all characters χ to the modulus q.

In special cases it is possible to prove a slightly better result. In particular, if $a_n = 1$ if n is a prime and 0 otherwise, there is a result of the same general type but without D and $d(n)$.

Theorem 3 has important consequences for the theory of the zeros of Dirichlet's L-functions and the distribution of prime numbers; in fact the large sieve was originally created by Linnik with a view to applications to classical problems in the theory of primes.

The principal result we shall prove on the distribution of the primes runs as follows. Let

$$\psi(z; q, a) = \sum_{\substack{n \leqslant z \\ n \equiv a \pmod q}} \Lambda(n),$$

where $(a, q) = 1$, and consider the error term in the prime number theorem for arithmetical progressions:

$$E(z; q, a) = \psi(z; q, a) - z/\phi(q). \tag{1.8}$$

Define $E(z, q)$ and $E^*(z, q)$ by

$$E(z, q) = \max_{(a,q)=1} |E(z; q, a)|, \tag{1.9}$$

$$E^*(z, q) = \max_{y \leq z} E(y, q). \tag{1.10}$$

THEOREM 4. *For any positive constant A there exists a positive constant B such that if $X \leqslant z^{\frac{1}{2}} (\log z)^{-B}$ then*

$$\sum_{q \leq X} E^*(z, q) \ll z(\log z)^{-A}. \tag{1.11}$$

We shall show that a possible value for B is $3A + 23$.

It seems likely that this result could also be proved by appealing to Roth's Theorem A; however, the use of Theorem 3 seems to be more appropriate.

We remark that nothing more precise than (1.11) can be proved even on the assumption of the generalized Riemann hypothesis, if we apply this in the form $E^*(z, q) \ll z^{\frac{1}{2}}(\log z)^2$ for $q \leqslant z$. One can say that Theorem 4 may serve as a good substitute for the generalized Riemann hypothesis in many additive problems involving primes. There are several instances of this general principle, and Professor Davenport and the author have worked out in detail an application to the study of small differences between prime numbers in a paper submitted to *Proc. Royal Soc. A.*

Results like (1.11), such as

$$\sum_{q\leqslant z^{\eta-\epsilon}} \mu^2(q)\, E(z,q) \ll z(\log z)^{-A} \tag{1.12}$$

for some positive constant η have been claimed by various authors. The work of Linnik and Rényi [2, 3] on the large sieve led to an inequality slightly weaker than (1.12), for some η. More recently, work on this subject has been published by Barban†‡ and Pan Cheng-Dong§‖. However, Barban's work has been subjected to criticism by Pan Cheng-Dong§, and the present writer is unable to understand Pan Cheng-Dong's paper‖. (It appears that the exceptional set of primes in Lemma 1.2 of this paper depends on s and a, while the choices of a and $s(=\rho)$ in (2.7) depend on D, with many possible choices for ρ, so that Lemma 1.2 is not applicable.)

Theorem 4 will be deduced from a new type of density theorem (Theorem 5 below) for the zeros of L-functions; most of the known theorems in the so-called statistical theory of L-functions are contained in this density result.

Let $N(\alpha, T; \chi)$ denote the number of zeros of $L(s, \chi)$ in the rectangle

$$\alpha \leqslant \sigma \leqslant 1, \quad |t| \leqslant T, \tag{1.13}$$

where $\frac{1}{2} \leqslant \alpha \leqslant 1$. Our principal density theorem is:

THEOREM 5. *Let Q be a finite set of positive integers and let M and D be defined by* (1.3) *and* (1.4). *Then*

$$\sum_{q\in Q} \frac{1}{\phi(q)} \sum_{\chi} |\tau(\chi)|^2 N(\alpha, T; \chi) \ll DT(M^2+MT)^{4(1-\alpha)/(3-2\alpha)} \log^{10}(M+T) \tag{1.14}$$

uniformly with respect to Q, for $\frac{1}{2} \leqslant \alpha \leqslant 1$, $T \geqslant 2$.

The proofs of Theorems 4 and 5 are self-contained, except for references to classical work of Landau, Littlewood and Titchmarsh, and we hope that they are given with an adequate amount of detail.

It may be useful if we add some remarks on the significance of (1.14). It was remarked by Littlewood that many results in the theory of Dirichlet's L-functions $L(s, \chi)$, valid for fixed χ and variable s, have

† M. B. Barban, *Trudy Mat. Inst. Akad. Nauk Uz. S.S.R.*, 22 (1961), 1–20.

‡ M. B. Barban, *Mat. Sbornik* (N.S.), 61 (103) (1963), 418–425.

§ Pan Cheng-Dong, *Acta Math. Sinica*, 14 (1964), 597–606 = *Chinese Math.*, 5 (1964), 642–652.

‖ Pan Cheng-Dong, *Acta Math. Sinica*, 13 (1963), 262–268 = *Chinese Math.*, 4 (1963), 283–290.

analogues ("q-analogues") for fixed s and variable χ (to variable modulus). A good example of this is

$$\overline{\lim_{t\to\infty}}\, |L(1+it,\chi)|/\log\log t > 0,$$

where the q-analogue is

$$\overline{\lim_{q\to\infty}}\, L(1,\chi)/\log\log q > 0$$

for the quadratic character $\chi \pmod q$.

It is easily seen that our inequality (1.14) is related to the q-analogue of the density hypothesis for the zeros of L-functions. This hypothesis asserts that

$$\sum_{\chi} N(\alpha, T;\chi) \ll q^{1+\epsilon} T^{2(1-\alpha)+\epsilon}, \tag{1.15}$$

and its q-analogue is

$$\sum_{\chi} N(\alpha, T;\chi) \ll q^{2(1-\alpha)+\epsilon} T^{1+\epsilon}. \tag{1.16}$$

Here $\sum_{\chi}$ denotes as usual a sum over all characters $\chi \pmod q$. The last two inequalities are unproved and probably very difficult. However, it is possible to prove something very nearly as good as (1.16). In fact, as we shall see later, it is possible to deduce from Theorem 5 the

COROLLARY. *We have, uniformly for* $\frac{1}{2} \leqslant \alpha \leqslant 1$ *and* $2 \leqslant T \leqslant \sqrt{X}$, *that*

$$\sum_{q\leqslant X} \sum_{\chi} N(\alpha, T;\chi) \ll X^{1+2(1-\alpha)+\epsilon} T^{1+\epsilon}. \tag{1.17}$$

Further,

$$\sum_{q\leqslant X} \sum_{\chi} N(\alpha, T;\chi) \ll X^{1+\epsilon} T^{2+\epsilon} \tag{1.18}$$

uniformly for $\frac{5}{8} \leqslant \alpha \leqslant 1$, $2 \leqslant T \leqslant X^2$.

(1.17) shows that the density hypothesis (1.16) is true on the average with respect to q if $2 \leqslant T \leqslant (\max q)^{\frac{1}{2}}$, and (1.18), shows that even more is true on the average with respect to q if $\frac{5}{8} \leqslant \alpha \leqslant 1$ and $T \leqslant (\max q)^2$. The latter result is in a sense surprising, and the explanation is that Theorem 5 is really a new type of density result. We conjecture the following

Density Hypothesis. If $\frac{1}{2} \leqslant \alpha \leqslant 1$ *and* $T \geqslant 2$, *then*

$$\sum_{q\leqslant X} \sum_{\chi}{}^{*} N(\alpha, T;\chi) \ll X^{4(1-\alpha)+\epsilon} T^{1+\epsilon} \tag{1.19}$$

uniformly in α, *where* $\sum_{\chi}^{*}$ *denotes a sum over the primitive characters* $\pmod q$.

Finally, the author wishes to express his deep gratitude to Professor Davenport for a discussion which originated this work and for his help in revising this paper.

2. In this section we shall prove Theorems 2 and 3. A rectangle in the (m, n) plane of the type

$$y < m \leqslant z, \quad y' < n \leqslant z'$$

will be denoted by $R(y, z; y', z')$, or briefly by R. Let $c_{m,n}$ be a double sequence of complex numbers, defined when (m, n) is in the square $Y < m \leqslant Z$, $Y < n \leqslant Z$; to every such sequence we can associate a subrectangle

$$R_0 = R_0(Y, Z_0; Y, Z_0')$$

of the square, depending on the sequence $c_{m,n}$ and on Y, Z, with the property that:

for every rectangle $R = R(Y, z; Y, z')$ contained in $R(Y, Z; Y, Z)$ we have

$$\left|\sum_R c_{m,n}\right| \leqslant \left|\sum_{R_0} c_{m,n}\right|. \tag{2.1}$$

Plainly such a rectangle R_0 always exists, though it need not be unique.

LEMMA 1. (Abel's inequality.) *Let $b_{m,n}$ be real numbers defined for $Y < m \leqslant Z$, $Y < n \leqslant Z$ and satisfying the conditions*

$$\text{(i)} \begin{cases} b_{m,n} \geqslant 0, \quad b_{m,n} - b_{m+1,n} \geqslant 0, \quad b_{m,n} - b_{m,n+1} \geqslant 0, \\ b_{m,n} - b_{m+1,n} - b_{m,n+1} + b_{m+1,n+1} \geqslant 0. \end{cases}$$

Let $B = \max b_{m,n}$. *Then*

$$\left|\sum_{R_0} c_{m,n} b_{m,n}\right| \leqslant B \left|\sum_{R_0} c_{m,n}\right|. \tag{2.2}$$

Proof. Put $b^*_{m,n} = b_{m,n}$ if $(m, n) \in R_0$ and $b^*_{m,n} = 0$ otherwise. Partial summation gives

$$\sum_{R_0} c_{m,n} b_{m,n} = \sum_{R_0} \left(\sum_{R(Y, m;\, Y, n)} c_{h,k} \right) (b^*_{m,n} - b^*_{m+1,n} - b^*_{m,n+1} + b^*_{m+1,n+1}).$$

Hence

$$\left|\sum_{R_0} c_{m,n} b_{m,n}\right| \leqslant \left(\max_R \left|\sum_R c_{m,n}\right| \right) \left(\sum_{R_0} |b^*_{m,n} - b^*_{m+1,n} - b^*_{m,n+1} + b^*_{m+1,n+1}| \right).$$

By (2.1) we have

$$\max_R \left|\sum_R c_{m,n}\right| \leqslant \left|\sum_{R_0} c_{m,n}\right|,$$

and from the conditions (i) we have

$$\begin{aligned} &\sum_{R_0} |b^*_{m,n} - b^*_{m+1,n} - b^*_{m,n+1} + b^*_{m+1,n+1}| \\ &= \sum_{R_0} (b^*_{m,n} - b^*_{m+1,n+1} - b^*_{m,n+1} + b^*_{m+1,n+1}) \\ &= b_{Y+1,Y+1} \leqslant B. \end{aligned}$$

This proves (2.2).

LEMMA 2. *Let $c_{m,n}$ and R_0 be as before, and suppose that $\eta > 0$. Then*

$$\left|\sum_{R_0} c_{m,n} - (2\eta)^{-1} \sum_{R_0} c_{m,n} \int_{-\eta}^{\eta} e\Big((m-n)\beta\Big)\, d\beta\right| \leqslant \left(\frac{\sinh x}{x} - 1\right) \left|\sum_{R_0} c_{m,n}\right|, \tag{2.3}$$

where $x = 4\pi\eta(Z-Y)$.

Proof. We have

$$(2\eta)^{-1} \sum_{R_0} c_{m,n} \int_{-\eta}^{\eta} e\Big((m-n)\beta\Big)\, d\beta = \sum_{k=0}^{\infty} (-1)^k \frac{(2\pi\eta)^{2k}}{(2k+1)!} \sum_{R_0} c_{m,n} (m-n)^{2k}$$

$$= \sum_{R_0} c_{m,n} \quad + \quad T,$$

where

$$T = \sum_{k=1}^{\infty} \frac{(-1)^k (2\pi\eta)^{2k}}{(2k+1)!} \sum_{r=0}^{2k} (-1)^r \binom{2k}{r} \sum_{R_0} c_{m,n} (Z-m)^r (Z-n)^{2k-r}.$$

The sequence $b_{m,n} = (Z-m)^r (Z-n)^{2k-r}$ satisfies the conditions (i) of Lemma 1, and $B \leqslant (Z-Y)^{2k}$. Hence, by (2.2),

$$\left|\sum_{R_0} c_{m,n} (Z-m)^r (Z-n)^{2k-r}\right| \leqslant (Z-Y)^{2k} \left|\sum_{R_0} c_{m,n}\right|.$$

Thus

$$|T| \leqslant \sum_{k=1}^{\infty} \frac{(2\pi\eta)^{2k}}{(2k+1)!} \sum_{r=0}^{2k} \binom{2k}{r} (Z-Y)^{2k} \left|\sum_{R_0} c_{m,n}\right|$$

$$= \left(\frac{\sinh x}{x} - 1\right) \left|\sum_{R_0} c_{m,n}\right|,$$

where $x = 4\pi\eta(Z-Y)$. This proves Lemma 2.

Proof of Theorem 2. Let

$$S_{m,q} = \sum_{\substack{a=1 \\ (a,q)=1}}^{q} e(am/q) \tag{2.4}$$

be the well-known Ramanujan sum. Take

$$c_{m,n} = a_m \bar{a}_n \sum_{q \leqslant X} S_{m-n,q} \tag{2.5}$$

for $(m,n) \in R(Y, Z;\, Y, Z)$. Choose η so that

$$x = 4\pi\eta(Z-Y) = \min\Big(1{\cdot}3168,\ 2\pi(Z-Y)X^{-2}\Big). \tag{2.6}$$

Then $\sinh x < 2x$, and (2.3) implies that

$$\left|\sum_{R_0} c_{m,n}\right| \leqslant \frac{2\pi(Z-Y)}{2x - \sinh x} \left|\sum_{R_0} c_{m,n} \int_{-\eta}^{\eta} e\Big((m-n)\beta\Big)\, d\beta\right|.$$

Since

$$2x-\sinh x>\frac{x}{1\cdot 4632}$$

for $0<x\leqslant 1\cdot 3168$, we obtain

$$\left|\sum_{R_0} c_{m,n}\right| \leqslant \max\Big(7(Z-Y),\ 1\cdot 47X^2\Big)\left|\sum_{R_0} c_{m,n}\int_{-\eta}^{\eta} e\Big((m-n)\beta\Big)\,d\beta\right|.$$

Let $\mathfrak{M}_{a,q}$ denote the interval $|\alpha-a/q|<\eta$, and put

$$S(\alpha;\ Y,Z)=\sum_{Y<n<Z} a_n\, e(n\alpha),$$

this being the same as $S(\alpha)$ in (1.1). We have

$$\sum_{R_0} c_{m,n}\int_{-\eta}^{\eta} e\Big((m-n)\beta\Big)\,d\beta$$

$$=\sum_{Y<m\leqslant Z_0}\ \sum_{Y<n\leqslant Z_0'} a_m\bar{a}_n \sum_{q\leqslant X}\ \sum_{\substack{a=1\\(a,q)=1}}^{q}\int_{\mathfrak{M}_{a,q}} e\Big((m-n)\alpha\Big)\,d\alpha$$

$$=\sum_{q\leqslant X}\ \sum_{\substack{a=1\\(a,q)=1}}^{q}\int_{\mathfrak{M}_{a,q}} S(\alpha;\ Y,Z_0)\,\overline{S(\alpha;\ Y,Z_0')}\,d\alpha.$$

This has absolute value

$$\leqslant \tfrac{1}{2}\sum_{q\leqslant X}\ \sum_{\substack{a=1\\(a,q)=1}}^{q}\int_{\mathfrak{M}_{a,q}}\Big\{|S(\alpha;\ Y,Z_0)|^2+|S(\alpha;\ Y,Z_0')|^2\Big\}\,d\alpha$$

$$\leqslant \max_z \sum_{q\leqslant X}\ \sum_{\substack{a=1\\(a,q)=1}}^{q}\int_{\mathfrak{M}_{a,q}} |S(\alpha;\ Y,z)|^2\,d\alpha$$

$$\leqslant \max_z \int_0^1 |S(\alpha;\ Y,z)|^2\,d\alpha$$

$$=\max_z \sum_{Y<n\leqslant z} |a_n|^2=\sum_{Y<n\leqslant Z}|a_n|^2.$$

Here we have used the fact that the intervals $\mathfrak{M}_{a,q}$ do not overlap, and this follows from the fact that $q\leqslant X$, $(a,q)=1$, and that the length 2η of $\mathfrak{M}_{a,q}$ satisfies $2\eta\leqslant X^{-2}$ by our choice of x in (2.6).

We have now proved that

$$\left|\sum_{R_0} c_{m,n}\right|\leqslant \max\Big(7(Z-Y),\ 1\cdot 47\,X^2\Big)\sum_{Y<n\leqslant Z}|a_n|^2.$$

Since

$$\left|\sum_{R} c_{m,n}\right|\leqslant\left|\sum_{R_0} c_{m,n}\right|$$

by (2.1), and

$$\sum_{R(Y,Z;\,Y,Z)} c_{m,n} = \sum_{q\leq X} \sum_{\substack{a=1\\(a,q)=1}}^{q} \sum_{Y<m\leq Z} \sum_{Y<n\leq Z} a_m \bar{a}_n e\big(a(m-n)/q\big)$$

$$= \sum_{q\leq X} \sum_{\substack{a=1\\(a,q)=1}}^{q} |S(a/q;\, Y, Z)|^2,$$

we obtain (1.2).

The proof of Theorem 3 is on similar lines, but we need also the following lemma relating multiplicative characters to Ramanujan sums.

LEMMA 3. *We have*

$$\sum_{\chi} |\tau(\chi)|^2 \chi(m)\bar{\chi}(n) = \begin{cases} \phi(q)\, S_{m-n,q} \text{ if } (mn, q)=1, \\ 0 \text{ if } (mn,q)>1, \end{cases} \tag{2.7}$$

where the summation is over all characters χ *to the modulus* q.

Proof. If $(mn, q)>1$ the result is trivial, since then $\chi(m)\bar{\chi}(n)=0$ for every χ. Now suppose that $(mn, q)=1$. Write Σ' for summation over all residues (mod q) that are relatively prime to q. We have

$$\sum_{\chi} |\tau(\chi)|^2 \chi(m)\bar{\chi}(n) = \sum_a{}' \sum_b{}' \sum_{\chi} \chi(am)\bar{\chi}(bn)\, e\big((a-b)/q\big)$$

$$= \phi(q) \sum_{\substack{a \quad b\\ am\equiv bn \pmod q}}{}' \sum{}' \; e\big((a-b)/q\big)$$

$$= \phi(q) \sum_h{}' e\big(h(n-m)/q\big)$$

$$= \phi(q)\, S_{n-m,q} = \phi(q) S_{m-n,q},$$

since all solutions of $am\equiv bn \pmod q$ are given by $a\equiv hn, b\equiv hm$. This proves Lemma 3.

Proof of Theorem 3. We take

$$c_{m,n} = a_m \bar{a}_n \sum_{q\in Q}{}^{*} S_{m-n,q}, \tag{2.8}$$

where Σ^* means that we restrict ourselves to those q which satisfy $(q, mn)=1$. Let

$$S_q(\alpha;\, Y, Z) = \sum_{\substack{Y<n\leq Z\\(n,q)=1}} a_n e(n\alpha), \tag{2.9}$$

$$S^{(d)}(\alpha;\, Y, Z) = \sum_{\substack{Y<n\leq Z\\ d\mid n}} a_n e(n\alpha). \tag{2.10}$$

Choosing η so that

$$x = 4\pi\eta(Z-Y) = \min\big(1{\cdot}3168,\, 2\pi(Z-Y)M^{-2}\big),$$

we obtain as before

$$\left|\sum_{R_0} c_{m,n}\right| \leqslant 7\max(Z-Y, M^2)\left|\sum_{R_0} c_{m,n}\int_{-\eta}^{\eta} e\Big((m-n)\beta\Big)\,d\beta\right|$$

$$= 7\max(Z-Y, M^2)\left|\sum_{q\in Q}\sum_a{}'\int_{\mathfrak{M}_{a,q}} S_q(\alpha;\ Y, Z_0)\,\overline{S_q(\alpha;\ Y, Z_0')}\,d\alpha\right|$$

$$\leqslant 7\max(Z-Y, M^2)\max_z\left(\sum_{q\in Q}\sum_a{}'\int_{\mathfrak{M}_{a,q}} |S_q(\alpha;\ Y, z)|^2\,d\alpha\right).$$

By a well-known identity, followed by the use of Cauchy's inequality, we have

$$|S_q(\alpha;\ Y, Z)|^2 = \left|\sum_{d\mid q}\mu(d)\,S^{(d)}(\alpha;\ Y, Z)\right|^2$$

$$\leqslant d(q)\sum_{d\mid q}|S^{(d)}(\alpha;\ Y, Z)|^2$$

$$\leqslant D\sum_{d=1}^{\infty}|S^{(d)}(\alpha;\ Y, Z)|^2. \tag{2.11}$$

Hence

$$\max_z\left(\sum_{q\in Q}\sum_a{}'\int_{\mathfrak{M}_{a,q}}|S_q(\alpha;\ Y, z)|^2\,d\alpha\right) \leqslant D\sum_{d=1}^{\infty}\max_z\int_0^1|S^{(d)}(\alpha;\ Y, z)|^2\,d\alpha$$

$$= D\sum_{d=1}^{\infty}\max_z\sum_{\substack{Y<n\leqslant z\\ d\mid n}}|a_n|^2$$

$$= D\sum_{Y<n\leqslant Z} d(n)|a_n|^2.$$

Theorem 3 follows easily, because by Lemma 3

$$\sum_{R(Y,Z;\,Y,Z)} c_{m,n} = \sum_{q\in Q}\sum_{\substack{Y<m\leqslant Z\\ (m,q)=1}}\sum_{\substack{Y<n\leqslant Z\\ (n,q)=1}} a_m\bar{a}_n\,S_{m-n,q}$$

$$= \sum_{q\in Q}\sum_{Y<m\leqslant Z}\sum_{Y<n\leqslant Z} a_m\bar{a}_n\,\frac{1}{\phi(q)}\sum_{\chi}|\tau(\chi)|^2\chi(m)\,\bar{\chi}(n)$$

$$= \sum_{q\in Q}\frac{1}{\phi(q)}\sum_{\chi}|\tau(\chi)|^2\left|\sum_{Y<n\leqslant Z}\chi(n)\,a_n\right|^2.$$

3. In this section we give the proof of Theorem 4. We shall adhere to the following notation. For any character χ (mod q) we shall denote by χ^* the (unique) primitive character associated with χ and by q^* its modulus, that is, the conductor of χ. By $\sum_{\chi}^*$ we shall denote a sum over the primitive

characters to the modulus q. The principal character (mod q) will be denoted by χ_0. For any character χ we define

$$\psi(z,\chi)=\sum_{n\leqslant z}\chi(n)\Lambda(n). \tag{3.1}$$

LEMMA 4. *Let N be arbitrarily large but fixed, and let $X_0=(\log z)^N$. Suppose that $X\leqslant z^{\frac{1}{2}}$. For any $D\geqslant 2$ and any positive integer M, let Q_M denote the set of integers q satisfying*

$$1<q\leqslant M,\quad d(q)\leqslant D. \tag{3.2}$$

Then we have

$$\sum_{q\leqslant X}E^*(z,q)\ll z(\log z)^{-A}+zD^{-1}(\log z)^3$$
$$+(\log z)^3\max_{X_0<M\leqslant X}M^{-1}\sum_{Q_M}\sum_{\chi}{}^{*}\max_{y\leqslant z}|\psi(y,\chi)|, \tag{3.3}$$

for every (arbitrarily large) fixed A.

Proof. We have

$$\sum_{q\leqslant X}E^*(z,q)=\sum_{q\in Q_X}+\sum_{q\notin Q_X}=\Sigma_1+\Sigma_2,\ \text{say}. \tag{3.4}$$

It is easy to estimate Σ_2. Plainly

$$\psi(z;q,a)\ll(\log z)\sum_{\substack{n\leqslant z\\ n\equiv a(\text{mod } q)}}1\ll(\log z)\left(1+z/\phi(q)\right),$$

whence, by the definition of $E^*(z,q)$ in (1.10),

$$E^*(z,q)\ll z(\log z)/\phi(q)\ \text{ for }\ q\leqslant z.$$

Thus
$$\Sigma_2\ll E^*(z,1)+\sum_{\substack{q\leqslant X\\ d(q)>D}}z(\log z)/\phi(q)$$
$$\ll z(\log z)^{-A}+z(\log z)D^{-1}\sum_{q\leqslant X}d(q)/\phi(q)$$
$$\ll z(\log z)^{-A}+zD^{-1}(\log z)^3.$$

For the sum Σ_1, we express $E^*(z,q)$ in terms of the values of $\psi(z,\chi)$. We have

$$\psi(z;q,a)=\frac{1}{\phi(q)}\sum_{\chi}\bar{\chi}(a)\psi(z,\chi),$$

and this gives

$$\phi(q)E(z,q)\leqslant|\psi(z,\chi_0)-z|+\sum_{\chi\neq\chi_0}|\psi(z,\chi)|.$$

Now

$$|\psi(z,\chi_0)-z|\ll z\exp\left(-C(\log z)^{\frac{1}{2}}\right)\ll z(\log z)^{-A-1}$$

by the prime number theorem in its classical form; and for $\chi \neq \chi_0$

$$\psi(z,\chi) = \sum_{\substack{m\leqslant z\\(m,q)=1}} \chi^*(m)\Lambda(m)$$

$$= \psi(z,\chi^*) - \sum_{\substack{m\leqslant z\\(m,q)>1}} \chi^*(m)\Lambda(m)$$

$$= \psi(z,\chi^*) + O\Big(\sum_{\substack{p^\nu\leqslant z\\p\mid q}} \log p\Big)$$

$$= \psi(z,\chi^*) + O\big((\log z)(\log q)\big).$$

Hence

$$\phi(q)\,E^*(z,q) \ll z(\log z)^{-A-1} + \phi(q)(\log z)^2 + \sum_{\chi\neq\chi_0}\max_{y\leqslant z}|\psi(y,\chi^*)|.$$

It follows that

$$\Sigma_1 \ll z(\log z)^{-A-1}\sum_{q\leqslant X} 1/\phi(q) + X(\log z)^2 + \sum_{q\in Q_X}\frac{1}{\phi(q)}\sum_{\chi\neq\chi_0}\max_{y\leqslant z}|\psi(y,\chi^*)|$$

$$\ll z(\log z)^{-A} + \sum_{q\in Q_X}\frac{1}{\phi(q)}\sum_{\chi\neq\chi_0}\max_{y\leqslant z}|\psi(y,\chi^*)|.$$

Since $q^*|q$ we have $d(q^*) \leqslant d(q) \leqslant D$, which implies that $q^* \in Q_X$, since $q^* > 1$ for $\chi \neq \chi_0$. Hence, collecting together all the terms containing the primitive characters χ^* belonging to the same modulus q^*, we get

$$\sum_{q\in Q_X}\frac{1}{\phi(q)}\sum_{\chi\neq\chi_0}\max_{y\leqslant z}|\psi(y,\chi^*)| = \sum_{q^*\in Q_X}\sum_{\chi}{}^*\max_{y\leqslant z}|\psi(y,\chi)|\sum_{\substack{q\in Q_X\\q\equiv 0(\text{mod } q^*)}} 1/\phi(q).$$

Now $\phi(q^*r) \geqslant \phi(q^*)\,\phi(r) \gg q^*\phi(r)(\log X)^{-1}$, and $X < z$. Hence the last expression is

$$\ll (\log z)^2 \sum_{q^*\in Q_X}(q^*)^{-1}\sum_{\chi}{}^*\max_{y\leqslant z}|\psi(y,\chi)|.$$

By the Siegel–Walfisz theorem (Prachar [4; ch. IV, Satz 7.2 and Satz 8.2]) we have

$$|\psi(z,\chi)| \ll z\exp\big(-c(\log z)^{\frac12}\big)$$

for $\chi \neq \chi_0$, and uniformly in q for $q \leqslant (\log z)^N = X_0$, where $c = c(N)$. It is easily deduced that the same estimate holds for $\max_{y\leqslant z}|\psi(y,\chi)|$, with possibly a different value of c. Hence

$$\sum_{q^*\in Q_{X_0}}(q^*)^{-1}\sum_{\chi}{}^*\max_{y\leqslant z}|\psi(y,\chi)| \ll z(\log z)^{-A-2}.$$

The remaining sum, that is, the sum over $X_0 < q \leqslant X$, can be divided into $\ll \log X$ sums over intervals of the type $2^{m-1} < q \leqslant 2^m$. This gives

$$\sum_{\substack{q^*\in Q_X\\q^*>X_0}}(q^*)^{-1}\sum_{\chi}{}^*\max_{y\leqslant z}|\psi(y,\chi)| \ll (\log z)\max_{X_0<M\leqslant X} M^{-1}\sum_{Q_M}\sum_{\chi}{}^*\max_{y\leqslant z}|\psi(y,\chi)|.$$

It follows that

$$\Sigma_1 \ll z(\log z)^{-A} + (\log z)^3 \max_{X_0 < M \leq X} M^{-1} \sum_{Q_M} \sum_{\chi}{}^* \max_{y \leq z} |\psi(y, \chi)|,$$

and on substitution in (3.4) we obtain (3.3). This proves Lemma 4.

Proof of Theorem 4. By a well-known explicit formula in the theory of primes (see *e.g.*, Prachar [4; ch. VII, Satz 4.6]), for $\chi \neq \chi_0$,

$$|\psi(z, \chi)| \ll \sum_{|\gamma| \leq T} \frac{z^\beta}{|\rho|} + \frac{z(\log z)^2}{T} + z^{\frac{1}{2}}$$

uniformly for $q \leq z$, $2 \leq T \leq z$, where $\rho = \beta + i\gamma$ runs through the zeros of $L(s, \chi)$ with $0 < \beta < 1$, multiple zeros being counted multiply. It follows that

$$\max_{y \leq z} |\psi(y, \chi)| \ll \sum_{|\gamma| \leq T} \frac{z^\beta}{|\rho|} + \frac{z(\log z)^2}{T} + z^{\frac{1}{2}} \tag{3.5}$$

uniformly for $q \leq z^{\frac{1}{2}}$, $2 \leq T \leq z^{\frac{1}{2}}$, because $|\psi(y, \chi)| \ll z^{\frac{1}{2}}$ if $y \leq z^{\frac{1}{2}}$.

Consider first the contribution of any zeros with $|\rho| < \frac{1}{4}$. The number of these is $\ll \log z$ (see Prachar [4; ch. VII, Satz 3.3]), and from the consideration of the corresponding zeros $1 - \rho$ of $L(s, \bar{\chi})$ we deduce that

$$|\rho| > z^{-\epsilon}$$

for any fixed positive ϵ, provided q is sufficiently large (see Prachar [4; ch. VII, Satz 6.9 and Satz 8.1]). Hence the contribution of these zeros to the sum is

$$\ll \sum_{\rho} z^{\beta+\epsilon} \ll (\log z) z^{\frac{1}{4}+\epsilon} \ll z^{\frac{1}{2}}.$$

As regards the zeros with $|\rho| \geq \frac{1}{4}$, it suffices to take only those with $\beta \geq \frac{1}{2}$. We divide the range $|\gamma| \leq T$ into $|\gamma| < 1$ and $2^{m-1} \leq |\gamma| < 2^m$ for $m = 1, 2, \ldots$. Then

$$\sum_{\substack{|\gamma| \leq T \\ |\rho| \geq \frac{1}{4}}} \frac{z^\beta}{|\rho|} \ll \sum_{2^{m-1} \leq T} 2^{-m} \sum_{\substack{|\gamma| \leq 2^m \\ \beta \geq \frac{1}{2}}} z^\beta.$$

Further,

$$\sum_{\substack{|\gamma| \leq 2^m \\ \beta \geq \frac{1}{2}}} z^\beta = \sum_{\substack{|\gamma| \leq 2^m \\ \beta \geq \frac{1}{2}}} \left(z^{\frac{1}{2}} + \int_{\frac{1}{2}}^{\beta} z^\sigma \log z \, d\sigma \right)$$

$$= z^{\frac{1}{2}} N(\tfrac{1}{2}, 2^m; \chi) + (\log z) \int_{\frac{1}{2}}^{1} N(\alpha, 2^m; \chi) z^\alpha \, d\alpha.$$

Using these results in (3.5), we obtain

$$\max_{y \leq z} |\psi(y, \chi)| \ll z^{\frac{1}{2}} + z(\log z)^2 T^{-1}$$
$$+ (\log z) \sum_{2^{m-1} \leq T} 2^{-m} \left(z^{\frac{1}{2}} N(\tfrac{1}{2}, 2^m; \chi) + \int_{\frac{1}{2}}^{1} N(\alpha, 2^m; \chi) z^\alpha \, d\alpha \right).$$

Hence

$$M^{-1}\sum_{Q_M}\sum_{\chi}{}^{*}\max_{y\leqslant z}|\psi(y,\chi)|$$

$$\ll M(z^{\frac12}+z(\log z)^2T^{-1})+M^{-1}(\log z)\sum_{2^{m-1}\leqslant T}2^{-m}\Big\{z^{\frac12}\sum_{Q_M}\sum_{\chi}{}^{*}N(\tfrac12,2^m;\chi)$$

$$+\int_{\frac12}^{1}\sum_{Q_M}\sum_{\chi}{}^{*}N(\alpha,2^m;\chi)z^{\alpha}\,d\alpha\Big\}$$

$$\ll M\Big(z^{\frac12}+z(\log z)^2T^{-1}\Big)+M^{-1}(\log z)\sum_{2^{m-1}\leqslant T}2^{-m}\max_{\alpha}\Big\{\sum_{Q_M}\sum_{\chi}{}^{*}N(\alpha,2^m;\chi)z^{\alpha}\Big\}$$

$$\ll M\Big(z^{\frac12}+z(\log z)^2T^{-1}\Big)$$

$$+M^{-1}(\log z)^2\max_{2\leqslant T'\leqslant T}(T')^{-1}\max_{\alpha}\Big\{\sum_{Q_M}\sum_{\chi}{}^{*}N(\alpha,T';\chi)z^{\alpha}\Big\}. \tag{3.6}$$

We now appeal to Theorem 5. Noting that for a primitive character $\chi \pmod q$ we have $|\tau(\chi)|^2=q>\phi(q)$, we deduce from Theorem 5 that

$$\sum_{Q_M}\sum_{\chi}{}^{*}N(\alpha,T';\chi)\leqslant\sum_{Q_M}\frac{1}{\phi(q)}\sum_{\chi}|\tau(\chi)|^2N(\alpha,T';\chi)$$

$$\ll DT'(M^2+MT')^{4(1-\alpha)/(3-2\alpha)}(\log z)^{10}.$$

Hence

$$\max_{2\leqslant T'\leqslant T}(T')^{-1}\max_{\alpha}\Big\{\sum_{Q_M}\sum_{\chi}{}^{*}N(\alpha,T';\chi)z^{\alpha}\Big\}$$

$$\ll D(\log z)^{10}\max_{\alpha}(M^2+MT)^{4(1-\alpha)/(3-2\alpha)}z^{\alpha}.$$

The conditions we have imposed on M and T are $M\leqslant X\leqslant z^{\frac12}$ and $T\leqslant z^{\frac12}$. The parameter D is at our disposal, and is independent of M.

Now take $D=(\log z)^{A+3}$, $T=M(\log z)^{A+5}$, $X\leqslant z^{\frac12}(\log z)^{-A-5}$; the condition $T\leqslant z^{\frac12}$ is satisfied since we retain the requirement that $M\leqslant X$. Substituting from the last inequality in (3.6), we obtain

$$M^{-1}\sum_{Q_M}\sum_{\chi}{}^{*}\max_{y\leqslant z}|\psi(y,\chi)|$$

$$\ll Mz^{\frac12}+z(\log z)^{-A-3}+M^{-1}(\log z)^{2A+20}\max_{\alpha}M^{8(1-\alpha)/(3-2\alpha)}z^{\alpha}. \tag{3.7}$$

Now

$$\frac{8(1-\alpha)}{3-2\alpha}-1=2(1-\alpha)-\frac{(2\alpha-1)^2}{3-2\alpha}\leqslant 2(1-\alpha)-\tfrac12(2\alpha-1)^2=\tfrac32-2\alpha^2.$$

The function $z^{\alpha} M^{\frac{3}{2}-2\alpha^2}$ increases for $\alpha < \alpha_0$ and decreases for $\alpha > \alpha_0$, where $\alpha_0 = (\log z)/(4 \log M)$. If $M < z^{\frac{1}{4}}$ then $\alpha_0 > 1$; the function increases with α for $\frac{1}{2} \leqslant \alpha \leqslant 1$, and its maximum is

$$zM^{-\frac{1}{2}} \leqslant zX_0^{-\frac{1}{2}} = z(\log z)^{-\frac{1}{2}N}.$$

If $z^{\frac{1}{4}} \leqslant M \leqslant X(<z^{\frac{1}{2}})$, the maximum of the function is

$$\exp\left(\tfrac{3}{2} \log M + \tfrac{1}{8}(\log z)^2/(\log M)\right).$$

Considered as a function of $\log M$, the expression in brackets is convex, and its maximum for

$$\tfrac{1}{4} \log z \leqslant \log M \leqslant \log X$$

is

$$\max\left(\tfrac{7}{8} \log z,\quad \tfrac{1}{8}\frac{(\log z)^2}{\log X} + \tfrac{3}{2} \log X\right).$$

We take $X = z^{\frac{1}{2}}(\log z)^{-B}$, in accordance with the hypothesis of Theorem 4. Then the last expression is $\leqslant \log z - B \log\log z + O(1)$, and it follows that

$$z^{\alpha} M^{\frac{3}{2}-2\alpha^2} \ll z(\log z)^{-\frac{1}{2}N} + z(\log z)^{-B}.$$

We take $N = 2B$, and suppose that $B \geqslant A+5$ so that the earlier condition $X \leqslant z^{\frac{1}{2}}(\log z)^{-A-5}$ shall be satisfied.

Applying the results just proved in (3.7), we obtain

$$M^{-1} \sum_{Q_M} \sum_{\chi}{}^{*} \max_{y \leqslant z} |\psi(y, \chi)| \ll Mz^{\frac{1}{2}} + z(\log z)^{-A-3} + z(\log z)^{2A+20-B}$$

for $X_0 \leqslant M \leqslant X$. Hence, by Lemma 4,

$$\sum_{q \leqslant X} E^*(z, q) \ll z(\log z)^{-A} + z(\log z)^{2A+23-B},$$

since $D = (\log z)^{A+3}$. Taking $B = 3A+23$ $(>A+5)$, we obtain (1.11), and this proves Theorem 4.

4. In this section we prove Theorem 5, the proof being based on Theorem 3.

Let Q be a finite set of positive integers and let M and D be defined by (1.3) and (1.4); also let

$$z = M^2, \tag{4.1}$$

$$Q(s, \chi) = \sum_{n \leqslant z} \chi(n)\mu(n) n^{-s}, \tag{4.2}$$

$$f(s, \chi) = L(s, \chi)\, Q(s, \chi) - 1. \tag{4.3}$$

We define

$$F(s) = \prod_{q \in Q} \prod_{\chi \neq \chi_0} \left(1 - f^2(s, \chi)\right)^{e(\chi)}, \tag{4.4}$$

where

$$e(\chi) = \frac{M!}{\phi(q)} |\tau(\chi)|^2. \tag{4.5}$$

Plainly $F(s)$ is an integral function of s, since $L(s, \chi)$ is an integral function for $\chi \neq \chi_0$, and $e(\chi)$ is a positive integer. Also $F(s)$ is real for real s, since then

$$\overline{f(s, \chi)} = f(s, \bar{\chi}), \quad |\tau(\bar{\chi})|^2 = |\tau(\chi)|^2.$$

As we shall prove later, we have $F(s) \neq 0$ on $\sigma = 2$, provided M is sufficiently large. We define $\arg F(\sigma + it)$ in the usual way (*cf.* Prachar [4; p. 398]) by continuous variation from $\arg F(2) = 0$ along the line segments $(2, 2+it, \sigma+it)$, with the proviso that $\arg F(s)$ is to be increased by $-\pi m \operatorname{sgn} t$ whenever the second segment passes through a zero of $F(s)$ of multiplicity m.

We write

$$\log^+ x = \begin{cases} \log x \text{ if } x > 1, \\ 0 \quad \text{otherwise.} \end{cases}$$

LEMMA 5. *We have*

$$2\pi M! \int_\alpha^\beta \sum_{q \in Q} \frac{1}{\phi(q)} \sum_{\chi \neq \chi_0} |\tau(\chi)|^2 N(\sigma, T; \chi)\, d\sigma$$

$$\leqslant \int_{-T}^{T} \{\log|F(\alpha+it)| - \log|F(\beta+it)|\}\, dt$$

$$+ \int_\alpha^\beta \{\arg F(\sigma+iT) - \arg F(\sigma-iT)\}\, d\sigma. \tag{4.6}$$

Proof. If ρ is a zero of $L(s, \chi)$ of multiplicity m, then ρ is a zero of $1 - f^2(s, \chi)$ and hence a zero of $F(s)$ of multiplicity at least $me(\chi)$. Hence Lemma 5 follows from a familiar theorem of Littlewood (see Prachar [4], Anhang, Satz 8.1).

LEMMA 6. *We have, for* $\frac{1}{2} \leqslant \alpha \leqslant 1$,

$$\int_\alpha^2 \{\arg F(\sigma+it) - \arg F(\sigma-it)\}\, d\sigma \ll M! + \int_0^{2\pi} \log^+ \left| F\left(2+it+(2-\alpha)e^{i\theta}\right) \right| d\theta.$$

Proof. If $\sigma > 1$ it follows from (4.2) and (4.3) that

$$f(s, \chi) = \sum_{n > z} \chi(n) A_z(n) n^{-s},$$

where

$$A_z(n) = \sum_{\substack{d \mid n \\ d \leqslant z}} \mu(d), \quad |A_z(n)| \leqslant d(n).$$

Hence, if M is large enough,

$$|f(2+it,\chi)|^2 \leqslant \Big(\sum_{n>z} d(n)\,n^{-2}\Big)^2 \ll (z^{-1}\log z)^2.$$

Thus $|f(2+it,\chi)|$ is small, and this justifies the earlier remark that $F(2+it)\neq 0$.

We have

$$\Big|\log\Big(1-f^2(2+it,\chi)\Big)\Big| \ll z^{-2}(\log z)^2;$$

also

$$\sum_{q\in Q}\frac{1}{\phi(q)}\sum_{\chi\neq\chi_0}|\tau(\chi)^2| \leqslant \sum_{q\leqslant M} q < M^2 = z.$$

It follows from (4.4) that

$$|\log F(2+it)| \leqslant \sum_{q\in Q}\frac{M!}{\phi(q)}\sum_{\chi\neq\chi_0}|\tau(\chi)|^2\Big|\log\Big(1-f^2(2+it,\chi)\Big)\Big|$$

$$\ll M!\,z^{-1}(\log z)^2 \ll M!. \tag{4.7}$$

We follow the general line of argument of Titchmarsh [5; p. 180]. For fixed t, let

$$g_t(s)=\tfrac{1}{2}\{F(s+it)+F(s-it)\}; \tag{4.8}$$

then $g_t(s)$ is an integral function of s, and

$$g_t(\sigma)=\mathscr{R}F(\sigma+it)$$

by the reflection principle. Let $n(r)$ denote the number of zeros of $g_t(s)$, counted with multiplicity, in the circle $|s-2|\leqslant r$. For $\sigma\leqslant 2$, we have

$$|\arg F(\sigma+it)| \leqslant |\arg F(2+it)| + (N+1)\pi,$$

where N is the number of zeros of $g_t(s)$ on the segment $\sigma\leqslant s\leqslant 2$. Thus, by (4.7),

$$|\arg F(\sigma+it)| \ll M! + n(2-\sigma).$$

By this inequality and Jensen's formula, if $\frac{1}{2}\leqslant\alpha\leqslant 2$ and $g_t(2)\neq 0$, we have

$$\int_\alpha^2 |\arg F(\sigma+it)|\,d\sigma \ll M! + \int_0^{2-\alpha} n(r)\,dr$$

$$\ll M! + \int_0^{2-\alpha} r^{-1}n(r)\,dr$$

$$= M! + \frac{1}{2\pi}\int_0^{2\pi}\log\Big|g_t\Big(2+(2-\alpha)e^{i\theta}\Big)\Big|\,d\theta - \log|g_t(2)|.$$

Also, using the inequality

$$\log^+(a+b) \leqslant 2+\log^+ a+\log^+ b,$$

we have

$$\int_0^{2\pi} \log^+ \left| g_t\left(2+(2-\alpha)e^{i\theta}\right)\right| d\theta \leqslant 4\pi + \int_0^{2\pi} \log^+ \left| F\left(2+it+(2-\alpha)e^{i\theta}\right)\right| d\theta$$

$$+ \int_0^{2\pi} \log^+ \left| F\left(2-it+(2-\alpha)e^{-i\theta}\right)\right| d\theta$$

$$\ll 1 + \int_0^{2\pi} \log^+ \left| F\left(2+it+(2-\alpha)e^{i\theta}\right)\right| d\theta,$$

since $F(\sigma - it)$ is conjugate complex to $F(\sigma+it)$. Substituting in the previous inequality, we obtain the result of Lemma 6, provided $-\log|g_t(2)| \ll M!$. However, we can dispense with this hypothesis by considering also the function

$$h_t(s) = \frac{1}{2i}\{F(s+it) - F(s-it)\}.$$

Then $|F(2+it)|^2 = |g_t(2)|^2 + |h_t(2)|^2$, and by (4.7) we have either $-\log|g_t(2)| \ll M!$ or $-\log|h_t(2)| \ll M!$. The first alternative we have dealt with, and for the second alternative there is the same argument with $h_t(s)$ in place of $g_t(s)$. This completes the proof of Lemma 6.

Lemma 7. *If χ is a non-principal character (mod q), then*

$$L(s,\chi) = \sum_{n \leqslant x} \chi(n) n^{-s} + O(qx^{-\sigma}) \tag{4.9}$$

uniformly for $\sigma \geqslant \frac{1}{2}$, $x \geqslant 2q$, $|t| \leqslant x/q$.

Proof. Write, as usual,

$$\zeta(s,w) = \sum_{n=0}^{\infty} (n+w)^{-s}$$

for $0 < w \leqslant 1$ and $\sigma > 1$. By well-known methods (Titchmarsh [5; §4.11 or §4.14]) we derive the approximation

$$\zeta(s,w) = \sum_{0 \leqslant n \leqslant y} (n+w)^{-s} - \frac{y^{1-s}}{1-s} + O(y^{-\sigma}),$$

valid uniformly for $\sigma \geqslant \frac{1}{2}$, any positive integer y, and $|t| \leqslant \pi y$.

We have

$$L(s,\chi) = q^{-s} \sum_{a=1}^{q} \chi(a)\zeta(s, a/q),$$

and on substituting the above approximation we obtain

$$L(s,\chi) = \sum_{0 < n \leqslant qy+q} \chi(n) n^{-s} + O(q^{1-\sigma} y^{-\sigma}),$$

since $\sum_{a=1}^{q} \chi(a) = 0$ for $\chi \neq \chi_0$. Taking $x = qy+q$, we have $|t| \leqslant \pi y$ and we obtain (4.9) when x is an integral multiple of q. But we can omit the latter condition, since the sum over less than q terms can be absorbed in $O(qx^{-\sigma})$.

LEMMA 8. *We have*

$$\sum_{q\in Q}\frac{1}{\phi(q)}\sum_{\chi\neq\chi_0}|\tau(\chi)|^2|f(\tfrac{1}{2}+it,\chi)|\ll D(M^2+M|t|)\log^2(M+|t|). \quad (4.10)$$

Proof. By (4.3)

$$|f(s,\chi)|\leqslant 1+|L(s,\chi)\,Q(s,\chi)|\leqslant 1+\tfrac{1}{2}|L(s,\chi)|^2+\tfrac{1}{2}|Q(s,\chi)|^2.$$

Hence the sum on the left of (4.10) is $\leqslant\Sigma_1+\Sigma_2+\Sigma_3$, where

$$\Sigma_1=\sum_{q\in Q}\frac{1}{\phi(q)}\sum_{\chi\neq\chi_0}|\tau(\chi)|^2,$$

$$\Sigma_2=\sum_{q\in Q}\frac{1}{\phi(q)}\sum_{\chi\neq\chi_0}|\tau(\chi)|^2|L(\tfrac{1}{2}+it,\chi)|^2,$$

$$\Sigma_3=\sum_{q\in Q}\frac{1}{\phi(q)}\sum_{\chi\neq\chi_0}|\tau(\chi)|^2|Q(\tfrac{1}{2}+it,\chi)|^2.$$

Since $|\tau(\chi)|^2\leqslant q$ we have $\Sigma_1\leqslant M^2$.

Now consider Σ_3. We have

$$Q(\tfrac{1}{2}+it,\chi)=\sum_{n\leqslant z}\chi(n)\,\mu(n)\,n^{-\frac{1}{2}-it},$$

and on appealing to Theorem 3 with $Y=0$, $Z=z$, $a_n=\mu(n)\,n^{-\frac{1}{2}-it}$ we obtain

$$\Sigma_3\ll D\max(z,M^2)\sum_{n\leqslant z}d(n)\,n^{-1}\ll DM^2(\log M)^2.$$

There remains Σ_2. Here we first approximate to $L(\tfrac{1}{2}+it,\chi)$ by a finite sum, using Lemma 7 with $x=M^2+M|t|$, and $q\leqslant M$, which is permissible since then $x\geqslant 2q$ and $|t|\leqslant x/q$. We obtain

$$|L(\tfrac{1}{2}+it,\chi)|^2\ll\Big|\sum_{n\leqslant x}\chi(n)\,n^{-\frac{1}{2}-it}\Big|^2+1.$$

Appealing to Theorem 3 again, with $Y=0$, $Z=x$, $a_n=n^{-\frac{1}{2}-it}$, we get

$$\Sigma_2\ll\Sigma_1+\sum_{q\in Q}\frac{1}{\phi(q)}\sum_{\chi\neq\chi_0}|\tau(\chi)|^2\Big|\sum_{n\leqslant x}\chi(n)\,n^{-\frac{1}{2}-it}\Big|^2$$
$$\ll M^2+D\max(x,M^2)\sum_{n\leqslant x}d(n)\,n^{-1}\ll D(M^2+M|t|)\log^2(M+|t|).$$

Adding the estimates for Σ_1, Σ_2, Σ_3 we obtain (4.10).

LEMMA 9. *We have, uniformly for* $\sigma\geqslant 1$,

$$\sum_{q\in Q}\frac{1}{\phi(q)}\sum_{\chi\neq\chi_0}|\tau(\chi)|^2|f(\sigma+it,\chi)|^2\ll D\log^9(M+|t|).$$

Proof. Let $x=M^2+M|t|$ as in the preceding proof. Then Lemma 7 gives

$$f(\sigma+it,\chi)=\Big(\sum_{n\leqslant x}\chi(n)\,n^{-\sigma-it}\Big)\Big(\sum_{n\leqslant z}\chi(n)\,\mu(n)\,n^{-\sigma-it}\Big)-1$$
$$+O\Big(Mx^{-\sigma}|Q(\sigma+it,\chi)|\Big)$$
$$=\sum_{z<n\leqslant zx}\chi(n)\,a_n(x,z)\,n^{-\sigma-it}+O\Big(M^{1-2\sigma}|Q(\sigma+it,\chi)|\Big),$$

where $a_n(x, z) = \Sigma\mu(d)$ over $d \mid n$, $nx^{-1} \leqslant d \leqslant z$.

Denoting by S the sum of the present lemma, we have

$$S \ll S_1 + M^{2-4\sigma} S_2,$$

where

$$S_1 = \sum_{q \in Q} \frac{1}{\phi(q)} \sum_{\chi \neq \chi_0} |\tau(\chi)|^2 \left| \sum_{z<n\leqslant zx} \chi(n)\, a_n(x, z) n^{-\sigma-it} \right|^2,$$

$$S_2 = \sum_{q \in Q} \frac{1}{\phi(q)} \sum_{\chi \neq \chi_0} |\tau(\chi)|^2 |Q(\sigma+it, \chi)|^2.$$

By Theorem 3 applied to S_2, with $Y = 0$, $Z = z$, $a_n = \mu(n)\, n^{-\sigma-it}$, we have

$$S_2 \ll D \max(z, M^2) \sum_{n\leqslant z} d(n) n^{-2\sigma} \ll DM^2.$$

Now consider S_1. We divide the range $z < n \leqslant zx$ into $\ll \log x$ intervals $(2^{h-1}z, 2^h z)$, $h = 1, 2, \ldots, h_0$, together with a partial interval $(2^{h_0}z, xz)$. By Cauchy's inequality,

$$\left| \sum_{z<n\leqslant zx} \chi(n)\, a_n(x, z)\, n^{-\sigma-it} \right|^2 \ll (\log x) \sum_{h=1}^{h_0+1} \left| \sum_{2^{h-1} z<n\leqslant 2^h z} \chi(n)\, a_n(x, z)\, n^{-\sigma-it} \right|^2,$$

with the convention that the upper bound for n in the inner sum is xz when $h = h_0 + 1$. This gives an inequality for S_1 in terms of $h_0 + 1$ sums, the typical one being

$$\sum_{q \in Q} \frac{1}{\phi(q)} \sum_{\chi} |\tau(\chi)|^2 \left| \sum_{2^{h-1} z<n\leqslant 2^h z} \chi(n)\, a_n(x, z)\, n^{-\sigma-it} \right|^2.$$

To each such sum we apply Theorem 3, with $Y = 2^{h-1}z$, $Z = 2^h z$ (or xz), $a_n = a_n(x, z)\, n^{-\sigma-it}$. Noting that $|a_n(x, z)| \leqslant d(n)$, we obtain for the last sum the estimate

$$\begin{aligned} D \max(2^{h-1}z, M^2) \sum_{2^{h-1} z<n\leqslant 2^h z} d(n)\, a_n{}^2(x, z)\, n^{-2\sigma} &\ll D 2^h z \sum_{2^{h-1} z<n\leqslant 2^h z} d^3(n)\, n^{-2\sigma} \\ &\ll D(2^h z)^{1-2\sigma} \sum_{n=1}^{2^h z} d^3(n) \\ &\ll D(2^h z)^{2-2\sigma} (\log x)^7 \\ &\ll Dz^{2-2\sigma} (\log x)^7, \end{aligned}$$

since

$$\sum_{n=1}^{N} d^3(n) \ll N (\log N)^7$$

and $\log(2^h z) \ll \log x$. On substituting in S_1 we get

$$S_1 \ll (\log x) \sum_{h=1}^{h_0+1} Dz^{2-2\sigma} (\log x)^7 \ll D(\log x)^9.$$

Collecting the results, we obtain Lemma 9.

LEMMA 10. *Let $f_1(s), \ldots, f_K(s)$ be regular functions of s in the strip $\alpha<\sigma<\beta$ and continuous onto the boundary, and suppose that each of them $\to 0$ as $|t|\to\infty$, uniformly in σ. Let $c_1, \ldots, c_K$ be positive numbers, and define*

$$J(\sigma;\ \lambda)=\left\{\int_{-\infty}^{\infty}\sum_{k=1}^{K} c_k|f_k(\sigma+it)|^{1/\lambda}\,dt\right\}^{\lambda}. \tag{4.11}$$

Then

$$J(\sigma;\ \lambda u+\mu v)\leqslant J(\alpha;\ \lambda)^u\,J(\beta;\ \mu)^v, \tag{4.12}$$

where

$$u=(\beta-\sigma)/(\beta-\alpha),\quad v=(\sigma-\alpha)/(\beta-\alpha).$$

Proof. When $K=1$ this is a theorem of R. M. Gabriel [6], and his proof extends without difficulty to the more general case. In the proof of Gabriel's Theorem 1, one considers

$$\int_{AB}\sum_{k=1}^{K} c_k\,\phi_k(z)\,\bar{\phi}_k(z)\,dz$$

instead of $\int\phi(z)\,\bar{\phi}(z)\,dz$, and follows the same line of argument but with an additional application of Hölder's inequality. This is the only modification of any substance that is needed.

Let us write for brevity

$$\Phi(\alpha,\ T)=\int_{-T}^{T}\sum_{q\in Q}\frac{1}{\phi(q)}\sum_{\chi\neq\chi_0}|\tau(\chi)|^2\log^+|1-f^2(\alpha+it,\ \chi)|\,dt. \tag{4.13}$$

LEMMA 11. *We have*

$$\Phi(\alpha,\ T)\ll DT(M^2+MT)^{4(1-\alpha)/(3-2\alpha)}\log^9(M+T), \tag{4.14}$$

uniformly for $\frac{1}{2}\leqslant\alpha\leqslant 1$, $T\geqslant 2$. Also

$$\Phi(\alpha,\ T)\ll DT\log^9(M+T) \tag{4.15}$$

uniformly for $\alpha\geqslant 1$, $T\geqslant 2$.

Proof. For $T\geqslant 4$, put

$$f_T(s,\chi)=f(s,\chi)/\cos(s/T),$$

$$J_T(\sigma;\ \lambda)=\left\{\int_{-\infty}^{\infty}\sum_{q\in Q}\frac{1}{\phi(q)}\sum_{\chi\neq\chi_0}|\tau(\chi)|^2|f_T(\sigma+it,\ \lambda)|^{1/\lambda}\,dt\right\}^{\lambda}.$$

For $T\geqslant 4$, $\frac{1}{2}\leqslant\sigma\leqslant 1$, we have

$$\tfrac{1}{2}\exp(|t|/T)\leqslant|\cos(s/T)|\leqslant\exp(|t|/T), \tag{4.16}$$

so that $f_T(s,\chi)$ is a regular function of s for $\frac{1}{2}\leqslant\sigma\leqslant 1$ and $\to 0$ as $|t|\to\infty$, uniformly in the strip $\frac{1}{2}\leqslant\sigma\leqslant 1$.

From (4.16) and Lemma 8, we obtain

$$J_T(\tfrac{1}{2};1) \ll \int_{-\infty}^{\infty} e^{-|t|/T} \sum_{q\in Q} \frac{1}{\phi(q)} \sum_{\chi\neq\chi_0} |\tau(\chi)|^2 |f(\tfrac{1}{2}+it,\chi)|\,dt$$

$$\ll \int_{-\infty}^{\infty} e^{-|t|/T} D(M^2+M|t|)\log^2(M+|t|)\,dt$$

$$\ll DT(M^2+MT)\log^2(M+T).$$

In the same way, Lemma 9 gives

$$J_T(1;\tfrac{1}{2}) \ll \left\{\int_{-\infty}^{\infty} e^{-2|t|/T} \sum_{q\in Q} \frac{1}{\phi(q)} \sum_{\chi\neq\chi_0} |\tau(\chi)|^2 |f(1+it,\chi)|^2\,dt\right\}^{\frac{1}{2}}$$

$$\ll \{DT\log^9(M+T)\}^{\frac{1}{2}}.$$

On applying the two-variable convexity result of Lemma 10 with

$$\alpha=\tfrac{1}{2},\quad \beta=1,\quad \lambda=1,\quad \mu=\tfrac{1}{2},\quad u=2(1-\sigma),\quad v=2\sigma-1,$$

$$c_k=\frac{1}{\phi(q)}|\tau(\chi)|^2,\quad f_k(s)=f_T(s,\chi),$$

we obtain

$$J_T(\sigma;\tfrac{3}{2}-\sigma) \ll \{DT(M^2+MT)\log^2(M+T)\}^{2-2\sigma}\{DT\log^9(M+T)\}^{\sigma-\frac{1}{2}}$$

$$\ll \{DT\log^9(M+T)\}^{\frac{3}{2}-\sigma}(M^2+MT)^{2-2\sigma}, \tag{4.17}$$

uniformly for $\frac{1}{2}\leqslant\sigma\leqslant 1$, $T\geqslant 4$.

For every complex w and every λ in $\frac{1}{2}\leqslant\lambda\leqslant 1$ we have

$$\log^+|1-w^2| \ll |w|^{1/\lambda}. \tag{4.18}$$

Hence it follows from the definition of $\Phi(\alpha, T)$ in (4.13) that, for $\frac{1}{2}\leqslant\sigma\leqslant 1$,

$$\Phi(\sigma,T) \ll \int_{-T}^{T} \sum_{q\in Q} \frac{1}{\phi(q)} \sum_{\chi\neq\chi_0} |\tau(\chi)|^2 |f(\sigma+it,\chi)|^{1/(\frac{3}{2}-\sigma)}\,dt.$$

By (4.16) we can introduce a factor

$$\left|\cos\Big((\sigma+it)/T\Big)\right|^{-1/(\frac{3}{2}-\sigma)}$$

into the integral, and this has the effect of replacing $f(\sigma+it,\chi)$ by $f_T(\sigma+it,\chi)$. Hence

$$\Phi(\sigma,T) \ll \{J_T(\sigma;\tfrac{3}{2}-\sigma)\}^{1/(\frac{3}{2}-\sigma)}.$$

Now the first conclusion of Lemma 11, namely (4.14), follows from (4.17).

In order to obtain the second conclusion, namely (4.15), we use again the inequality (4.18), which implies that

$$\Phi(\alpha,T) \ll \int_{-T}^{T} \sum_{q\in Q} \frac{1}{\phi(q)} \sum_{\chi\neq\chi_0} |\tau(\chi)|^2 |f(\alpha+it,\chi)|^2\,dt$$

Now (4.15) for $\alpha \geqslant 1$ follows at once from Lemma 9. This completes the proof of Lemma 11.

Proof of Theorem 5. We write for brevity

$$\mathscr{N}_Q(\sigma, T) = \sum_{q \in Q} \frac{1}{\phi(q)} \sum_{\chi \neq \chi_0} |\tau(\chi)|^2 N(\sigma, T;\ \chi).$$

We start from Lemma 5 with $\beta = 2$; using Lemma 6 and (4.7) we obtain

$$\begin{aligned} 2\pi M! \int_\alpha^2 \mathscr{N}_Q(\sigma, T)\, d\sigma &\leqslant \int_{-T}^{T} \{\log|F(\alpha+it)| - \log|F(2+it)|\}\, dt \\ &\quad + \int_\alpha^2 \{\arg F(\sigma+it) - \arg F(\sigma-it)\}\, d\sigma \\ &\ll \int_{-T}^{T} \log^+|F(\alpha+it)|\, dt \\ &\quad + \int_0^{2\pi} \log^+\left|F\left(2+iT+(2-\alpha)e^{i\theta}\right)\right| d\theta + M!\,T. \qquad (4.19) \end{aligned}$$

The function $\mathscr{N}_Q(\sigma, T)$ is a non-decreasing function of T for fixed σ, so on integrating (4.19) with respect to T from 0 to $2T$ we get

$$\begin{aligned} 2\pi M!\,T \int_\alpha^2 \mathscr{N}_Q(\sigma, T)\, d\sigma &\leqslant 2\pi M! \int_0^{2T} \int_\alpha^2 \mathscr{N}_Q(\sigma, U)\, d\sigma\, dU \\ &\ll \int_0^{2T} \int_{-U}^{U} \log^+|F(\alpha+it)|\, dt\, dU \\ &\quad + \int_0^{2T} \int_0^{2\pi} \log^+\left|F\left(2+iU+(2-\alpha)e^{i\theta}\right)\right| d\theta\, dU \\ &\quad + M!\,T^2. \qquad (4.20) \end{aligned}$$

Obviously

$$\int_0^{2T} \int_{-U}^{U} \log^+|F(\alpha+it)|\, dt\, dU \leqslant 2T \int_{-2T}^{2T} \log^+|F(\alpha+it)|\, dt.$$

Also

$$\begin{aligned} &\int_0^{2T} \int_0^{2\pi} \log^+\left|F\left(2+iU+(2-\alpha)e^{i\theta}\right)\right| d\theta\, dU \\ &\leqslant 2\pi \max_\theta \int_0^{2T} \log^+\left|F\left(2+iU+(2-\alpha)e^{i\theta}\right)\right| dU \\ &\ll \max_{\alpha \leqslant \sigma \leqslant 4} \int_{-2}^{2T+2} \log^+|F(\sigma+it)|\, dt. \end{aligned}$$

Using these results in (4.20), we find that

$$M! \int_\alpha^2 \mathscr{N}_Q(\sigma, T)\, d\sigma \ll M!\,T + \max_{\alpha \leqslant \sigma \leqslant 4} \int_{-2T-2}^{2T+2} \log^+|F(\sigma+it)|\, dt. \qquad (4.21)$$

We have

$$\log^+|F(s)| = \log^+ \prod_{q\in Q} \prod_{\chi\neq\chi_0} |1-f^2(s,\chi)|^{e(\chi)}$$

$$\leqslant M! \sum_{q\in Q} \frac{1}{\phi(q)} \sum_{\chi\neq\chi_0} |\tau(\chi)|^2 \log^+|1-f^2(s,\chi)|,$$

so that

$$\int_{-2T-2}^{2T+2} \log^+|F(\sigma+it)|\,dt \leqslant M!\,\Phi(\sigma, 2T+2)$$

by the definition (4.13) of $\Phi(\alpha, T)$. Hence, by (4.21) and Lemma 11, we have

$$\int_\alpha^2 \mathcal{N}_Q(\sigma, T)\,d\sigma \ll DT(M^2+MT)^{4(1-\alpha)/(3-2\alpha)}\log^9(M+T), \qquad (4.22)$$

provided $T \geqslant 2$ and $\frac{1}{2} \leqslant \alpha \leqslant 1$.

The function $\mathcal{N}_Q(\sigma, T)$ is a non-increasing function of σ for fixed T. Hence if $0<\delta<1$ we have

$$\mathcal{N}_Q(\alpha+\delta, T) \leqslant \delta^{-1}\int_\alpha^{\alpha+\delta} \mathcal{N}_Q(\sigma, T)\,d\sigma$$

$$\ll \delta^{-1} DT(M^2+MT)^{4(1-\alpha)/(3-2\alpha)}\log^9(M+T)$$

provided $T \geqslant 2$ and $\frac{1}{2} \leqslant \alpha \leqslant 1$. We take

$$\delta = 1/\log(M+T),$$

and note that

$$4(1-\alpha)/(3-2\alpha) = 4(1-\alpha-\delta)/(3-2\alpha-2\delta) + O(\delta)$$

and that

$$(M^2+MT)^\delta = O(1).$$

Hence

$$\mathcal{N}_Q(\alpha, T) \ll DT(M^2+MT)^{4(1-\alpha)/(3-2\alpha)}\log^{10}(M+T), \qquad (4.23)$$

uniformly for $\frac{1}{2}+\delta \leqslant \alpha \leqslant 1$.

We have also

$$\sum_{q\in Q} \frac{1}{\phi(q)} |\tau(\chi_0)|^2 N(\alpha, T; \chi_0) = N(\alpha, T) \sum_{q\in Q} \frac{\mu^2(q)}{\phi(q)} \ll T(\log T)(\log M), \qquad (4.24)$$

where $N(\alpha, T)$ denotes as usual the number of zeros of $\zeta(s)$ in the rectangle $\frac{1}{2} \leqslant \sigma \leqslant 1$, $|t| \leqslant T$. On adding (4.23) and (4.24) we obtain the conclusion of Theorem 5, namely (1.14), for $\frac{1}{2}+\delta \leqslant \alpha \leqslant 1$.

Finally, suppose that $\frac{1}{2} \leqslant \alpha \leqslant \frac{1}{2}+\delta$. By a known result (Prachar [4; p. 223]), we have

$$\sum_\chi N(\alpha, T; \chi) \ll \phi(q)\, T \log(M+T).$$

Hence

$$\sum_{q\in Q}\frac{1}{\phi(q)}\sum_{\chi}|\tau(\chi)|^2 N(\alpha, T;\chi)\ll\sum_{q\in Q} qT\log(M+T)\ll M^2 T\log(M+T).$$

This inequality is superior to (1.14) when $\frac{1}{2}\leqslant\alpha\leqslant\frac{1}{2}+\delta$, in view of the definition of δ, and the proof of Theorem 5 is now complete.

We now deduce the corollary (1.17) and (1.18). Each character χ mod q arises from a primitive character χ^* mod q^*, where $q^*|q$, and

$$N(\alpha, T;\chi)=N(\alpha, T;\chi^*).$$

Since the number of values of q for a given q^* is at most X/q^*, we have

$$\sum_{q\leqslant X}\sum_{\chi}N(\alpha, T;\chi)\leqslant\sum_{q^*\leqslant X}X/q^*\sum_{\chi^*}N(\alpha, T;\chi^*).$$

Dividing the sum over q^* into intervals $(2^h, 2^{h+1})$, we get the estimate

$$(\log X)\max_{M\leqslant X}XM^{-1}\sum_{q^*\leqslant M}\sum_{\chi^*}N(\alpha, T;\chi^*)\ll\max_{M\leqslant X}XM^{-1}T(M^2+MT)^{\beta}(XT)^{\epsilon},$$

where $\beta=4(1-\alpha)/(3-2\alpha)$. This is

$$\ll\max(X^{1+\epsilon}T^{1+\beta+\epsilon}, X^{2\beta+\epsilon}T^{1+\epsilon}).$$

Since $T\leqslant X^{\frac{1}{2}}$ we have

$$T^{\beta}\leqslant X^{2(1-\alpha)/(3-2\alpha)}\leqslant X^{2(1-\alpha)}.$$

Also $2\beta\leqslant 1+2(1-\alpha)$. Hence (1.17). For (1.18) we note that $\beta\leqslant\frac{1}{2}$ when $\frac{5}{6}\leqslant\alpha\leqslant 1$.

We end the paper with two simple remarks about Theorem 5. It is possible to prove many other similar inequalities, for example

$$\sum_{q\in Q}1/\phi(q)\sum_{\chi}|\tau(\chi)|^2 N(\alpha, T;\chi)\ll DT^2M^{5(1-\alpha)}\log^{10}(M+T);$$

which is better than our Theorem 5 if $\alpha>7/10$ and T is not too large. The inequality of Theorem 5 is analogous to another result of Ingham (see Titchmarsh [5; Theorem 9.19(B)]), and, by a happy circumstance, it gives a useful bound in the whole range $T\ll M^{1+\epsilon}$; this seems to be essential in the proof of Theorem 4.

References

1. K. F. Roth, " On the large sieve of Linnik and Rényi ", *Mathematika*, 12 (1965), 1–9.
2. Yu. V. Linnik, " The large sieve ", *Doklady Akad. Nauk SSSR*, 30 (1941), 292–294 (in Russian).
3. A. Rényi, " On the representation of an even number as the sum of a single prime and an almost prime number ", *Izv. Akad. Nauk SSSR*, Ser. Mat. 12 (1948), 57–78 (in Russian); also *American Math. Soc. Translations* (2), 19 (1961), 299–321.
4. K. Prachar, *Primzahlverteilung* (Springer, 1957).
5. E. C. Titchmarsh, *The theory of the Riemann zeta-function* (Oxford, 1951).
6. R. M. Gabriel, " Some results concerning the integrals of moduli of regular functions along certain curves ", *Journal London Math. Soc.*, 2 (1927), 112–117.

Istituto Matematico,
Via C. Saldini 50, Milan.

(*Received on the 27th of May, 1965.*)

Noted by the editor: It follows (1,3) from Theorem 4 and the arguments of the Appendix in the preceding paper of Wang Yuan.

Vol. XVI, No. 2 SCIENTIA SINICA May, 1973

ON THE REPRESENTATION OF A LARGER EVEN INTEGER AS THE SUM OF A PRIME AND THE PRODUCT OF AT MOST TWO PRIMES

CHEN JING-RUN (陈景润)
(*Institute of Mathematics, Academia Sinica*)

Received March 13, 1973.

ABSTRACT

In this paper we shall prove that every sufficiently large even integer is a sum of a prime and a product of at most 2 primes. The method used is simple without any complicated numerical calculations.

I. INTRODUCTION

For brevity, we denote the following proposition by $(1, a)$:

Every sufficiently large even integer is the sum of a prime and the product of at most two primes.

The sieve method and some results in the distribution of prime numbers have been employed to prove the above proposition by many mathematicians, for example,

$(1, c)$ Renyi[1],

$(1, 5)$ Pan Cheng-tung[2], Барбан[3],

$(1, 4)$ Wang Yuan[4], Pan Cheng-tung[5], Барбан[6],

$(1, 3)$ Бухштаб[7], А. И. Виноградов[8], Bombieri[9].

In a previous paper of the author[10] a sketch proof of $(1, 2)$ has been given. In this paper we shall give a detailed proof of $(1, 2)$.

Let x be a large even integer, h be any even integer, and C_x be $\prod_{\substack{p\mid x\\ p>2}} \frac{p-1}{p-2} \prod_{p>2} \cdot \left(1 - \frac{1}{(p-1)^2}\right)$.

Let $P_x(1, 2)$ be the number of primes p satisfying the following conditions:

$$x - p = p_1 \quad \text{or} \quad x - p = p_2 p_3,$$

where p_1, p_2, p_3 are primes.

Let $x_h(1, 2)$ be the number of primes $p \leqslant x$ satisfying the following conditions:

$$p + h = p_1 \quad \text{or} \quad p + h = p_2 p_3.$$

In this paper, we shall give a detailed proof of

$$P_x(1, 2) \geqslant \frac{0.67 x C_x}{(\log x)^2}. \tag{$*$}$$

In [10] we proved $(*)$ with factor 0.098 instead of 0.67. By the same method we can prove that

$$x_h(1, 2) \geqslant \frac{0.67xC_x}{(\log x)^2}.$$

The method used is simple without any complicated numerical calculations. In proving Lemma 9, a result from Richert[11] and a well known Bombieri's theorem are employed.

Now we state our results as follows:

Theorem I. Every sufficiently large even integer is a sum of a prime and a product of at most 2 primes, and it is found

$$P_x(1, 2) \geqslant \frac{0.67xC_x}{(\log x)^2}.$$

Theorem II. There exist infinitely many primes p such that $p + h$ is a product of at most 2 primes, h being any even integer, and

$$x_h(1, 2) \geqslant \frac{0.67xC_h}{(\log x)^2}.$$

The author is indebted to Professor L. K. Hua for his encouragement and to Professor S. H. Min and Professor Wang Yuan for their great help.

II. Some Lemmas

Lemma 1. For any real number $x > 1$ we denote by $[\log x]$ the integral part of $\log x$. Set $y \geqslant 0$, and

$$\Phi(y) = \frac{1}{2\pi i}\int_{2-i\infty}^{2+i\infty} \frac{y^\omega d\omega}{\omega\left(1 + \dfrac{\omega}{(\log x)^{1.1}}\right)^{[\log x]+1}}.$$

Set $\log x \geqslant 10^3$, and $y \geqslant e^{2(\log x)^{-0.1}}$. Then it follows

$$1 - x^{-0.1} \leqslant \Phi(y) \leqslant 1,$$

and $\Phi(y)$ is non-decreasing for all $y \geqslant 0$.

Proof. Besides the evident relation $\Phi(y) = 0$ for $0 \leqslant y \leqslant 1$ we need

$$\frac{\partial^r}{\partial\omega^r}\left(\frac{y^\omega}{\omega}\right) = \left(\frac{y^\omega}{\omega}\right)\left\{(\log y)^r + \sum_{i=1}^{r} \frac{(-1)^i r\cdots(r-i+1)(\log y)^{r-i}}{\omega^i}\right\}. \quad (1)$$

We now proceed by induction with respect to r. It is obvious that $\frac{\partial}{\partial\omega}\left(\frac{y^\omega}{\omega}\right) = \left(\frac{y^\omega}{\omega}\right)\left\{\log y - \frac{1}{\omega}\right\}$ and (1) is therefore true for $r = 1$. Suppose (1) has been proved for $r = 1, \cdots, S$. We have

$$\frac{\partial^{S+1}}{\partial\omega^{S+1}}\left(\frac{y^\omega}{\omega}\right) = \frac{\partial}{\partial\omega}\left\{y^\omega\left(\frac{(\log y)^S}{\omega} + \sum_{i=1}^{S} \frac{(-1)^i S\cdots(S-i+1)(\log y)^{S-i}}{\omega^{i+1}}\right)\right\}$$

$$= y^\omega\left\{\frac{(\log y)^{S+1}}{\omega} + \sum_{i=1}^{S} \frac{(-1)^i S\cdots(S-i+1)(\log y)^{S+1-i}}{\omega^{i+1}} - \frac{(\log y)^S}{\omega^2}\right.$$

$$+\sum_{i=1}^{S}\frac{(-1)^{i+1}S\cdots(S-i+1)(i+1)(\log y)^{S-i}}{\omega^{i+2}}\Bigg\}=\left(\frac{y^{\omega}}{\omega}\right)\Bigg\{(\log y)^{S+1}$$

$$-\frac{(S+1)(\log y)^{S}}{\omega}+\frac{(-1)^{S+1}(S+1)!}{\omega^{S+1}}+\sum_{i=2}^{S}\Bigg(\frac{(-1)^{i}S\cdots(S-i+1)(\log y)^{S+1-i}}{\omega^{i}}$$

$$+\frac{(-1)^{i}S\cdots(S+2-i)i(\log y)^{S+1-i}}{\omega^{i}}\Bigg)\Bigg\}=\left(\frac{y^{\omega}}{\omega}\right)\Bigg\{(\log y)^{S+1}$$

$$+\sum_{i=1}^{S+1}\frac{(-1)^{i}(S+1)\cdots(S+1-i+1)(\log y)^{S+1-i}}{\omega^{i}}\Bigg\}.$$

Consequently, (1) is also true for $S+1$. We have

$$\Phi(y)=1+\left\{\frac{(\log x)^{1.1+1.1[\log x]}}{[\log x]!}\right\}\left\{\frac{\partial^{[\log x]}}{\partial\omega^{[\log x]}}\left(\frac{y^{\omega}}{\omega}\right)\right\}_{\omega=-(\log x)^{1.1}}$$

$$=1-e^{-(\log x)^{1.1}(\log y)}\sum_{\nu=0}^{[\log x]}\frac{\{(\log x)^{1.1}(\log y)\}^{\nu}}{\nu!}$$

$$=\left\{\frac{1}{[\log x]!}\right\}\int_{0}^{(\log x)^{1.1}(\log y)}e^{-\lambda}\lambda^{[\log x]}d\lambda,$$

for $y\geqslant 1$, which, by using also the relation $\Phi(y)=0$ for $0\leqslant y\leqslant 1$, puts the non-decreasing property into evidence. From $\log x\geqslant 10^{3}$, and $e^{\log(1+\lambda)}\leqslant e^{\lambda\log 2}$ we obtain

$$0<1-\Phi(y)=\left\{\frac{1}{[\log x]!}\right\}\int_{(\log x)^{1.1}(\log y)}^{\infty}e^{-\lambda}\lambda^{[\log x]}d\lambda$$

$$\leqslant\left\{\frac{1}{[\log x]!}\right\}\int_{2[\log x]}^{\infty}e^{-\lambda}\lambda^{[\log x]}d\lambda=\left\{\frac{([\log x])^{1+[\log x]}}{[\log x]!}\right\}$$

$$\cdot\int_{2}^{\infty}e^{-\lambda[\log x]}\lambda^{[\log x]}d\lambda=\left\{\frac{e^{-[\log x]}([\log x])^{1+[\log x]}}{[\log x]!}\right\}$$

$$\cdot\int_{1}^{\infty}e^{-\lambda[\log x]}(1+\lambda)^{[\log x]}d\lambda\leqslant x^{-0.1},\text{ when } y\geqslant e^{2(\log x)^{-0.1}}.$$

Lemma 2. Set $e(\alpha)=e^{2\pi i\alpha}$ and

$$S(\alpha)=\sum_{n=M+1}^{M+N}a_{n}e(n\alpha),\qquad Z=\sum_{n=M+1}^{M+N}|a_{n}|^{2},$$

a_n being any real numbers. We let $\sum_{\chi_q}^{*}$ denote a sum over all primitive characters modulo q. Then it follows

$$\sum_{q\leqslant X}\frac{q}{\varphi(q)}\sum_{\chi_q}^{*}\left|\sum_{n=M+1}^{M+N}a_{n}\chi_{q}(n)\right|^{2}\leqslant(X^{2}+\pi N)Z,\tag{2}$$

and

$$\sum_{D<q\leqslant Q}\frac{1}{\varphi(q)}\sum_{\chi_q}^{*}\left|\sum_{n=M+1}^{M+N}a_{n}\chi_{q}(n)\right|^{2}\ll\left(Q+\frac{N}{D}\right)Z.\tag{3}$$

Proof. Let F be any complex-valued function with continuous derivative and period 1. We average the inequality

$$\left|F\left(\frac{a}{q}\right)\right| \leqslant |F(\alpha)| + \int_{\frac{a}{q}}^{\alpha} |F'(\beta)|\,|d\beta|$$

over the interval $I(a, q)$ of length $\frac{1}{Q^2}$ centred at $\frac{a}{q}$. The intervals $I(a, q)$ with $1 \leqslant a \leqslant q$, $(a, q) = 1$, and $q \leqslant Q$ do not overlap. Hence we have

$$\sum_{q\leqslant Q}\sum_{\substack{(a,q)=1\\1\leqslant a<q}}\left|F\left(\frac{a}{q}\right)\right| \leqslant \sum_{q\leqslant Q}\sum_{\substack{(a,q)=1\\1\leqslant a<q}}\left\{Q^2\int_{I(a,q)}|F(\alpha)|d\alpha + \frac{1}{2}\int_{I(a,q)}|F'(\beta)|d\beta\right\}$$

$$\leqslant Q^2\int_0^1|F(\alpha)|d\alpha + \frac{1}{2}\int_0^1|F'(\beta)|d\beta.$$

Now put $F(\alpha) = \{S(\alpha)\}^2$. Since $\int_0^1 |F(\alpha)|d\alpha = Z$ and

$$\frac{1}{2}\int_0^1|F'(\beta)|d\beta = \int_0^1|S(\alpha)|\,|S'(\alpha)|d\alpha$$

$$\leqslant \left\{\left(\int_0^1|S(\alpha)|^2d\alpha\right)\left(\int_0^1|S'(\alpha)|^2d\alpha\right)\right\}^{\frac{1}{2}} = Z^{\frac{1}{2}}\left(\int_0^1|S'(\alpha)|^2d\alpha\right)^{\frac{1}{2}},$$

therefore we have

$$\sum_{q\leqslant Q}\sum_{\substack{(a,q)=1\\1\leqslant a<q}}\left|S\left(\frac{a}{q}\right)\right|^2 = \sum_{q\leqslant Q}\sum_{\substack{(a,q)=1\\1\leqslant a<q}}\left\{\left|S\left(\frac{a}{q}\right)\right|\left|e\left(-\frac{a\left(M+\left[\frac{N}{2}\right]\right)}{q}\right)\right|\right\}^2$$

$$= \sum_{q\leqslant Q}\sum_{\substack{(a,q)=1\\1\leqslant a<q}}\left|\sum_{n=M+1}^{M+N}a_n e\left(\left\{n-\left(M+\left[\frac{N}{2}\right]\right)\right\}\frac{a}{q}\right)\right|^2$$

$$= \sum_{q\leqslant Q}\sum_{\substack{(a,q)=1\\1\leqslant a<q}}\left|\sum_{-\left[\frac{N}{2}\right]+1\leqslant n\leqslant N-\left[\frac{N}{2}\right]} a_{n+M+\left[\frac{N}{2}\right]}\, e\left(\frac{na}{q}\right)\right|^2$$

$$\leqslant ZQ^2 + Z^{\frac{1}{2}}\left\{\sum_{n=-\left[\frac{N}{2}\right]+1}^{N-\left[\frac{N}{2}\right]}\left((2\pi n)a_{n+M+\left[\frac{N}{2}\right]}\right)^2\right\}^{\frac{1}{2}} \leqslant ZQ^2$$

$$+ \pi N Z^{\frac{1}{2}}\left(\sum_{n=-\left[\frac{N}{2}\right]+1}^{N-\left[\frac{N}{2}\right]}\left|a_{n+M+\left[\frac{N}{2}\right]}\right|^2\right)^{\frac{1}{2}} \leqslant (Q^2+\pi N)Z. \qquad (4)$$

For each primitive character χ, we put $\tau(\chi_q^*) = \sum_{1\leqslant a<q}\chi_q^*(a)e\left(\frac{a}{q}\right)$. We have $\tau(\overline{\chi_q^*})\cdot$ $\cdot\chi_q^*(n) = \sum_{a=1}^{q}\overline{\chi_q^*}(a)e\left(\frac{na}{q}\right)$. Since $|\tau(\overline{\chi_q^*})|^2 = q$, we obtain

$$\left(\frac{1}{\varphi(q)}\right)\sum_{\chi_q}{}^*\left|\sum_{n=M+1}^{M+N}a_n\chi_q(n)\right|^2 \leqslant \left(\frac{1}{q\varphi(q)}\right)\sum_{\chi_q}{}^*\left|\tau(\overline{\chi_q})\sum_{n=M+1}^{M+N}a_n\chi_q(n)\right|^2$$

$$= \left(\frac{1}{q\varphi(q)}\right)\sum_{\chi_q}{}^*\left|\sum_{a=1}^{q}\overline{\chi_q}(a)\sum_{n=M+1}^{M+N}a_n e\left(\frac{na}{q}\right)\right|^2$$

$$\leqslant \left(\frac{1}{q\varphi(q)}\right)\sum_{\chi_q}\left|\sum_{a=1}^{q}\overline{\chi_q}(a)\sum_{n=M+1}^{M+N}a_n e\left(\frac{na}{q}\right)\right|^2$$

$$\leqslant \frac{1}{q}\sum_{\substack{a=1\\(a,q)=1}}^{q}\left|\sum_{n=M+1}^{M+N}a_n e\left(\frac{na}{q}\right)\right|^2.$$

(2) now follows from (4). Let h be a positive integer, satisfying the inequality $2^hD < Q \leqslant 2^{h+1}D$. We have

$$\sum_{D<q\leqslant Q}\frac{1}{\varphi(q)}\sum_{\chi_q}{}^{*}\left|\sum_{n=M+1}^{M+N}a_n\chi_q(n)\right|^2 \leqslant \sum_{i=0}^{h}\left(\sum_{2^iD<q\leqslant 2^{i+1}D}\frac{1}{\varphi(q)}\sum_{\chi_q}{}^{*}\left|\sum_{n=M+1}^{M+N}a_n\chi_q(n)\right|^2\right)$$

$$\leqslant \sum_{i=0}^{h}\left(\frac{1}{2^iD}\right)\left(\sum_{2^iD<q\leqslant 2^{i+1}D}\frac{q}{\varphi(q)}\sum_{\chi_q}{}^{*}\left|\sum_{n=M+1}^{M+N}a_n\chi_q(n)\right|^2\right)$$

$$\leqslant \sum_{i=0}^{h}\left(2^{i+2}D + \frac{\pi N}{2^iD}\right)\sum_{n=M+1}^{M+N}|a_n|^2 \ll \left(Q + \frac{N}{D}\right)\sum_{n=M+1}^{M+N}|a_n|^2.$$

Thus the lemma is proved.

Lemma 3. Let $\sum_{\chi_q}^{*}$ denote a sum over all primitive characters, modulo q. Set $S = \sigma + it$, and suppose that $\sigma \geqslant \frac{1}{2}$. Then it is inferred that

$$\sum_{q\leqslant Q}\sum_{\chi_q}{}^{*}|L(S, \chi_q)|^4 \ll Q^2|S|^2(\log Q)^4.$$

Proof. We have

$$L(S, \chi) = \sum_{n=1}^{\infty}\frac{\chi(n)}{n^S} = \sum_{n=1}^{N}\frac{\chi(n)}{n^S} + \sum_{n=N+1}^{\infty}\frac{\sum_{i\leqslant n}\chi(i) - \sum_{i\leqslant n-1}\chi(i)}{n^S}$$

$$= \sum_{n=1}^{N}\frac{\chi(n)}{n^S} + \sum_{n=N+1}^{\infty}\left(\sum_{i\leqslant n}\chi(i)\right)\left(\frac{1}{n^S} - \frac{1}{(n+1)^S}\right) - \frac{\sum_{i\leqslant N}\chi(i)}{(N+1)^S}$$

$$= \sum_{n=1}^{N}\frac{\chi(n)}{n^S} + O\left(\frac{|S|q^{\frac{1}{2}}\log q}{N^\sigma}\right).$$

Using $\sigma \geqslant \frac{1}{2}$ and Lemma 2, we obtain

$$\sum_{q\leqslant Q}\sum_{\chi_q}{}^{*}|L(S, \chi_q)|^4 \ll \sum_{q\leqslant Q}\sum_{\chi_q}{}^{*}\left(\left|\sum_{n=1}^{[Q|S|]}\frac{\chi_q(n)}{n^S}\right|^4 + Q^{-2}|S|^2q^2(\log q)^4\right)$$

$$\ll |S|^2Q^2(\log Q)^4 + (Q^2 + Q^2|S|^2)\sum_{n=1}^{[Q|S|]^2}\frac{d^2(n)}{n} \ll Q^2|S|^2(\log Q)^4.$$

This proves the lemma.

Lemma 4. Let m be an integer, while $m \neq 1$. For square-free odd k the estimation

$$\left|\sum_{\chi_k}{}^{*}\chi_k(m)\right| \leqslant |(m-1, k)|$$

holds.

Proof. For the proof we remark that if $k = p_1 \cdots p_l$, $p_1 < \cdots < p_l$, g_j is a primitive root mod p_j and, further, if $m \equiv g_j^{\xi_j} (\bmod\, p_j)$, $0 \leqslant \xi_j \leqslant p_j - 2$, $j = 1, \cdots, l$ then for fixed $\nu_j'S$ with $1 \leqslant \nu_j \leqslant p_j - 2$, $j = 1, \cdots, l$ the primitive characters belonging to modulo k are given by $\chi_k^*(m) = e^{2\pi i\left(\frac{\nu_1\xi_1}{p_1-1} + \cdots + \frac{\nu_l\xi_l}{p_l-1}\right)}$. Set $Z(m, k) = \left|\sum_{\chi_k}^* \chi_k(m)\right|$. We have

$$Z(m, k) = \prod_{j=1}^{l} Z(m, p_i) = \prod_{j=1}^{l} \left| \sum_{\nu_j=1}^{p_j-2} e^{2\pi i \frac{\nu_j\xi_j}{p_j-1}} \right|$$

$$= \prod_{\substack{j=1 \\ \xi_j=0}}^{l} (p_i - 2) < \prod_{p_j|(m-1)} p_i = |(m-1, k)|.$$

This proves the lemma.

Let x be an even integer, λ_1 be equal to 1, and λ_d be equal to 0 for $d > x^{\frac{1}{4}-\frac{\epsilon}{2}}$. Set $g(k) = \dfrac{1}{\varphi(k)}$, $f(k) = \varphi(k) \prod\limits_{p|k} \dfrac{p-2}{p-1}$, and $\lambda_d = \dfrac{\mu(d)}{f(d)g(d)} \left\{ \sum\limits_{\substack{1 \leqslant k \leqslant (x^{\frac{1}{2}-\epsilon})^{\frac{1}{2}}/d \\ (k, xd)=1}} \dfrac{\mu^2(k)}{f(k)} \right\}$ $\cdot \left\{ \sum\limits_{\substack{1 \leqslant k \leqslant (x^{\frac{1}{2}-\epsilon})^{\frac{1}{2}} \\ (k, x)=1}} \dfrac{\mu^2(k)}{f(k)} \right\}^{-1}$ for $1 < d \leqslant x^{\frac{1}{4}-\frac{\epsilon}{2}}$. If d be an odd integer, $\mu(d) \neq 0$, then we have

$$\sum_{\substack{1 \leqslant k \leqslant (x^{\frac{1}{2}-\epsilon})^{\frac{1}{2}} \\ (k, x)=1}} \frac{\mu^2(k)}{f(k)} = \sum_{t|d} \sum_{\substack{1 \leqslant k \leqslant (x^{\frac{1}{2}-\epsilon})^{\frac{1}{2}} \\ (k, x)=1,\ (k, d)=t}} \frac{\mu^2(k)}{f(k)} = \sum_{t|d} \left\{ \frac{1}{\prod\limits_{p|t} (p-2)} \right\} \sum_{\substack{1 \leqslant k \leqslant (x^{\frac{1}{2}-\epsilon})^{\frac{1}{2}}/t \\ (k, xd)=1}} \frac{\mu^2(k)}{f(k)}$$

$$\geqslant \left\{ \prod_{p|d} \left(1 + \frac{1}{p-2}\right) \right\} \left\{ \sum_{\substack{1 \leqslant k \leqslant (x^{\frac{1}{2}-\epsilon})^{\frac{1}{2}}/d \\ (k, xd)=1}} \frac{\mu^2(k)}{f(k)} \right\}.$$

Thus we have $|\lambda_d| \leqslant 1$ for all positive integers d. Denote by x an even integer satisfying $\log x \geqslant 10^6$. We use the following notations:

$$Q = \prod_{2 < p < x^{\frac{1}{4}}} p,$$

$$\Omega = \sum_{\substack{x^{\frac{1}{10}} < p_1 \leqslant x^{\frac{1}{3}} < p_2 \leqslant \left(\frac{x}{p_1}\right)^{\frac{1}{2}} \\ p_3 \leqslant \frac{x}{p_1 p_2} \\ (x - p_1 p_2 p_3, Q)=1}} 1, \quad M = \sum_{x^{\frac{1}{10}} < p_1 \leqslant x^{\frac{1}{3}} < p_2 \leqslant \left(\frac{x}{p_1}\right)^{\frac{1}{2}}} \left(\frac{1}{\log \frac{x}{p_1 p_2}} \right) \left(\sum_{\substack{n \leqslant \frac{x}{p_1 p_2} \\ (x - p_1 p_2 n, Q)=1}} \Lambda(n) \right).$$

We have $\Omega \leqslant \dfrac{M}{1-\epsilon} + N$, where

$$N \ll \sum_{x^{\frac{1}{10}} < p_1 \leqslant x^{\frac{1}{3}} < p_2 \leqslant \left(\frac{x}{p_1}\right)^{\frac{1}{2}}} \left(\frac{x}{p_1 p_2} \right)^{1-\epsilon} \ll x^{1-\epsilon} \int_{x^{\frac{1}{10}}}^{x^{\frac{1}{3}}} \frac{dS}{S^{1-\epsilon}} \int_{x^{\frac{1}{3}}}^{\left(\frac{x}{s}\right)^{\frac{1}{2}}}$$

$$\cdot \frac{dt}{t^{1-\epsilon}} \ll x^{1-\frac{\epsilon}{2}} \int_{x^{\frac{1}{10}}}^{x^{\frac{1}{3}}} \frac{dS}{S^{1-\frac{\epsilon}{2}}} \ll x^{1-\frac{\epsilon}{3}}.$$

It now follows from Lemma 1 that

$$M \leqslant \sum_{x^{\frac{1}{10}}<p_1\leqslant x^{\frac{1}{3}}<p_2\leqslant\left(\frac{x}{p_1}\right)^{\frac{1}{2}}} \left(\frac{1}{\log\frac{x}{p_1p_2}}\right) \sum_{\substack{n\leqslant\frac{x}{p_1p_2}\\(x-p_1p_2n,\,Q)=1}} \Lambda(n)\Phi\left(\frac{x}{p_1p_2n}\right) + O\left(\frac{x}{(\log x)^{2.01}}\right)$$

$$\leqslant \sum_{x^{\frac{1}{10}}<p_1\leqslant x^{\frac{1}{3}}<p_2\leqslant\left(\frac{x}{p_1}\right)^{\frac{1}{2}}} \left(\frac{1}{\log\frac{x}{p_1p_2}}\right) \sum_{n\leqslant\frac{x}{p_1p_2}} \Lambda(n)\Phi\left(\frac{x}{p_1p_2n}\right)\Big(\sum_{\substack{d|(x-p_1p_2n,\,Q)\\(d,\,x)=1}} \lambda_d\Big)^2$$

$$+ O\left(\frac{x}{(\log x)^{2.01}}\right) = \sum_{\substack{(d_1,x)=1\\d_1|Q}} \sum_{\substack{(d_2,x)=1\\d_2|Q}} \lambda_{d_1}\lambda_{d_2} N_{\frac{d_1d_2}{(d_1,d_2)}} + O\left(\frac{x}{(\log x)^{2.01}}\right), \tag{5}$$

where

$$N_{\frac{d_1d_2}{(d_1,d_2)}} = \sum_{x^{\frac{1}{10}}<p_1\leqslant x^{\frac{1}{3}}<p_2\leqslant\left(\frac{x}{p_1}\right)^{\frac{1}{2}}} \left(\frac{1}{\log\frac{x}{p_1p_2}}\right) \sum_{\substack{n\leqslant\frac{x}{p_1p_2}\\x-p_1p_2n\equiv0\left(\bmod\frac{d_1d_2}{(d_1,d_2)}\right)}} \Lambda(n)\Phi\left(\frac{x}{p_1p_2n}\right)$$

$$= \left\{\frac{1}{\varphi\left(\frac{d_1d_2}{(d_1,d_2)}\right)}\right\}\Bigg\{ \sum_{\substack{x^{\frac{1}{10}}<p_1\leqslant x^{\frac{1}{3}}<p_2\leqslant\left(\frac{x}{p_1}\right)^{\frac{1}{2}}\\n\leqslant\frac{x}{p_1p_2}\\(p_1p_2n,\,d_1d_2)=1}} \left(\frac{1}{\log\frac{x}{p_1p_2}}\right)\Lambda(n)\Phi\left(\frac{x}{p_1p_2n}\right)$$

$$+ \sum_{\chi_{\frac{d_1d_2}{(d_1,d_2)}}\neq\chi_0} \overline{\chi_{\frac{d_1d_2}{(d_1,d_2)}}(x)} \sum_{\substack{x^{\frac{1}{10}}<p_1\leqslant x^{\frac{1}{3}}<p_2\leqslant\left(\frac{x}{p_1}\right)^{\frac{1}{2}}\\n\leqslant\frac{x}{p_1p_2}}} \left(\frac{\Lambda(n)}{\log\frac{x}{p_1p_2}}\right)\Phi\left(\frac{x}{p_1p_2n}\right)\chi_{\frac{d_1d_2}{(d_1,d_2)}}(p_1p_2n)\Bigg\}$$

$$= \left\{\frac{1}{\varphi\left(\frac{d_1d_2}{(d_1,d_2)}\right)}\right\}\Bigg\{ \sum_{\substack{x^{\frac{1}{10}}<p_1\leqslant x^{\frac{1}{3}}<p_2\leqslant\left(\frac{x}{p_1}\right)^{\frac{1}{2}}\\n\leqslant\frac{x}{p_1p_2}\\(p_1p_2n,\,d_1d_2)=1}} \left(\frac{1}{\log\frac{x}{p_1p_2}}\right)\Lambda(n)\Phi\left(\frac{x}{p_1p_2n}\right)\Bigg\} - \left\{\frac{1}{2\pi i\,\varphi\left(\frac{d_1d_2}{(d_1,d_2)}\right)}\right\}$$

$$\cdot\Bigg\{\int_{2-i\infty}^{2+i\infty}\left(1+\frac{\omega}{(\log x)^{1.1}}\right)^{-[\log x]-1}\left(\frac{x^\omega}{\omega}\right) \sum_{\chi_{\frac{d_1d_2}{(d_1,d_2)}}\neq\chi_0} \overline{\chi_{\frac{d_1d_2}{(d_1,d_2)}}(x)}\,\frac{L'}{L}\left(\omega,\chi_{\frac{d_1d_2}{(d_1,d_2)}}\right)$$

$$\cdot \sum_{x^{\frac{1}{10}}<p_1\leqslant x^{\frac{1}{3}}<p_2\leqslant\left(\frac{x}{p_1}\right)^{\frac{1}{2}}} \chi_{\frac{d_1d_2}{(d_1,d_2)}}(p_1p_2)\cdot\left(\frac{1}{\log\frac{x}{p_1p_2}}\right)\left(\frac{d\omega}{(p_1p_2)^\omega}\right)\Bigg\}. \tag{6}$$

We denote by $\nu(d)$ the number of prime factors of d. For a character χ_d, let d^* be its conductor and $\chi^*_{d^*}$ the corresponding primitive character. We use the following notations:

$$M_1 = \sum_{(d_1,x)=1}\sum_{(d_2,x)=1} \frac{\lambda_{d_1}\lambda_{d_2}}{\varphi\left(\frac{d_1d_2}{(d_1,d_2)}\right)} \sum_{\substack{x^{\frac{1}{10}}<p_1\leqslant x^{\frac{1}{3}}<p_2\leqslant\left(\frac{x}{p_1}\right)^{\frac{1}{2}}\\n\leqslant\frac{x}{p_1p_2}}} \left(\frac{1}{\log\frac{x}{p_1p_2}}\right)\Lambda(n)\Phi\left(\frac{x}{p_1p_2n}\right),$$

$$M_2 = \sum_{\substack{d\leqslant x^{\frac{1}{2}-\epsilon}\\(d,x)=1}} \frac{|\mu(d)|3^{\nu(d)}}{\varphi(d)} \Bigg| \sum_{\chi_d\neq\chi_0} \overline{\chi^*_{d^*}(x)} \int_{2-i\infty}^{2+i\infty}\left(\frac{x^\omega}{\omega}\right)\left(1+\frac{\omega}{(\log x)^{1.1}}\right)^{-[\log x]-1}$$

$$\cdot \frac{L'}{L}(\omega, \chi^*_{d^*}) \sum_{\substack{x^{\frac{1}{10}}<p_1\leqslant x^{\frac{1}{3}}<p_2\leqslant(\frac{x}{p_1})^{\frac{1}{2}} \\ (p_1p_2,d)=1}} \chi^*_{d^*}(p_1p_2)\left((p_1p_2)^\omega \log \frac{x}{p_1p_2}\right)^{-1} d\omega \Bigg|.$$

Lemma 5. Let x be an even integer. Then we obtain $\Omega \leqslant \frac{M_1+M_2}{1-\epsilon} + O\left(\frac{x}{(\log x)^{2.01}}\right)$.

Proof. From (5) and (6) we have

$$M \leqslant M_1 + |M_3| + M_4 + O\left(\frac{x}{(\log x)^{2.01}}\right), \tag{7}$$

where

$$M_3 = \sum_{(d_1,x)=1} \sum_{(d_2,x)=1} \frac{\lambda_{d_1}\lambda_{d_2}}{\varphi\left(\frac{d_1d_2}{(d_1,d_2)}\right)} \sum_{\substack{x^{\frac{1}{10}}<p_1\leqslant x^{\frac{1}{3}}<p_2\leqslant(\frac{x}{p_1})^{\frac{1}{2}} \\ n\leqslant\frac{x}{p_1p_2} \\ (d_1d_2,p_1p_2n)>1}} \left(\frac{1}{\log\frac{x}{p_1p_2}}\right) \Lambda(n)\Phi\left(\frac{x}{p_1p_2n}\right),$$

$$M_4 = \sum_{(d_1,x)=1} \sum_{(d_2,x)=1} \left(-\frac{\lambda_{d_1}\lambda_{d_2}}{2\pi i\varphi\left(\frac{d_1d_2}{(d_1,d_2)}\right)}\right) \int_{2-i\infty}^{2+i\infty} \left(\frac{x^\omega}{\omega}\right)\left(1+\frac{\omega}{(\log x)^{1.1}}\right)^{-[\log x]-1}$$

$$\cdot \sum_{\chi_{\frac{d_1d_2}{(d_1,d_2)}}\neq\chi_0} \overline{\chi_{\frac{d_1d_2}{(d_1,d_2)}}}(x) \frac{L'}{L}(\omega, \chi_{\frac{d_1d_2}{(d_1,d_2)}}) \sum_{x^{\frac{1}{10}}<p_1\leqslant x^{\frac{1}{3}}<p_2\leqslant(\frac{x}{p_1})^{\frac{1}{2}}}$$

$$\cdot \left(\frac{1}{(p_1p_2)^\omega \log\frac{x}{p_1p_2}}\right) \chi_{\frac{d_1d_2}{(d_1,d_2)}}(p_1p_2)d\omega.$$

Now the sum M_3 will be estimated. We have

$$M_3 \ll x^\epsilon \sum_{d\leqslant x^{\frac{1}{2}-\epsilon}} \frac{1}{d} \sum_{\substack{x^{\frac{1}{10}}<p_1\leqslant x^{\frac{1}{3}}<p_2\leqslant(\frac{x}{p_1})^{\frac{1}{2}} \\ n\leqslant\frac{x}{p_1p_2} \\ (d,p_1p_2n)>1}} \Lambda(n) \ll \sum_{x^{\frac{1}{10}}<p_1\leqslant x^{\frac{1}{3}}<p_2\leqslant(\frac{x}{p_1})^{\frac{1}{2}}} \left(\frac{x^{1+\epsilon}}{p_1p_2}\right)\left(\sum_{\substack{d\leqslant x^{\frac{1}{2}-\epsilon} \\ p_1|d}} \frac{1}{d}\right.$$

$$\left. + \sum_{\substack{d\leqslant x^{\frac{1}{2}-\epsilon} \\ p_2|d}} \frac{1}{d}\right) + \sum_{x^{\frac{1}{10}}<p_1\leqslant x^{\frac{1}{3}}<p_2\leqslant(\frac{x}{p_1})^{\frac{1}{2}}} \sum_{p\leqslant\frac{x}{p_1p_2}} (\log p) \sum_{\substack{d\leqslant x^{\frac{1}{2}-\epsilon} \\ p|d}} \frac{x^\epsilon}{d} + x^{1-\epsilon} \ll x^{1-\epsilon}. \tag{8}$$

Now the sum M_4 will be estimated. Set $d>0$ and $\mu(d)\neq 0$. The number of solutions of the equation $\frac{d_1d_2}{(d_1,d_2)} = d$, where d_1 and d_2 are positive integers, is given by $3^{\nu(d)}$. Since $|\lambda_d| \leqslant 1$, we obtain

$$M_4 \leqslant \sum_{\substack{d\leqslant x^{\frac{1}{2}-\epsilon} \\ (d,x)=1}} \frac{3^{\nu(d)}|\mu(d)|}{\varphi(d)} \Bigg| \sum_{\chi_d\neq\chi_0} \int_{2-i\infty}^{2+i\infty} \left(\frac{x^\omega}{\omega}\right)\left(1+\frac{\omega}{(\log x)^{1.1}}\right)^{-[\log x]-1}$$

$$\cdot \overline{\chi_d}(x) \frac{L'}{L}(\omega, \chi_d) \sum_{x^{\frac{1}{10}}<p_1\leqslant x^{\frac{1}{3}}<p_2\leqslant(\frac{x}{p_1})^{\frac{1}{2}}} \chi_d(p_1p_2) \left(\frac{1}{(p_1p_2)^\omega}\right)\left(\frac{d\omega}{\log\frac{x}{p_1p_2}}\right)\Bigg|.$$

Since $\frac{L'}{L}(\omega, \chi_d) = \frac{L'}{L}(\omega, \chi^*_{d^*}) + \sum_{p \mid \frac{d}{d^*}} \frac{\chi^*_{d^*}(p)\log p}{p^\omega - \chi^*_{d^*}(p)}$, it follows that

$$M_4 \leqslant M_2 + M_5, \tag{9}$$

where

$$M_5 = \sum_{\substack{d \leqslant x^{\frac{1}{2}-\epsilon} \\ (d,x)=1}} \frac{|\mu(d)|\,3^{\nu(d)}}{\varphi(d)} \Bigg| \sum_{\chi_d \neq \chi_0} \overline{\chi^*_{d^*}}(x) \int_{2-i\infty}^{2+i\infty} \left(\frac{x^\omega}{\omega}\right)\left(1 + \frac{\omega}{(\log x)^{1.1}}\right)^{-[\log x]-1}$$
$$\cdot \left(\sum_{p \mid \frac{d}{d^*}} \frac{\chi^*_{d^*}(p)\log p}{p^\omega - \chi^*_{d^*}(p)}\right) \sum_{\substack{x^{\frac{1}{10}} < p_1 \leqslant x^{\frac{1}{3}} < p_2 \leqslant \left(\frac{x}{p_1}\right)^{\frac{1}{2}} \\ (p_1p_2, d)=1}} \frac{\chi^*_{d^*}(p_1p_2)}{(p_1p_2)^\omega \log \frac{x}{p_1p_2}} \, d\omega \Bigg|.$$

We have $\frac{\chi^*_{d^*}(p)}{p^\omega - \chi^*_{d^*}(p)} = \sum_{\lambda=1}^{\infty} \left(\frac{\chi^*_{d^*}(p)}{p^\omega}\right)^\lambda$ when $\operatorname{Re}\omega = 2$. Let y denote the solution of the congruence $xy \equiv 1 \pmod{d^*}$. By Lemma 4 we have

$$\left|\sum_{\chi_{d^*}}{}^{*}\, \overline{\chi_{d^*}}(x)\chi_{d^*}(p_1p_2p^\lambda)\right| = \left|\sum_{\chi_{d^*}}{}^{*}\, \chi_{d^*}(p_1p_2p^\lambda y)\right|$$
$$\leqslant |(p_1p_2p^\lambda y - 1,\ d^*)| = |(x - p_1p_2p^\lambda,\ d^*)|, \tag{10}$$

when $\lambda \geqslant 1$, $\mu(d^*) \neq 0$ and $(d^*, xp_1p_2p^\lambda) = 1$.

From (10) and Lemma 1 we have

$$M_5 \ll \sum_{\substack{d \leqslant x^{\frac{1}{2}-\epsilon} \\ (d,x)=1}} \frac{|\mu(d)|\,3^{\nu(d)}}{\varphi(d)} \Bigg| \sum_{\substack{d^* \mid d \\ d^* > 1}} \sum_{p \mid \frac{d}{d^*}} (\log p) \sum_{\lambda=1}^{\infty} \sum_{\substack{x^{\frac{1}{10}} < p_1 \leqslant x^{\frac{1}{3}} < p_2 \leqslant \left(\frac{x}{p_1}\right)^{\frac{1}{2}} \\ (p_1p_2, d)=1}} \sum_{\chi_{d^*}}{}^{*}\, \overline{\chi_{d^*}}(x)\chi_{d^*}(p_1p_2p^\lambda)$$
$$\cdot \left(\frac{1}{\log \frac{x}{p_1p_2}}\right) \Phi\left(\frac{x}{p_1p_2p^\lambda}\right) \Bigg| \ll \sum_{\substack{d \leqslant x^{\frac{1}{2}-\epsilon} \\ (d,x)=1}} \frac{|\mu(d)|\,3^{\nu(d)}}{\varphi(d)} \sum_{\substack{d^* \mid d \\ d^* > 1}} \sum_{p \mid \frac{d}{d^*}} \sum_{\substack{x^{\frac{1}{10}} < p_1 \leqslant x^{\frac{1}{3}} < p_2 \leqslant \left(\frac{x}{p_1}\right)^{\frac{1}{2}} \\ (p_1p_2, d)=1}}$$
$$\cdot \sum_{1 \leqslant \lambda \leqslant \left(\log \frac{x}{p_1p_2}\right)(\log p)^{-1}} \left(\frac{\log p}{\log \frac{x}{p_1p_2}}\right) ((x - p_1p_2p^\lambda,\ d^*)) \ll \sum_{\substack{k_1k_2 \leqslant x^{\frac{1}{2}-\epsilon} \\ (k_1k_2, x)=1}} \frac{|\mu(k_1)|\,|\mu(k_2)|\,x^{\frac{\epsilon}{4}}}{\varphi(k_1)\varphi(k_2)}$$
$$\cdot \sum_{p \mid k_2} \sum_{x^{\frac{1}{10}} < p_1 \leqslant x^{\frac{1}{3}} < p_2 \leqslant \left(\frac{x}{p_1}\right)^{\frac{1}{2}}} \sum_{1 \leqslant \lambda \leqslant \left(\log \frac{x}{p_1p_2}\right)(\log p)^{-1}} ((x - p_1p_2p^\lambda,\ k_1)) \ll x^{\frac{\epsilon}{3}} \sum_{\substack{k_1 \leqslant x^{\frac{1}{2}-\epsilon} \\ (k_1, x)=1}}$$
$$\cdot \frac{1}{k_1} \sum_{\substack{x^{\frac{1}{10}} < p_1 \leqslant x^{\frac{1}{3}} < p_2 \leqslant \left(\frac{x}{p_1}\right)^{\frac{1}{2}} \\ p^\lambda \leqslant \frac{x}{p_1p_2}}} (x - p_1p_2p^\lambda,\ k_1) \sum_{\substack{k_2 \leqslant x^{\frac{1}{2}-\epsilon} \\ k_2 \equiv 0 \pmod{p}}} \frac{1}{k_2} \ll x^{\frac{\epsilon}{2}} \sum_{\substack{x^{\frac{1}{10}} < p_1 \leqslant x^{\frac{1}{3}} < p_2 \leqslant \left(\frac{x}{p_1}\right)^{\frac{1}{2}} \\ p^\lambda \leqslant \frac{x}{p_1p_2}}}$$
$$\cdot \frac{1}{p} \sum_{d \mid (x - p_1p_2p^\lambda)} d \sum_{\substack{k_1 \leqslant x^{\frac{1}{2}-\epsilon} \\ d \mid k_1}} \frac{1}{k_1} \ll x^{1-\epsilon}. \tag{11}$$

From (7), (8), (9) and (11) we complete the proof of Lemma 5.

Lemma 6. We have

$$M_2 \ll \frac{x}{(\log x)^{2.01}}.$$

Proof. Set

$$\Phi(y, \chi) = \int_{2-i\infty}^{2+i\infty} \left(\frac{y^\omega}{\omega}\right)\left(1 + \frac{\omega}{(\log x)^{1.1}}\right)^{-[\log x]-1} \frac{L'}{L}(\omega, \chi)d\omega$$

$$= \int_{1+\frac{1}{\log x}-i\infty}^{1+\frac{1}{\log x}+i\infty} \left(\frac{y^\omega}{\omega}\right)\left(1 + \frac{\omega}{(\log x)^{1.1}}\right)^{-[\log x]-1} \frac{L'}{L}(\omega, \chi)d\omega.$$

Then it follows

$$M_2 \leqslant \sum_{\substack{1<l\leqslant x^{\frac{1}{2}-\epsilon}\\(l,x)=1}} \left\{ \sum_{\substack{1<d\leqslant x^{\frac{1}{2}-\epsilon}\\ l|d,(d,x)=1}} \frac{|\mu(d)|3^{\nu(d)}}{\varphi(d)}\right\} \left|\sum_{\chi_l}{}^* \overline{\chi_l}(x) \sum_{\substack{x^{\frac{1}{10}}<p_1\leqslant x^{\frac{1}{3}}<p_2\leqslant\left(\frac{x}{p_1}\right)^{\frac{1}{2}}\\(p_1p_2,d)=1}} \left(\frac{1}{\log \frac{x}{p_1p_2}}\right)\right.$$

$$\left.\cdot \Phi\left(\frac{x}{p_1p_2}, \chi_l\right)\chi_l(p_1p_2)\right| \leqslant \sum_{\substack{1<d\leqslant x^{\frac{1}{2}-\epsilon}\\(d,x)=1}} \frac{|\mu(d)|3^{\nu(d)}}{\varphi(d)} \cdot$$

$$\cdot \left\{ \sum_{\substack{1<l\leqslant x^{\frac{1}{2}-\epsilon}\\(l,xd)=1}} \frac{|\mu(l)|3^{\nu(l)}}{\varphi(l)} \left|\sum_{\chi_l}{}^* \overline{\chi_l}(x) \sum_{\substack{x^{\frac{1}{10}}<p_1\leqslant x^{\frac{1}{3}}<p_2\leqslant\left(\frac{x}{p_1}\right)^{\frac{1}{2}}\\(p_1p_2,d)=1}} \left(\frac{1}{\log \frac{x}{p_1p_2}}\right)\right.\right.$$

$$\left.\left.\cdot \Phi\left(\frac{x}{p_1p_2}, \chi_l\right)\chi_l(p_1p_2)\right|\right\}.$$

We have

$$\sum_{1<d\leqslant x^{\frac{1}{2}-\epsilon}} \frac{3^{\nu(d)}|\mu(d)|}{\varphi(d)} \ll (\log x) \sum_{d\leqslant x^{\frac{1}{2}-\epsilon}} \frac{(\tau(d))^2}{d} \ll (\log x)^5,$$

where $\tau(l) = \sum_{d|l} 1$. Hence we have

$$M_2 \ll (\log x)^6 \operatorname{Max}_{1<m\leqslant x^{\frac{1}{2}}} N_m, \tag{12}$$

where

$$N_m = \sum_{\substack{1<l\leqslant x^{\frac{1}{2}-\epsilon}\\(l,x)=1}} \frac{|\mu(l)|3^{\nu(l)}}{l} \left|\sum_{\chi_l}{}^* \overline{\chi_l}(x) \sum_{\substack{x^{\frac{1}{10}}<p_1\leqslant x^{\frac{1}{3}}<p_2\leqslant\left(\frac{x}{p_1}\right)^{\frac{1}{2}}\\(p_1p_2,m)=1}}\right.$$

$$\left.\cdot\left(\frac{1}{\log \frac{x}{p_1p_2}}\right)\Phi\left(\frac{x}{p_1p_2}, \chi_l\right)\chi_l(p_1p_2)\right|.$$

Let $\sum_{(k,m)}$ denote a sum extended over all primes p_1, p_2, satisfying $x^{\frac{1}{10}} < p_1 \leqslant x^{\frac{1}{3}} < p_2 \leqslant \left(\frac{x}{p_1}\right)^{\frac{1}{2}}$, $x^{\frac{13}{30}}2^k < p_1p_2 \leqslant x^{\frac{13}{30}}2^{k+1}$ and $(p_1p_2, m) = 1$. Let I_1 be a positive integer satisfying the inequality $2^{I_1-1}(\log x)^{100} < x^{\frac{1}{2}-\epsilon} < 2^{I_1}(\log x)^{100}$, and let I_2 be equal to $\left[\frac{7 \log x}{30 \log 2}\right]$. We have

$$N_m \leqslant \sum_{l=0}^{I_1} \sum_{k=0}^{I_2} N_m^{(l,k)}, \tag{13}$$

where

$$N_m^{(0,k)} = \sum_{\substack{1<d\leqslant(\log x)^{100}\\(d,x)=1}} \frac{|\mu(d)|3^{\nu(d)}}{d} \left|\sum_{\chi_d}{}^* \overline{\chi_d}(x) \sum_{(k,m)} \left(\frac{1}{\log \frac{x}{p_1p_2}}\right)\Phi\left(\frac{x}{p_1p_2}, \chi_d\right)\chi_d(p_1p_2)\right|,$$

$$N_m^{(l,k)} = \sum_{\substack{2^{l-1}(\log x)^{100}<d\leqslant 2^l(\log x)^{100}\\(d,x)=1}} \frac{|\mu(d)|3^{\nu(d)}}{d}$$

$$\cdot\left|\sum_{\chi_d}{}^{*}\,\overline{\chi}_d(x)\sum_{(k,m)}\left(\frac{1}{\log\dfrac{x}{p_1p_2}}\right)\Phi\left(\frac{x}{p_1p_2},\chi_d\right)\chi_d(p_1p_2)\right| \quad \text{for } l\geqslant 1.$$

Set $S(H,\omega,\chi_d)=\sum_{n=1}^{H}\dfrac{\mu(n)\chi_d(n)}{n^{\omega}}$, where $H\ll x$. For $\operatorname{Re}\omega\geqslant 1$, we have

$$S(H,\omega,\chi_d)\ll\log x,\quad L(\omega,\chi_d)=\sum_{n=1}^{H}\frac{\chi_d(n)}{n^{\omega}}+O\left(\frac{|\omega|d^{\frac12}\log d}{H}\right).$$

For $\operatorname{Re}\omega\geqslant 1$, we have

$$1-L(\omega,\chi_d)\,S(H,\omega,\chi_d)=\sum_{n=1}^{\infty}\frac{C_H(n)\chi_d(n)}{n^{\omega}}+O\left(\frac{|\omega|d^{\frac12}(\log x)^2}{H}\right),$$

where $C_H(1)=0$, and for $n>1$, $C_H(n)=-\sum_{\substack{d\mid n,\ 1\leqslant d\leqslant H\\ \frac{n}{d}\leqslant H}}\mu(d)$, so that $C_H(n)=0$ for $1\leqslant n\leqslant H$ and $C_H(n)\leqslant\tau(n)$ if $n>H$, and $C_H(n)=0$ for $n>H^2$. Applying Schwarz's inequality we obtain

$$\left|\sum_{n=1}^{\infty}\frac{C_H(n)\chi_d(n)}{n^{\omega}}\right|^2\ll(\log x)\sum_{l=0}^{3l_1}\left|\sum_{n=2^lH+1}^{2^{l+1}H}\frac{C_H(n)\chi_d(n)}{n^{\omega}}\right|^2, \tag{14}$$

when $H\ll x$. When $Q\ll x$, from (3), (14), and $\sum_{n\leqslant x}\tau^2(n)\ll x(\log x)^3$ we have

$$\sum_{D<d\leqslant Q}\frac{1}{\varphi(d)}\sum_{\chi_d}{}^{*}\left|\sum_{n=2^lH+1}^{2^{l+1}H}\frac{C_H(n)\chi_d(n)}{n^{\alpha+i\nu}}\right|^2\ll\left(Q+\frac{2^lH}{D}\right)\sum_{n=2^lH+1}^{2^{l+1}H}\frac{(\tau(n))^2}{n^2}$$
$$\ll\left(\frac{Q}{2^lH}+\frac{1}{D}\right)(\log x)^3,$$

and

$$\sum_{D<d\leqslant Q}\frac{1}{\varphi(d)}\sum_{\chi_d}{}^{*}|1-L(\alpha+i\nu,\chi_d)S(H,\alpha+i\nu,\chi_d)|^2$$
$$\ll\sum_{D<d\leqslant Q}\frac{1}{\varphi(d)}\sum_{\chi_d}{}^{*}\left|\sum_{n=1}^{\infty}\frac{C_H(n)\chi_d(n)}{n^{\alpha+i\nu}}\right|^2+\frac{|\alpha+i\nu|^2Q^2(\log x)^4}{H^2}$$
$$\ll\left(\frac{Q}{H}+\frac{1}{D}+\frac{|\alpha+i\nu|^2Q^2}{H^2}\right)(\log x)^5, \tag{15}$$

where $\alpha=1+\dfrac{1}{\log x}$. We have

$$\{S(H,\beta+i\nu,\chi_d)\}^2=\sum_{n=1}^{H^2}\frac{j(n)\chi_d(n)}{n^{\beta+i\nu}}, \tag{16}$$

where $\beta = \frac{1}{2} + \frac{1}{\log x}$ and $|j(n)| \leqslant \tau(n)$.

From (3) and (16) we have

$$\sum_{2^{l-1}(\log x)^{100} < d \leqslant 2^l (\log x)^{100}} \frac{1}{\varphi(d)} \sum_{\chi_d}{}^* |S(H, \beta + iv, \chi_d)|^4$$

$$\ll \left(2^l (\log x)^{100} + \frac{H^2}{2^l (\log x)^{100}}\right) \sum_{n=1}^{H^2} \frac{(\tau(n))^2}{n} \ll 2^l (\log x)^{104} + \frac{H^2}{2^l (\log x)^{96}}, \quad (17)$$

when $l \geqslant 1$ and $H \ll x$. Using $L'(\omega, \chi_d) = \frac{1}{2\pi i} \int_r \frac{L(\xi, \chi_d)}{(\xi - \omega)^2} d\xi$, where r is a circle with centre ω and radius $(\log x)^{-1}$, we have $|L'(\omega, \chi_d)| \ll (\log x)^2 \int_r |L(\xi, \chi_d)| d\xi$. By Holder's inequality we have $|L'(\omega, \chi_d)|^4 \ll (\log x)^5 \int_r |L(\xi, \chi_d)|^4 |d\xi|$. It follows from Lemma 3 that

$$\sum_{2^{l-1}(\log x)^{100} < d \leqslant 2^l (\log x)^{100}} \left(\frac{1}{\varphi(d)}\right) \sum_{\chi_d}{}^* |L'(\beta + iv, \chi_d)|^4 \ll 2^l (\log x)^{109} (|\beta + iv|)^2.$$

We have

$$\frac{L'}{L}(\omega, \chi_d) = \left\{\frac{L'}{L}(\omega, \chi_d)\right\} \{1 - L(\omega, \chi_d) S(H, \omega, \chi_d)\} + L'(\omega, \chi_d) S(H, \omega, \chi_d). \quad (18)$$

The following notations are used:

$$A(l, k, \omega, m, H) = \sum_{\substack{2^{l-1}(\log x)^{100} < d \leqslant 2^l (\log x)^{100} \\ (d,x)=1}} \frac{|\mu(d)| 3^{\nu(d)}}{d}$$

$$\cdot \sum_{\chi_d}{}^* \left| \sum_{(k,m)} \frac{\chi_d(p_1 p_2)}{(p_1 p_2)^\omega \log \frac{x}{p_1 p_2}} \right| |1 - L(\omega, \chi_d) S(H, \omega, \chi_d)|,$$

$$B(l, k, \omega, m, H) = \sum_{\substack{2^{l-1}(\log x)^{100} < d \leqslant 2^l (\log x)^{100} \\ (d,x)=1}} \frac{|\mu(d)| 3^{\nu(d)}}{d}$$

$$\cdot \sum_{\chi_d}{}^* \left| \sum_{(k,m)} \frac{\chi_d(p_1 p_2)}{(p_1 p_2)^\omega \log \frac{x}{p_1 p_2}} \right| |L'(\omega, \chi_d) S(H, \omega, \chi_d)|.$$

When $l \geqslant 1$, from (18) we have

$$N_m'^{(l,k)} \ll x (\log x)^2 \int_0^\infty \frac{A(l, k, \alpha + iv, m, H)}{|\alpha + iv| \left(1 + \frac{|\alpha + iv|}{(\log x)^{1.1}}\right)^{[\log x]+1}} dv$$

$$+ x^{\frac{1}{2}} \int_0^\infty \frac{B(l, k, \beta + iv, m, H)}{|\beta + iv| \left(1 + \frac{|\beta + iv|}{(\log x)^{1.1}}\right)^{[\log x]+1}} dv. \quad (19)$$

It is obvious that

$$3^{\nu(d)} \leqslant e^{\frac{3 \log d}{\log \log d}}, \quad (20)$$

when $|\mu(d)| \neq 0$ and d is large.

We now treat $N_m^{(l,k)}$ with three cases.

Case 1. Set $l \geqslant 1$. Suppose that l and k satisfy $2^k x^{\frac{13}{30}} > x^{\frac{1}{2}-\epsilon}$ or $x^{\frac{1}{2}-\epsilon} \geqslant 2^k x^{\frac{13}{30}} > 2^l (\log x)^{100}$.

We put

$$H = 2^l (\log x)^{200} I_{l,x}, \quad \text{where } I_{l,x} = e^{\frac{6 \log \{2^l (\log x)^{100}\}}{\log\log \{2^l (\log x)^{100}\}}}.$$

From (15), (17), (18), (19) and (20) we have

$$\begin{aligned}
N_m^{(l,k)} \ll\ & x(\log x)^4 \int_0^\infty \Bigg[\Bigg\{ \sum_{\substack{2^{l-1}(\log x)^{100} < d \leqslant 2^l (\log x)^{100} \\ (d,x)=1}} \frac{|\mu(d)|}{d} \sum_{\chi_d}{}^* \Bigg| \sum_{(k,m)} \frac{\chi_d(p_1 p_2)}{(p_1 p_2)^{\alpha+i\nu} \log \frac{x}{p_1 p_2}} \Bigg|^2 \Bigg\} \\
& \cdot \Bigg\{ \sum_{\substack{2^{l-1}(\log x)^{100} < d \leqslant 2^l (\log x)^{100} \\ (d,x)=1}} \frac{|\mu(d)|}{d} \sum_{\chi_d}{}^* \Big| 1 - L(\alpha+i\nu, \chi_d) S(H, \alpha+i\nu, \chi_d) \Big|^2 \Bigg\} I_{l,x} \Bigg]^{\frac{1}{2}} \\
& \cdot \left(\frac{d\nu}{1+\nu^{2.1}}\right) + x^{\frac{1}{2}} (\log x)^4 \int_0^\infty \Bigg\{\Bigg(\sum_{\substack{2^{l-1}(\log x)^{100} < d \leqslant 2^l (\log x)^{100} \\ (d,x)=1}} \frac{|\mu(d)|}{d} \sum_{\chi_d}{}^* \Bigg| \sum_{(k,m)} \\
& \cdot \frac{\chi_d(p_1 p_2)}{(p_1 p_2)^{\beta+i\nu} \log \frac{x}{p_1 p_2}} \Bigg|^2 (I_{l,x}) \Bigg\}^{\frac{1}{2}} \Bigg\{\Bigg(\sum_{\substack{2^{l-1}(\log x)^{100} < d \leqslant 2^l (\log x)^{100} \\ (d,x)=1}} \frac{|\mu(d)|}{d} \sum_{\chi_d}{}^* |L'(\beta+i\nu, \chi_d)|^4 \Bigg) \\
& \cdot \Bigg(\sum_{\substack{2^{l-1}(\log x)^{100} < d \leqslant 2^l (\log x)^{100} \\ (d,x)=1}} \frac{|\mu(d)|}{d} \sum_{\chi_d}{}^* \Big| S(H, \beta+i\nu, \chi_d) \Big|^4 \Bigg)^{\frac{1}{4}} \left(\frac{d\nu}{1+\nu^4}\right) \\
\ll\ & x(\log x)^8 \int_0^\infty \Bigg\{\Bigg(2^l (\log x)^{100} + \frac{2^k x^{\frac{13}{30}}}{2^l (\log x)^{100}} \Bigg) \Bigg(\sum_{2^k x^{\frac{13}{30}} < n \leqslant 2^{k+1} x^{\frac{13}{30}}} \frac{1}{n^2} \Bigg) \Bigg(\frac{2^l (\log x)^{100}}{H} \\
& + \frac{1}{2^l (\log x)^{100}} + \frac{(1+\nu^2) 2^{2l} (\log x)^{200}}{H^2} \Bigg) I_{l,x} \Bigg\}^{\frac{1}{2}} \left(\frac{d\nu}{1+\nu^{2.1}}\right) + x^{\frac{1}{2}} (\log x)^8 \int_0^\infty \Bigg\{\Bigg(2^l (\log x)^{100} \\
& + \frac{2^k x^{\frac{13}{30}}}{2^l (\log x)^{100}} \Bigg) I_{l,x} \Bigg\}^{\frac{1}{2}} \Big\{ 2^{2l} (\log x)^{213} + H^2 (\log x)^{13} \Big\}^{\frac{1}{4}} (1+\nu^2)^{\frac{1}{4}} \left(\frac{d\nu}{1+\nu^4}\right) \ll \frac{x}{(\log x)^{20}}. \qquad (21)
\end{aligned}$$

Case 2. Suppose that l and k satisfy

$$2^k x^{\frac{13}{30}} \leqslant 2^l (\log x)^{100} < 2 x^{\frac{1}{2}-\epsilon}.$$

Putting $H = \max\left(x^{\frac{1}{2}-\epsilon}, 2^{2l-k} x^{-\frac{13}{30}} (\log x)^{400} I_{l,x}\right)$, we have

$$\begin{aligned}
N_m^{(l,k)} \ll\ & x(\log x)^8 \int_0^\infty \Bigg\{\Bigg(2^l (\log x)^{100} + \frac{2^k x^{\frac{13}{30}}}{2^l (\log x)^{100}} \Bigg) \Bigg(\sum_{2^k x^{\frac{13}{30}} < n \leqslant 2^{k+1} x^{\frac{13}{30}}} \frac{1}{n^2} \Bigg) \\
& \cdot \Bigg(\frac{2^l (\log x)^{100}}{H} + \frac{1}{2^l (\log x)^{100}} + \frac{(1+\nu^2) 2^{2l} (\log x)^{200}}{H^2} \Bigg) (I_{l,x}) \Bigg\}^{\frac{1}{2}} \left(\frac{d\nu}{1+\nu^{2.1}}\right) \\
& + x^{\frac{1}{2}} (\log x)^4 \int_0^\infty \Bigg\{ \sum_{2^{l-1}(\log x)^{100} < d \leqslant 2^l (\log x)^{100}} \frac{|\mu(d)|}{d} \sum_{\chi_d}{}^* |S(H, \beta+i\nu, \chi_d)|^2 \Bigg\}^{\frac{1}{2}} (I_{l,x})^{\frac{1}{2}}
\end{aligned}$$

$$\cdot\Big\{\sum_{2^{l-1}(\log x)^{100}<d\leqslant 2^l(\log x)^{100}}\frac{|\mu(d)|}{d}\sum_{\chi_d}{}^{*}|L'(\beta+iv,\ \chi_d)|^4\Big\}^{\frac{1}{4}}$$

$$\cdot\Big\{\sum_{2^{l-1}(\log x)^{100}<d\leqslant 2^l(\log x)^{100}}\frac{|\mu(d)|}{d}\sum_{\chi_d}{}^{*}\Big|\Big(\sum_{(k,\ m)}\frac{\chi_d(p_1p_2)}{(p_1p_2)^{\beta+iv}\log\dfrac{x}{p_1p_2}}\Big)^2\Big|^2\Big\}^{\frac{1}{4}}\Big(\frac{dv}{1+v^4}\Big)$$

$$\ll x^{\frac{1}{2}}(\log x)^{20}\Big\{2^l(\log x)^{100}+\frac{H}{2^l(\log x)^{100}}\Big\}^{\frac{1}{2}}(I_{l,\,x})^{\frac{1}{2}}(2^l(\log x)^{109})^{\frac{1}{4}}$$

$$\cdot\Big(2^l(\log x)^{100}+\frac{2^{2k}x^{\frac{13}{15}}}{2^l(\log x)^{100}}\Big)^{\frac{1}{4}}\int_0^\infty\frac{(1+v^2)^{\frac{1}{4}}}{1+v^4}\,dv+\frac{x}{(\log x)^{20}}\ll\frac{x}{(\log x)^{20}}. \tag{22}$$

Case 3. Set $l=0$, and suppose that $0\leqslant k\leqslant I_2$.

Let c denote a positive constant, and χ_d denote a primitive character. It is well known that

$$L(S,\chi_d)\neq 0,$$

when $\operatorname{Re} S\geqslant 1-\dfrac{c}{d^{\frac{1}{300}}}$. Hence we have

$$N_m^{(0,\,k)}\ll\sum_{1<d\leqslant(\log x)^{100}}\frac{3^{\nu(d)}|\mu(d)|}{d}\sum_{\chi_d}{}^{*}\Big|\int_{1-\frac{1}{(\log x)^{1/2}}-i\infty}^{1-\frac{1}{(\log x)^{1/2}}+i\infty}\sum_{(k,\ m)}\Big(\frac{1}{\log\dfrac{x}{p_1p_2}}\Big)$$

$$\cdot\ \chi_d(p_1p_2)\Big(\frac{x}{p_1p_2}\Big)^{\omega}\Big(1+\frac{\omega}{(\log x)^{1.1}}\Big)^{-[\log x]-1}\frac{L'}{L}(\omega,\ \chi_d)\frac{d\omega}{\omega}\Big|$$

$$\ll(\log x)^{200}\sum_{x^{\frac{1}{10}}<p_1\leqslant x^{\frac{1}{3}}<p_2\leqslant(\frac{x}{p_1})^{\frac{1}{2}}}\Big(\frac{x}{p_1p_2}\Big)^{1-\frac{1}{(\log x)^{1/2}}}\ll\frac{x}{(\log x)^{20}}. \tag{23}$$

From (12), (13), (21), (22) and (23) we complete the proof of Lemma 6.

Lemma 7. Let x be a large even integer. Then we have

$$M_1\leqslant\Big\{\frac{(8+24\epsilon)xC_x}{\log x}\Big\}\Big\{\sum_{x^{\frac{1}{10}}<p_1\leqslant x^{\frac{1}{3}}<p_2\leqslant(\frac{x}{p_1})^{\frac{1}{2}}}\frac{1}{p_1p_2\log\dfrac{x}{p_1p_2}}\Big\},$$

where $C_x=\prod\limits_{\substack{p|x\\ p>2}}\dfrac{p-1}{p-2}\prod\limits_{p>2}\Big(1-\dfrac{1}{(p-1)^2}\Big)$.

Proof. Set $S=\sum\limits_{\substack{1\leqslant k\leqslant(x^{\frac{1}{2}-\epsilon})^{\frac{1}{2}}\\ (k,x)=1}}\dfrac{\mu^2(k)}{f(k)}$. Then it follows

$$\lambda_d g(d)=\Big(\frac{1}{S}\Big)\sum_{\substack{1\leqslant k\leqslant(x^{\frac{1}{2}-\epsilon})^{\frac{1}{2}}/d\\ (k,xd)=1}}\frac{\mu(kd)\mu(k)}{f(kd)}.$$

Hence, if $(m,x)=1$, we have

$$\sum_{\substack{d\leqslant(x^{\frac{1}{2}-\epsilon})^{\frac{1}{2}}\\(d,x)=1,\ m|d}}\lambda_d g(d)=\left(\frac{1}{S}\right)\left(\sum_{\substack{d\leqslant(x^{\frac{1}{2}-\epsilon})^{\frac{1}{2}}\\(d,x)=1,\ m|d}}\ \sum_{\substack{1\leqslant k\leqslant(x^{\frac{1}{2}-\epsilon})^{\frac{1}{2}}/d\\(k,xd)=1}}\frac{\mu(kd)\mu(k)}{f(kd)}\right)$$

$$=\left(\frac{1}{S}\right)\sum_{\substack{1\leqslant r\leqslant(x^{\frac{1}{2}-\epsilon})^{\frac{1}{2}}\\(r,x)=1}}\frac{\mu(r)}{f(r)}\sum_{m|d|r}\mu\left(\frac{r}{d}\right)=\frac{\mu(m)}{Sf(m)}.$$

Since $\dfrac{1}{\varphi\left(\dfrac{d_1d_2}{(d_1,d_2)}\right)}=g(d_1)g(d_2)\sum\limits_{d|(d_1,d_2)}f(d)$, therefore we have

$$\sum_{d\leqslant(x^{\frac{1}{2}-\epsilon})^{\frac{1}{2}}}\ \sum_{\substack{d_2\leqslant(x^{\frac{1}{2}-\epsilon})^{\frac{1}{2}}\\(d_1d_2,x)=1}}\frac{\lambda_{d_1}\lambda_{d_2}}{\varphi\left(\dfrac{d_1d_2}{(d_1,d_2)}\right)}=\sum_{d_1\leqslant(x^{\frac{1}{2}-\epsilon})^{\frac{1}{2}}}\ \sum_{\substack{d_2\leqslant(x^{\frac{1}{2}-\epsilon})^{\frac{1}{2}}\\(d_1d_2,x)=1}}\lambda_{d_1}\lambda_{d_2}g(d_1)g(d_2)\sum_{k|(d_1,d_2)}f(k)$$

$$=\sum_{\substack{k\leqslant(x^{\frac{1}{2}-\epsilon})^{\frac{1}{2}}\\(k,x)=1}}f(k)\left(\sum_{\substack{d\leqslant(x^{\frac{1}{2}-\epsilon})^{\frac{1}{2}}\\k|d,(d,x)=1}}\lambda_d g(d)\right)^2=\frac{1}{S}. \tag{24}$$

Set $V_k(x)=\sum\limits_{\substack{1\leqslant n\leqslant x\\(n,k)=1}}\dfrac{\mu^2(n)}{\varphi(n)}$. Then we obtain

$$\log x\leqslant\sum_{n=1}^{x}\frac{1}{n}\leqslant\sum_{1\leqslant n\leqslant x}\frac{\mu^2(n)}{n}\prod_{p|n}\left(\sum_{l=0}^{\infty}\frac{1}{p^l}\right)=\sum_{1\leqslant n\leqslant x}\frac{\mu^2(n)}{n}\prod_{p|n}\left(1-\frac{1}{p}\right)^{-1}$$

$$=V_1(x)=\sum_{d|k}\sum_{\substack{1\leqslant n\leqslant x\\(n,k)=d}}\frac{\mu^2(n)}{\varphi(n)}=\sum_{d|k}\frac{\mu^2(d)}{\varphi(d)}\sum_{\substack{1\leqslant m\leqslant x/d\\(m,k)=1}}\frac{\mu^2(m)}{\varphi(m)}\leqslant\sum_{d|k}\frac{\mu^2(d)}{\varphi(d)}V_k(x)$$

$$=\frac{kV_k(x)}{\varphi(k)}.$$

Hence $V_k(x)\geqslant\dfrac{\varphi(k)\log x}{k}$ holds good. Set $\psi(1)=1$ and $\psi(q)=\prod\limits_{p|q}(p-2)$, where $q>2$. Then we have

$$S=\sum_{\substack{1\leqslant k\leqslant(x^{\frac{1}{2}-\epsilon})^{\frac{1}{2}}\\(k,x)=1}}\frac{\mu^2(k)}{\varphi(k)}\prod_{p\nmid k}\left(1+\frac{1}{p-2}\right)=\sum_{\substack{1\leqslant k\leqslant(x^{\frac{1}{2}-\epsilon})^{\frac{1}{2}}\\(k,x)=1}}\frac{\mu^2(k)}{\varphi(k)}\sum_{q|k}\frac{1}{\psi(q)}$$

$$=\sum_{\substack{q\leqslant(x^{\frac{1}{2}-\epsilon})^{\frac{1}{2}}\\(q,x)=1}}\frac{\mu^2(q)}{\psi(q)\varphi(q)}\sum_{\substack{r\leqslant(x^{\frac{1}{2}-\epsilon})^{\frac{1}{2}}/q\\(r,qx)=1}}\frac{\mu^2(r)}{\varphi(r)}\geqslant\sum_{\substack{q\leqslant(x^{\frac{1}{2}-\epsilon})^{\frac{1}{2}}\\(q,x)=1}}\frac{\mu^2(q)}{\psi(q)\varphi(q)}\left\{\frac{\varphi(qx)}{qx}\log\frac{x^{\frac{1}{4}-\frac{\epsilon}{2}}}{q}\right\}$$

$$=\left(\frac{\varphi(x)}{x}\right)(\log x^{\frac{1}{4}-\frac{\epsilon}{2}})\prod_{p\nmid x}\left(1+\frac{1}{p(p-2)}\right)+O(1)=\frac{\left(\dfrac{1}{8}-\dfrac{\epsilon}{4}\right)(\log x)}{C_x}+O(1). \tag{25}$$

When x is a large integer, from (24) and (25) we have

$$M_1\leqslant(8+24\epsilon)C_x(\log x)^{-1}\sum_{x^{\frac{1}{10}}<p_1\leqslant x^{\frac{1}{3}}<p_2\leqslant\left(\frac{x}{p_1}\right)^{\frac{1}{2}}}\ \sum_{n\leqslant\frac{x}{p_1p_2}}\left(\frac{\Lambda(n)}{\log\dfrac{x}{p_1p_2}}\right)\Phi\left(\frac{x}{p_1p_2n}\right). \tag{26}$$

Lemma 7 is true from (26) and Lemma 1.

Lemma 8. Let x be a large even integer. Then $\Omega \leqslant \frac{3.9404\, xC_x}{(\log x)^2}$ holds.

Proof. When x is a large even integer, from Lemmas 5, 6 and 7, we have

$$\Omega \leqslant \left\{\frac{8(1+5\epsilon)xC_x}{\log x}\right\}\left\{\sum_{x^{\frac{1}{10}}<p_1\leqslant x^{\frac{1}{3}}<p_2\leqslant\left(\frac{x}{p_1}\right)^{\frac{1}{2}}} \frac{1}{p_1p_2\log\frac{x}{p_1p_2}}\right\}. \tag{27}$$

We have

$$\sum_{x^{\frac{1}{10}}<p_1\leqslant x^{\frac{1}{3}}<p_2\leqslant\left(\frac{x}{p_1}\right)^{\frac{1}{2}}} \frac{1}{p_1p_2\log\frac{x}{p_1p_2}} \leqslant (1+\epsilon)\sum_{x^{\frac{1}{10}}<p_1\leqslant x^{\frac{1}{3}}}\int_{x^{\frac{1}{3}}}^{\left(\frac{x}{p_1}\right)^{\frac{1}{2}}} \frac{dt}{p_1t(\log t)\log\frac{x}{p_1t}}$$

$$\leqslant (1+2\epsilon)\int_{x^{\frac{1}{10}}}^{x^{\frac{1}{3}}}\frac{dS}{S\log S}\int_{x^{\frac{1}{3}}}^{\left(\frac{x}{S}\right)^{\frac{1}{2}}}\frac{dt}{t\,(\log t)\left(\log\frac{x}{St}\right)} \leqslant (1+2\epsilon)\int_{\frac{1}{10}}^{\frac{1}{3}}\frac{d\alpha}{\alpha}\int_{\frac{1}{3}}^{\frac{1-\alpha}{2}}\frac{d\beta}{\beta(1-\alpha-\beta)\log x},$$

$$\int_{\frac{1}{10}}^{\frac{1}{3}}\frac{d\alpha}{\alpha}\int_{\frac{1}{3}}^{\frac{1-\alpha}{2}}\left(\frac{1}{1-\alpha}\right)\left(\frac{1}{\beta}+\frac{1}{1-\alpha-\beta}\right)d\beta = \int_{\frac{1}{10}}^{\frac{1}{3}}\frac{\log\frac{1-\alpha}{2}-\log\frac{1}{3}-\log\frac{1-\alpha}{2}+\log\left(\frac{2}{3}-\alpha\right)}{\alpha(1-\alpha)}d\alpha$$

$$= \int_{\frac{1}{10}}^{\frac{1}{3}}\frac{\log(2-3\alpha)}{\alpha(1-\alpha)}d\alpha = \sum_{i=0}^{6}\int_{\frac{1}{10}+\frac{i}{30}}^{\frac{1}{10}+\frac{i+1}{30}}\frac{\log\left(1.6-\frac{i}{10}\right)}{\alpha(1-\alpha)}d\alpha + \sum_{i=0}^{6}\int_{\frac{1}{10}+\frac{i}{30}}^{\frac{1}{10}+\frac{i+1}{30}}\frac{\log\frac{2-3\alpha}{1.6-0.i}}{\alpha(1-\alpha)}d\alpha$$

$$\leqslant \sum_{i=0}^{6}\left\{\log\left(1.6-\frac{i}{10}\right)\right\}\left\{\log\frac{\frac{9}{10}-\frac{i}{30}}{\frac{1}{10}+\frac{i}{30}} - \log\frac{\frac{9}{10}-\frac{1}{30}-\frac{i}{30}}{\frac{1}{10}+\frac{i+1}{30}}\right\}$$

$$+ \sum_{i=0}^{6}\int_{\frac{1}{10}+\frac{i}{30}}^{\frac{1}{10}+\frac{i+1}{30}}\frac{(0.4+0.i-3\alpha)}{(1.6-0.i)\,\alpha(1-\alpha)}d\alpha \leqslant \sum_{i=0}^{6}\left\{\log(1.6-0.i)+\frac{4+i}{16-i}\right\}\left\{\log\frac{27-i}{3+i}\right.$$

$$\left.-\log\frac{26-i}{4+i}\right\} - 3\sum_{i=0}^{6}\int_{\frac{1}{10}+\frac{i}{30}}^{\frac{1}{10}+\frac{i+1}{30}}\frac{d\alpha}{(1.6-0.i)\,(1-\alpha)} = \sum_{i=0}^{6}\left\{\log(1.6-0.i)+\frac{4+i}{16-i}\right\}$$

$$\cdot\left\{\log\frac{108+23i-i^2}{78+23i-i^2}\right\} - 3\sum_{i=0}^{6}\left(\frac{1}{1.6-0.i}\right)\left(\log\frac{27-i}{26-i}\right)$$

$$\leqslant (0.47+0.25)(0.32542)+(0.40547+0.33334)(0.26236)+(0.33647$$
$$+0.42858)(0.22315)+(0.26236+0.53847)(0.19671)+(0.18232$$
$$+0.66667)(0.17799)+(0.09531+0.81819)(0.16431)$$
$$+0.15415-3\left(\frac{0.03774}{1.6}+\frac{0.03922}{1.5}+\frac{0.04082}{1.4}+\frac{0.04256}{1.3}+\frac{0.04445}{1.2}\right.$$
$$\left.+\frac{0.04652}{1.1}+0.04879\right) \leqslant 0.234303+0.193837+0.17073+0.15754+0.151115$$
$$+0.1501+0.15415-3(0.023587+0.026146+0.029157+0.032738$$
$$+0.037041+0.04229+0.04879) \leqslant 1.21178-0.71924 = 0.49254. \tag{28}$$

From (27) and (28) we complete the proof of Lemma 8.

Let x be a large even integer and $P_x(x, x^{\frac{1}{10}})$ be the number of primes p satisfying the following conditions:

$$p \leqslant x, \quad p \not\equiv x \pmod{p_i} \qquad (1 \leqslant i \leqslant j),$$

where $3 = p_1 < p_2 < \cdots < p_j \leqslant x^{\frac{1}{10}}$ is the set of odd primes not exceeding $x^{\frac{1}{10}}$. For a prime p', let $P_x(x, p', x^{\frac{1}{10}})$ be the number of primes p satisfying the following conditions:

$$p \leqslant x, \ p \equiv x (\bmod p'), \quad p \not\equiv x \pmod{p_i}, \qquad (1 \leqslant i \leqslant j),$$

where $p_1, \cdots, p_j$ are the same as mentioned above.

Lemma 9. Let x be a large even integer. Then we have

$$P_x(x, x^{\frac{1}{10}}) - \left(\frac{1}{2}\right) \sum_{x^{\frac{1}{10}} < p \leqslant x^{\frac{1}{3}}} P_x(x, p, x^{\frac{1}{10}}) \geqslant \frac{2.6408 x C_x}{(\log x)^2}.$$

Proof. Putting $r(p) = \dfrac{p}{p-1}$, $K = x$ and $z = x^{\frac{1}{10}}$ in (2.11) of [11], we see that (A_1) and (A_2) of [11] are satisfied. Therefore, applying (2.11) of [11], we obtain

$$\begin{aligned} \Gamma_x(x^{\frac{1}{10}}) &= \frac{x}{\varphi(x)} \prod_{p \nmid x} \frac{1 - \dfrac{1}{p-1}}{1 - \dfrac{1}{p}} \cdot \frac{e^{-r}}{\log x^{\frac{1}{10}}} \left\{1 + O\left(\frac{1}{\log x}\right)\right\} \\ &= \frac{x}{\varphi(x)} \prod_{\substack{p \mid x \\ p > 2}} \frac{(p-1)^2}{p(p-2)} \prod_{p > 2} \left(1 - \frac{1}{(p-1)^2}\right) \frac{e^{-r}}{\log x^{\frac{1}{10}}} \left\{1 + O\left(\frac{1}{\log x}\right)\right\} \\ &= \frac{20 e^{-r} C_x}{\log x} \left\{1 + O\left(\frac{1}{\log x}\right)\right\}, \end{aligned} \tag{29}$$

where r denotes Euler's constant. Set

$$F(u) = \frac{2e^r}{u}, \qquad f(u) = 0, \qquad 0 < u \leqslant 2,$$

$$(uF(u))' = f(u-1), \qquad (uf(u))' = F(u-1), \qquad u \geqslant 2. \tag{30}$$

When $2 < u \leqslant 3$, from (30) we have

$$uF(u) = 2F(2), \qquad F(u) = \frac{2e^r}{u}.$$

We have

$$uf(u) = \int_2^u F(t-1)dt = 2e^r \log(u-1), \text{ when } 2 < u \leqslant 4;$$

$$f(u) = \frac{2e^r \log(u-1)}{u}, \text{ when } 2 < u \leqslant 4;$$

$$uF(u) = 2e^r + \int_3^u f(t-1)dt = 2e^r \left(1 + \int_2^{u-1} \frac{\log(t-1)}{t} dt\right), \text{ when } 3 \leqslant u \leqslant 4;$$

$$5f(5) = 2e^r \log 3 + \int_4^5 F(u-1)\,du = 2e^r\left(\log 4 + \int_3^4 \frac{du}{u}\int_2^{u-1} \frac{\log(t-1)}{t}dt\right).$$

We put $\xi^2 = x^{\frac{1}{2}-\epsilon}$, $q = 1$ and $z = x^{\frac{1}{10}}$ in Theorem A of [11]. From (2.19), (4.18) and (3.24) of [11], and (29) of the present paper, we have

$$P_x(x, x^{\frac{1}{10}}) \geqslant \frac{2(1-\sqrt{\epsilon})e^{-r}xC_x f(5)}{(\log x)(\log x^{\frac{1}{10}})} \geqslant \left\{\frac{8(1-\sqrt{\epsilon})\,xC_x}{(\log x)^2}\right\}$$

$$\cdot\left\{\log 4 + \int_3^4 \frac{du}{u}\int_2^{u-1}\frac{\log(t-1)}{t}dt\right\}, \tag{31}$$

where x is a large integer.

Again we put $\xi^2 = \dfrac{x^{\frac{1}{2}-\epsilon}}{p}$, $q = p$ and $z = x^{\frac{1}{10}}$ in Theorem A of [11]. From (2.18), (3.24), and (4.18) of [11] and (29) of the present paper, we have

$$\sum_{x^{\frac{1}{10}}<p\leqslant x^{\frac{1}{3}}} P_x(x, p, x^{\frac{1}{10}}) \leqslant \left\{\frac{20(1+\sqrt{\epsilon})e^{-r}xC_x}{(\log x)^2}\right\}\left\{\sum_{x^{\frac{1}{10}}<p\leqslant x^{\frac{1}{3}}}\left(\frac{1}{p}\right)\right.$$

$$\left.\cdot\, 2e^r\left(1+\int_2^{4-\frac{10\log p}{\log x}}\frac{\log(t-1)}{t}dt\right)\left(\frac{\log x^{\frac{1}{10}}}{\log\frac{x^{\frac{1}{2}}}{p}}\right) + \sum_{x^{\frac{1}{5}}<p\leqslant x^{\frac{1}{3}}}\frac{2e^r\log x^{\frac{1}{10}}}{p\log\frac{x^{\frac{1}{2}}}{p}}\right\}$$

$$\leqslant \left\{\frac{(4+5\sqrt{\epsilon})\,xC_x}{\log x}\right\}\left\{\int_{x^{\frac{1}{10}}}^{x^{\frac{1}{5}}}\frac{dS}{S(\log S)\left(\log\frac{x^{\frac{1}{2}}}{S}\right)}\int_2^{4-\frac{10\log S}{\log x}}\frac{\log(t-1)}{t}dt\right.$$

$$\left. + \int_{x^{\frac{1}{10}}}^{x^{\frac{1}{3}}}\frac{dS}{S(\log S)\left(\log\frac{x^{\frac{1}{2}}}{S}\right)}\right\} = \left\{\frac{(4+5\sqrt{\epsilon})\,xC_x}{(\log x)^2}\right\}\left\{\int_{\frac{1}{10}}^{\frac{1}{5}}\frac{d\alpha}{\alpha\left(\frac{1}{2}-\alpha\right)}\int_2^{4-10\alpha}\frac{\log(t-1)}{t}dt\right.$$

$$\left. + \int_{\frac{1}{10}}^{\frac{1}{3}}\frac{d\alpha}{\alpha\left(\frac{1}{2}-\alpha\right)}\right\} = \left\{\frac{(8+10\sqrt{\epsilon})\,xC_x}{(\log x)^2}\right\}$$

$$\cdot\left\{\log 8 + \int_{\frac{1}{10}}^{\frac{1}{5}}\frac{d\alpha}{2\alpha\left(\frac{1}{2}-\alpha\right)}\int_2^{4-10\alpha}\frac{\log(t-1)}{t}dt\right\}. \tag{32}$$

By putting $4 - 10\alpha = u - 1$, it is found $\alpha = \dfrac{5-u}{10}$ and $\dfrac{d\alpha}{\alpha\left(\frac{1}{2}-\alpha\right)} = -\dfrac{10\,du}{u(5-u)}$.

We have

$$u = 4 \text{ when } \alpha = \frac{1}{10};$$

$$u = 3 \text{ when } \alpha = \frac{1}{5}.$$

Hence it follows

$$\int_{\frac{1}{10}}^{\frac{1}{3}} \frac{d\alpha}{\alpha\left(\frac{1}{2}-\alpha\right)} \int_{2}^{4-10\alpha} \frac{\log(t-1)}{t}\,dt = \int_{3}^{4} \frac{10du}{u(5-u)} \int_{2}^{u-1} \frac{\log(t-1)}{t}\,dt.$$

We have

$$\int_{3}^{4} \frac{du}{u} \int_{2}^{u-1} \frac{\log(t-1)}{t}\,dt - \left(\frac{1}{4}\right) \int_{\frac{1}{10}}^{\frac{1}{3}} \frac{d\alpha}{\alpha\left(\frac{1}{2}-\alpha\right)} \int_{2}^{4-1)\alpha} \frac{\log(t-1)}{t}\,dt$$

$$= \int_{3}^{4} \left(\frac{1}{u} - \frac{2.5}{u(5-u)}\right) du \int_{2}^{u-1} \frac{\log(t-1)}{t}\,dt \geqslant \int_{3}^{4} \left\{\frac{2.5-u}{u(5-u)}\right\} du$$

$$\cdot \int_{2}^{u-1} \left(\frac{t-2}{2} + \frac{t-2}{t}\right)\left(\frac{dt}{t}\right) = \int_{3}^{4} \left\{\frac{2.5-u}{2u(5-u)}\right\}\left(u-3+\frac{4}{u-1}-2\right) du$$

$$= \int_{3}^{4} \left(\frac{1}{2} - \frac{2.25}{u} - \frac{1}{4(5-u)} + \frac{0.75}{u-1}\right) du = \frac{1}{2} - 2.25 \log\frac{4}{3} - \frac{\log 2}{4}$$

$$+ 0.75 \log\frac{3}{2} = \frac{1}{2} + 0.75 \log\frac{9}{8} - 1.5 \log\frac{4}{3} - \frac{\log 2}{4}$$

$$\geqslant 0.588335 - 0.6048075 = -0.0164725, \tag{33}$$

be using

$$\log x \leqslant \frac{x-1}{2} + \frac{x-1}{1+x} \text{ for } 1 \leqslant x \leqslant 2.$$

From (31), (32) and (33), we have

$$P_x(x, x^{\frac{1}{10}}) - \left(\frac{1}{2}\right) \sum_{x^{\frac{1}{10}} < p \leqslant x^{\frac{1}{3}}} [P_x(x, p, x^{\frac{1}{10}}) \geqslant \left(\frac{(8-50\sqrt{\epsilon})xC_x}{(\log x)^2}\right)$$

$$\cdot \left(\log 4 - \frac{\log 8}{2} - 0.0164725\right) \geqslant \frac{(8xC_x)(0.3301)}{(\log x)^2},$$

which proves the Lemma.

III. The Proof of Our Main Results

It is obvious that

$$P_x(1,2) \geqslant P_x(x, x^{\frac{1}{10}}) - \left(\frac{1}{2}\right) \sum_{x^{\frac{1}{10}} < p \leqslant x^{\frac{1}{3}}} P_x(x, p, x^{\frac{1}{10}}) - \frac{\Omega}{2} - x^{0.91}. \tag{34}$$

By (34) and Lemmas 8 and 9, we obtain

$$P_x(1,2) \geqslant \frac{0.67\, xC_x}{(\log x)^2},$$

and Theorem 1 follows.

By the same method as used in estimating $P_x(1,2)$, we can easily find that

$$x_h(1,2) \geqslant \frac{0.67\, xC_h}{(\log x)^2},$$

and Theorem II follows.

References

[1] Renyi, A. 1948 On the representation of an even number as the sum of a prime and of an almost prime, *Изв. АН СССР*, сер. Мат. **12**, 57—78.

[2] Pan, Cheng-tung 1962 On the representation of an even number as the sum of a prime and of an almost prime, *Acta Mathematica Sinica*, **12**, 95—106.

[3] Барбан М. Б. 1961 Арифметические Функции на редких множествах, *Док. АН УзССР*, **8**, 9—11.

[4] Wang, Yuan 1962 On the representation of large integer as a sum of a prime and an almost prime, *Sci. Sin.*, **11**, 1033—1054.

[5] Пан Чэн-дун 1963 О представлении четных чисел в виде суммы простого и непревосходящего 4 простых произведения, *Sci. Sin.*, **12**, 455—474.

[6] Барбан М. Б. 1963 Плотность нулей L-рядов Дирихле и задача о сложении простых и почти простых чисел, *Мат. сб.*, **61**, 419—425.

[7] Бухштаб А. А. 1965 Новые результаты в исследовании проблемы Гольдбаха-Эйлера и проблемы простых чисел близнецов, *Док. АН СССР*, **162**, 739—742.

[8] Виноградов А. И. 1965 О плотностной гипотезе для L-рядов Дирихле, *Изв. АН СССР*, сер. Мат., **29**, 903—934.

[9] Bombieri, E. 1965 On the large sieve, *Mathematika*, **12**, 201—225.

[10] Chen, Jing-run 1966 On the representation of a large even integer as the sum of a prime and the product of at most 2 primes, *Kexue Tongbao*, **17**, 385—386.

[11] Richert, H. E. 1969 Selberg's sieve with weights, *Mathematika*, **16**, 1—22.

A New Mean Value Theorem and its Applications

PAN CHENG-DONG

Mathematics Department, Shandong University, People's Republic of China

1. INTRODUCTION

Let

$$\pi(X; d, l) = \sum_{\substack{p \leq X \\ p \equiv l (\bmod d)}} 1 .$$

In 1948, A. Renyi [**16**] proved the following Theorem:

THEOREM 1. *For any given positive $A > 0$, there exists a positive $\eta > 1$ such that*

$$R(X^{\eta}; X) = \sum_{d \leq X^{\eta}} \max_{y \leq X} \max_{(l,d)=1} \left| \pi(y; d, l) - \frac{\pi(y; 1, 1)}{\phi(d)} \right| \ll X \log^{-A} X$$

where $\phi(d)$ is Euler's function.

Precisely speaking, the result of A. Renyi was proved in a weighted form, but the elimination weights did not present any basic problems.

By this, he proved the following proposition:

Every large even integer is the sum of a prime number and an almost prime number with the number of prime factors not exceeding C.

For brevity, we denote the above proposition by $(1, C)$. Renyi did not give the quantitative estimate of η and C. By his method, we can say only that η is very small and C is very large.

M. B. Barban in 1961 [**12**] and I in 1962 [**5**] proved independently that Theorem 1 holds for $\eta<\frac{1}{6}$ and $\eta<\frac{1}{3}$ respectively. With $\eta<\frac{1}{3}$ I first proved the quantitative result—(1, 5). In 1962 Wang Yuan proved (1, 4) using only $\eta<\frac{1}{3}$. I in 1962 [**14**] and M. B. Barban in 1963 [**13**] proved independently that Theorem 1 holds for $\eta<\frac{3}{8}$, and we obtained (1, 4) without much numerical calculation. In 1965 A. A. Buchstab proved (1, 3) by use of $\eta<\frac{3}{8}$.

In 1965 A. I. Vinogradov and E. Bombieri [**1**] proved independently that Theorem 1 holds for $\eta<\frac{1}{2}$.

More precisely, E. Bombieri proved the following important theorem:

THEOREM 2 (Bombieri). *For any given positive $A>0$, we have*

$$\sum_{d\le X^{1/2}\log^{-B_1}X}\ \max_{y\le x}\ \max_{(l,d)=1}\left|\pi(y;d,l)-\frac{\pi(y;1,1)}{\phi(d)}\right|\ll X\log^{-A}X$$

where $B_1=3A+23$.

From this, (1, 3) can be derived without much numerical calculation.

In 1975 Ding and I proved the following new mean value theorem:

THEOREM 3. *Let*

$$\pi(X;a,d,l)=\sum_{\substack{ap\le X\\ ap\equiv l(\mathrm{mod}\,d)}}1$$

and let $f(a)$ be a real function, $f(a)\ll 1$; then, for any given $A>0$, we have

$$\sum_{d\le X^{1/2}\log^{-B_2}X}\ \max_{y\le X}\ \max_{(l,d)=1}\left|\sum_{\substack{a\le X^{1-\varepsilon}\\ (a,d)=1}}f(a)\left(\pi(y;a,d,l)-\frac{\pi(y;a,1,1)}{\phi(d)}\right)\right|$$

$$\ll X\log^{-A}X$$

where $B_2=\frac{3}{2}A+17$ and $0<\varepsilon<1$.

Putting

$$f(a)=\begin{cases}1, & a=1\\ 0, & a>1\end{cases}$$

we have

$$\sum_{\substack{a\le X^{1-\varepsilon}\\ (a,d)=1}}f(a)\left(\pi(y;a,d,l)-\frac{\pi(y;a,1,1)}{\phi(d)}\right)=\pi(y;d,l)-\frac{\pi(y;1,1)}{\phi(d)},$$

so that Theorem 3 is a generalization of Theorem 2. However, its interest is less a matter of generalization than of important applications. We give some examples in Section 3.

2. THE PROOF OF THEOREM 3

In order to prove Theorem 3 we require some well known lemmas.

LEMMA 1. *For any complex numbers a_n, we have*

$$\sum_{q\leq Q}\frac{q}{\phi(q)}\sum_{\chi_q}{}^*\left|\sum_{n=M+1}^{M+N}a_n\chi(n)\right|\ll(Q^2+N)\sum_{n=M+1}^{M+N}|a_n|^2$$

and

$$\sum_{H<q\leq Q}\frac{1}{\phi(q)}\sum_{\chi_q}{}^*\left|\sum_{n=M+1}^{M+N}a_n\chi(n)\right|\ll\left(Q+\frac{N}{H}\right)\sum_{n=M+1}^{M+N}|a_n|^2,$$

where the asterisk indicates that the sum is taken over all the primitive characters mod q.

LEMMA 2. *If $T\geq 2$ and $|\sigma-\frac{1}{2}|\leq 1/(200\log qT)$, we have*

$$\sum_{\chi_q}{}^*\int_{-T}^{T}|L(\sigma+it,\chi)|^4\,dt\ll\phi(q)T\log^4 qT$$

and

$$\sum_{\chi_q}{}^*\int_{-T}^{T}|L'(\sigma+it,\chi)|^4\,dt\ll\phi(q)T\log^8 qT.$$

Let

$$\Psi(X;a,d,l)=\sum_{\substack{an\leq X\\ an\equiv l(\mathrm{mod}\ d)}}\Lambda(n)$$

and let

$$R(D;X,f)=\sum_{d\leq D}\max_{y\leq X}\max_{(l,d)=1}\left|\sum_{\substack{a\leq X^{1-\epsilon}\\(a,d)=1}}f(a)\left(\psi(y;a,d,l)-\frac{\psi(y;a,1,1)}{\phi(d)}\right)\right|$$

where

$$D=X^{\frac{1}{2}}\log^{-B_2}X,\qquad B_2=\tfrac{3}{2}A+17.$$

For $(a,d)=(l,d)=1$, we have

$$\psi(y;a,d,l)=\frac{1}{\phi(d)}\sum_{an\leq y}\sum_{\chi_a}\chi(an)\overline{\chi(l)}\chi(n)$$

$$=\frac{1}{\phi(d)}\sum_{an\leq y}\chi_d^0(n)\Lambda(n)+\frac{1}{\phi(d)}\sum_{\chi_d\neq\chi_d^0}\bar{\chi}(l)\chi(a)\sum_{an\leq y}\chi(n)\Lambda(n)$$

$$=\frac{1}{\phi(d)}\sum_{an\leq y}\Lambda(n)+\frac{1}{\phi(d)}\sum_{1<q|d}\sum_{\chi_d}{}^*\bar{\chi}(l)\chi(a)$$

$$\sum_{\substack{an\leq y\\(n,d)=1}}\chi(n)\Lambda(n)+O\left(\frac{\log d\log y}{\phi(d)}\right).$$

From this, we have

$$R(D;X,f)\leqslant \sum_{d\leqslant D}\frac{1}{\phi(d)}\sum_{1<q|d}\max_{y\leqslant X}\sum_{\chi_q}{}^{*}\Bigg|\sum_{\substack{a\leqslant X^{1-\varepsilon}\\(a,d)=1}}f(a)\chi(a)\sum_{\substack{an\leqslant y\\(n,d)=1}}\Lambda(n)\chi(n)\Bigg|$$

$$+O\Big(\frac{X}{\log^A X}\Big)\leqslant \log X\max_{m\leqslant D}\sum_{1<q\leqslant D}\frac{1}{\phi(q)}\sum_{\chi_q}{}^{*}$$

$$\times\Bigg|\sum_{\substack{a\leqslant X^{1-\varepsilon}\\(a,m)=1}}f(a)\chi(a)\sum_{\substack{an\leqslant y\\(n,m)=1}}\Lambda(n)\chi(n)\Bigg|+O\Big(\frac{X}{\log^A X}\Big). \qquad (1)$$

Let h be any fixed positive number and $D_1=\log^h X$. From (1) and the Siegel–Walfisz theorem, we get

$$R(D,X,f)\leqslant \log X\max_{m\leqslant D}\sum_{D_1<q\leqslant D}\frac{1}{\phi(q)}\max_{y\leqslant X}\sum_{\chi_q}{}^{*}$$

$$\times\Bigg|\sum_{a\leqslant X^{1-\varepsilon}}f(a)\chi(a)\sum_{\substack{an\leqslant y\\(n,m)=1}}\Lambda(n)\chi(n)\Bigg|+O\Big(\frac{X}{\log^A X}\Big). \qquad (2)$$

Let $D_1\leqslant Q_1\leqslant D, Q<Q'\leqslant 2Q$ and let (q) denote the interval $Q<q\leqslant Q'$.

Let $\frac{1}{2}\leqslant E<X^{1-\varepsilon}, E<E'\leqslant 2E$ and let (a) denote the interval $E<a\leqslant E'$. Let

$$\mathrm{Im}\,(Q,E)=\sum_{(q)}\frac{1}{\phi(q)}\max_{y\leqslant X}\sum_{\chi_q}{}^{*}\Bigg|\sum_{\substack{(a)\\(a,m)=1}}f(a)\chi(a)\sum_{\substack{an\leqslant y\\(n,m)=1}}\Lambda(n)\chi(n)\Bigg|.$$

It is evident that Theorem 3 follows at once provided

$$\mathrm{Im}\,(Q,E)\ll\frac{X}{\log^{A+3}X}. \qquad (3)$$

For convenience, let

$$f^{(m)}(a)=\begin{cases}f(a), & (m,a)=1,\\ 0, & (m,a)>1,\end{cases}$$

and

$$d_E^{(m)}(n)=\Lambda(n),\qquad E\geqslant D_1^2,$$

$$d_E^{(m)}(n)=\begin{cases}\Lambda(n), & (n,m)=1,\\ 0, & (n,m)>1;\end{cases}\qquad E>D_1^2$$

and let

$$\mathrm{Im}'(Q,E)=\sum_{(q)}\frac{1}{\phi(q)}\max_{y\leqslant X}\sum_{\chi_q}{}^{*}\Bigg|\sum_{(a)}f^{(m)}(a)\chi(a)\sum_{an\leqslant y}d_E^{(m)}(n)\chi(n)\Bigg|.$$

Then we always have

$$\mathrm{Im}'(Q,E)=\mathrm{Im}'(Q,E)+O\left(\frac{X}{\log^{A+3}X}\right). \tag{4}$$

By Perron's formula we get

$$\mathrm{Im}'(Q,E)\ll\sum_{(q)}\frac{1}{\phi(q)}\max_{y\leq X}\sum_{\chi_q}{}^{*}$$
$$\times\left|\int_{b-iT}^{b+iT}f_E^{(m)}(s,\chi)d_E^{(m)}(S,\chi)\frac{y^s}{S}ds\right|+O\left(\frac{X}{\log^{A+3}X}\right) \tag{5}$$

where

$$S=\sigma+it,\qquad b=1+\frac{1}{\log X},\qquad T=X^{10},$$

$$d_E^{(m)}(s,\chi)=\sum_{n=1}^{\infty}d_E^{(m)}(n)\chi(n)n^{-s},\qquad \sigma>1,$$

$$f_E^{(m)}(s,\chi)=\sum_{(a)}f^{(m)}(a)\chi(a)a^{-s}.$$

LEMMA 3. *If $E\leqslant D_1^2$ we have*

$$\mathrm{Im}'(Q,E)\ll XD_1^{-1}\log^{13}X+X^{\frac{1}{2}}DD^{\frac{1}{2}}\log^{b}X. \tag{6}$$

Proof. Let $M_1=QD_1$ and

$$H(s,\chi)=\sum_{n\leq M_1}\mu(n)\chi(n)n^{-s},$$

and, for brevity, let G, F and H denote $d_E^{(m)}(s,\chi)$, $f_E^{(m)}(s,\chi)$ and $H(s,\chi)$. Then

$$FG=FG(1-LH)+FGLH=FG(1-LH)-FL'H. \tag{7}$$

We have

$$FG=\sum_{n=1}^{\infty}a(n)\chi(n)n^{-s}=F_1+F_2, \tag{8}$$

with

$$F_1=\sum_{n\leq M_1}a(n)\chi(n)n^{-s},\qquad F_2=\sum_{n>M_1}a(n)\chi(n)n^{-s}. \tag{9}$$

where

$$a(n)=\sum_{l|n}d_E^{(m)}(l)f^{(m)}\left(\frac{n}{l}\right).$$

From (7), (8), (9) we have

$$\int_{b-iT}^{b+iT} FG\frac{y^s}{s}\,ds=\int_{(b,T)} FG\frac{ys}{s}\,ds=\int_{(b,T)} F_2(1-LH)\frac{y^s}{s}\,ds$$
$$+\int_{(\frac{1}{2},T)}(F_1-F_1LH-FL'H)\frac{y^s}{s}\,ds+O(X^{-1}).$$

From this, by Schwarz's inequality, we get

$$\begin{aligned}\mathrm{Im}'(Q,E)\ll X\log X&\max_{\mathrm{Res}=b}\Big(\sum_{(q)}\frac{1}{\phi(q)}\sum_{\chi_q}{}^{*}|F_2|^2\Big)^{\frac{1}{2}}\\
&\times\max_{\mathrm{Res}=b}\Big(\sum_{(q)}\frac{1}{\phi(q)}\sum_{\chi_q}{}^{*}|1-LH|^2\Big)^{\frac{1}{2}}\\
&+X^{\frac{1}{2}}\log XQ^{\frac{1}{2}}\max_{\mathrm{Res}=\frac{1}{2}}\Big(\sum_{(q)}\frac{1}{\phi(q)}\sum_{\chi_q}{}^{*}|F_1|^2\Big)^{\frac{1}{2}}\\
&+X^{\frac{1}{2}}\log^{\frac{3}{4}}X\max_{\mathrm{Res}=\frac{1}{2}}\Big(\sum_{(q)}\frac{1}{\phi(q)}\sum_{\chi_q}{}^{*}|F_1|^2\Big)^{\frac{1}{2}}\\
&\times\max_{\mathrm{Res}=\frac{1}{2}}\Big(\sum_{(q)}\frac{1}{\phi(q)}\sum_{\chi_q}{}^{*}|H|^4\Big)^{\frac{1}{4}}\Big(\sum_{(q)}\frac{1}{\phi(q)}\sum_{\chi_q}{}^{*}\int_{(\frac{1}{2},T)}\frac{|L|^4}{|s|}|ds|\Big)^{\frac{1}{4}}\\
&+X^{\frac{1}{2}}\log^{\frac{3}{4}}X\max_{\mathrm{Res}=\frac{1}{2}}\Big(\sum_{(q)}\frac{1}{\phi(q)}\sum_{\chi_q}{}^{*}|F|^2\Big)\max_{\mathrm{Res}=\frac{1}{2}}\Big(\sum_{(q)}\frac{1}{\phi(q)}\sum_{\chi_q}{}^{*}|H|^4\Big)^{\frac{1}{4}}\\
&\times\Big(\sum_{(q)}\frac{1}{\phi(q)}\sum_{\chi_q}{}^{*}\int_{(\frac{1}{2},T)}\frac{|L'|^4}{|s|}|ds|\Big)^{\frac{1}{4}}.\end{aligned}\tag{10}$$

By using Lemmas 1 and 2 to estimate every term of (10), we can get (6) at once.

LEMMA 4. *If* $E>D_1^2$ *we have*

$$\mathrm{Im}'(Q,E)\ll XD_1^{-1}\log^4 X+X^{\frac{1}{2}}D\log^2 X.\tag{11}$$

Proof. Taking $M_2=Q^2$, when $\mathrm{Res}=b=1+1/(\log X)$, we have

$$G=d_E^{(m)}(s,\chi)=G_1+G_2,$$
$$G_1=\sum_{n\le M_2}d_E^{(M)}(n)\chi(n)n^{-s},\qquad G_2=\sum_{n>M_2}d_E^{(m)}(n)\chi(n)h^{-s}$$

and

$$\int_{(b,T)}FG\frac{ys}{s}\,ds=\int_{(b,T)}FG_2\frac{ys}{s}\,ds+\int_{(\frac{1}{2},T)}FG_1\frac{ys}{s}\,ds+O(X^{-1}).$$

From this, by Schwarz's inequality we get

$$\operatorname{Im}'(Q,E) \ll X \log X \max_{\mathrm{Res}=b} \Big(\sum_{(q)} \frac{1}{\phi(q)} \sum_{\chi_q}^{*} |G_2|^2\Big)^{\frac{1}{2}}$$
$$\times \max_{\mathrm{Res}=b} \Big(\sum_{(q)} \frac{1}{\phi(q)} \sum_{\chi_q}^{*} |G|^2\Big)^{\frac{1}{2}} + X^{\frac{1}{2}} \log X$$
$$\times \max_{\mathrm{Res}=\frac{1}{2}} \Big(\sum_{(q)} \frac{1}{\phi(q)} \sum_{\chi_q}^{*} |G_1|^2\Big)^{\frac{1}{2}} \max_{\mathrm{Res}=\frac{1}{2}} \Big(\sum_{(q)} \frac{1}{\phi(q)} \sum_{\chi_q}^{*} |F|^2\Big)^{\frac{1}{2}}. \qquad (12)$$

Similarly, by using Lemmas 1 and 2 to estimate every term in (12), we get (11) at once.

Choosing $h = A + 16$ from (6), (11) and (4) we get (3) at once, and Theorem 3 is proved.

Remark. If $f(a)$ satisfies conditions

$$\sum_{h \leqslant X} |f(n)| \ll X \log^{\lambda_1} X, \ \sum_{n \leqslant X} \sum_{d|n} |f(d)| \ll X \log^{\lambda_2} X, \qquad (\Delta)$$

where λ_1, λ_2 are positive constants, then Theorem 3 is still true ($B_2 \geqslant g(A, \lambda_1, \lambda_2)$).

3. APPLICATIONS

A. *To the result* (1, 2).

In 1966 and 1973 Chen devised a new weighted sieve method and proved (1, 2). Chen's principal contribution is that he pointed out that the key to proving the Proposition (1, 2) is to estimate the sum Ω

$$\Omega = \sum_{\substack{(p_{1,2}) \\ p_3 \leqslant N/p_1p_2 \\ N-p=p_1p_2p_3}} 1,$$

where N is a large even integer, and $(p_{1,2})$ denotes the condition $N^{\frac{1}{10}} < p_1 < N^{\frac{1}{3}} \leqslant p_2 \leqslant (N/p_1)^{\frac{1}{2}}$; and he was the first to propose a method to estimate the sum successfully. In 1975 we pointed out that the key to realizing Chen's weighted sieve method was precisely Theorem 3.

Let $P = \prod_{2 < p \leqslant N^{\frac{1}{4}-\epsilon/2}, p|N}$; then we have

$$\Omega \leqslant \sum_{(p_{1,2})} \sum_{\substack{p \leqslant N/p_1p_2 \\ (N-p_1p_2p_3, P)=1}} \Big\{ \sum_{d|(N-p_1p_2p_3, P)} \lambda_d \Big\}^2 + O(N^{\frac{1}{4}})$$

where λ_d are the Selberg functions ($\lambda_d = 0,\ d > N^{\frac{1}{4}-\varepsilon/2}$). Hence we have

$$\begin{aligned}
\Omega &\leqslant \sum_{d_1|P}\sum_{d_2|P}\lambda_{d_1}\lambda_{d_2}\sum_{(p_{1,2})}\pi(N;p_1p_2,[d_1,d_2],N)+O(N^{\frac{1}{4}})\\
&\leqslant \sum_{(p_{1,2})}\sum_{d_1|P}\sum_{d_2|P}\lambda_{d_1}\lambda_{d_2}\frac{\pi(N;p_1p_2,1,1)}{\phi([d_1,d_2])}\\
&\quad + O\Bigg(\sum_{\substack{d\leqslant N^{(1/2)-\varepsilon}\\(d,N)=1}}|\mu(d)|3^{\omega(d)}\Bigg|\sum_{\substack{(p_{1,2})\\(p_1p_2,d)=1}}\Bigg(\pi(N;p_1p_2,d,N)\\
&\qquad\qquad -\frac{\pi(N;p_1p_2,1,1)}{\phi(d)}\Bigg)\Bigg|\Bigg)+O(N^{\frac{1}{4}})\\
&\leqslant \sum_{(p_{1,2})}\sum_{d_1|P}\sum_{d_2|P}\lambda_{d_1}\lambda_{d_2}\frac{\pi(N;p_1p_2,1,1)}{\phi([d_1,d_2])}\\
&\quad + O\Bigg(\sum_{\substack{d\leqslant N^{(1/2)-\varepsilon}\\(d,N)=1}}|\mu(d)|3^{\omega(d)}\Bigg|\sum_{N^{13/30}<a\leqslant N^{2/3}}f(a)\Bigg(\pi(N;a,d,N)\\
&\qquad\qquad -\frac{\pi(N;a,1,1)}{\phi(d)}\Bigg)\Bigg|\Bigg)+O(N^{\frac{1}{4}}),
\end{aligned}$$

where

$$f(a)=\begin{cases}1, & \text{for } a=p_1p_2, \quad \text{and} \quad N^{\frac{1}{10}}<p_1\leqslant N^{\frac{1}{3}}\leqslant p_2\leqslant\left(\dfrac{N}{p_1}\right)^{\frac{1}{2}},\\ 0, & \text{otherwise}.\end{cases}$$

Therefore it follows from Theorem 3 that

$$\Omega \leqslant \text{principal term} + O(N/\log^3 N).$$

B. *The upper bound of* $D(N)$

Let

$$D(N)=\sum_{N=p_1+p_2} 1.$$

In 1949, A. Selberg proved

$$D(N)\leqslant 16(1+o(1)\mathfrak{S}(N)\frac{N}{\log^2 N}.$$

where

$$\mathfrak{S}(N)=\prod_{p|N}\frac{p-1}{p-2}\prod_{p>2}\left(1-\frac{1}{(p-1)^2}\right).$$

In 1964, using Theorem 1 with $\eta<\frac{1}{3}$, I improved the coefficient 16 to 12 [**15**]. Until 1978, the best result was due to E. Bombieri and H. Davenport [**2**] who improved the coefficient 12 to 8 as early as 1966.

It is very difficult to improve the coefficient 8. In 1978 Chen [**4**] improved the coefficient 8 to 7·8342, but his proof is very very complicated. Recently, Pan Cheng Biao gave a simple proof of Chen's result. He proved the following:

$$D(N) \leqslant 7{\cdot}928\mathfrak{S}(N)\frac{N}{\log^2 N}.$$

I am going to sketch his proof.

Let $\mathcal{B} = \{b = N - p, p < N\}$. It is easy to see that

$$D(N) \leqslant S(\mathcal{B}, \mathcal{P}, N^{\frac{1}{3}}) + O(N^{\frac{1}{3}}), \tag{13}$$

where

$$S(\mathcal{B}, \mathcal{P}, z) = \sum_{\substack{b \in \mathcal{B} \\ (b, p(z)) = 1}} 1$$

and

$$\mathcal{P} = \{p : p \nmid N\}, \qquad P(z) = \prod_{\substack{p \in \mathcal{P} \\ p < z}} p.$$

By the Buchstab identity

$$S(\mathcal{B}; \mathcal{P}, z) = S(\mathcal{B}; \mathcal{P}, w) - \sum_{\substack{w \leqslant p < z \\ p \in \mathcal{P}}} S(\mathcal{B}_p, \mathcal{P}, p) \tag{14}$$

where $z \geqslant w \geqslant 2$ and $\mathcal{B}_d = \{b \in \mathcal{B}, d|b\}$. It is easy to prove that

$$S(\mathcal{B}; \mathcal{P}, N^{\frac{1}{3}}) \leqslant S(\mathcal{B}; \mathcal{P}, N^{\frac{1}{7}}) - \tfrac{1}{2}\Omega_1 + \tfrac{1}{2}\Omega_2 + O(N^{\frac{6}{7}}) \tag{15}$$

where

$$\Omega_1 = \sum_{N^{1/7} \leqslant p_1 < N^{1/3}} S(\mathcal{B}_{p_1}; \mathcal{P}, N^{\frac{1}{7}}), \tag{16}$$

and

$$\Omega_2 = \sum_{N^{1/7} \leqslant p_2 < p_3 < p_1 < N^{1/3}} S(\mathcal{B}_{p_1 p_2 p_3}; \mathcal{P}, p_3). \tag{17}$$

By the Jurkat–Richert theorem [**11**] and Bombieri's theorem we can get $S(\mathcal{B}; \mathcal{P}, N^{\frac{1}{7}}) - \frac{1}{2}\Omega_1$

$$\leqslant 8(1 + o(1))\mathfrak{S}(N)\frac{N}{\log^2 N}\left[1 + \int_2^{2\cdot 5} \frac{\log(t-1)}{t}\,dt \right.$$

$$\left. - \frac{1}{2}\int_{1\cdot 5}^{2\cdot 5} \frac{\log(2{\cdot}5 - 3{\cdot}5/(t+1))}{t}\,dt\right]. \tag{18}$$

However, we cannot use the same way to estimate the upper bound of Ω_2 because in this case, $\max p_1 p_2 p_3 \geqslant N^{\frac{1}{2}}$.

For estimating Ω_2 we have to consider the set

$$\mathcal{L}=\left\{l=N-(np_2p_3)p_1;\ N^{\frac{1}{7}}\leqslant p_2<p_3<N^{\frac{1}{5}},\ 1\leqslant n\leqslant\frac{N}{p_2p_4^3},\right.$$

$$\left.\left(n,\frac{P(p_1)}{p_2}\right)=1,\ p_3<p_1<\min\left(N^{\frac{1}{5}},\frac{N}{np_0p_5}\right)\right\}.$$

It is clear that

$$\Omega_2\leqslant\sum_{p\in\mathcal{L}}1$$

so we can get

$$\Omega_2\leqslant S(\mathcal{L};\mathcal{P},N^{\frac{1}{4}-\varepsilon})+O(N^{\frac{6}{7}}). \tag{19}$$

When we use the simplest Selberg upper bound sieve method to estimate $S(\mathcal{L};\mathcal{P},N^{\frac{1}{4}-\varepsilon})$ the error term can just be estimated by using Theorem 3 but not Theorem 2; and then we get

$$S(\mathcal{L};\mathcal{P},N^{\frac{1}{4}-\varepsilon})\leqslant 8(1+o(1))\mathfrak{S}(N)\frac{X}{\log N} \tag{20}$$

where

$$X=\sum_{N^{1/7}\leqslant p_2<p_3<p_1<N^{1/5}}\ \sum_{1\leqslant n\leqslant N/p_1p_2p_3}1. \tag{21}$$

By the Buchstab asymptotic formula

$$\sum_{\substack{1\leqslant n\leqslant y\\(n,P(y^{1/u}))=1}}1=\frac{y}{\log y^{1/u}}\,\omega(u)+O\left(\frac{y}{(\log y^{(1/u)})^2}\right), \tag{22}$$

$$\begin{cases}\omega(u)=\dfrac{1}{u}, & 1\leqslant u<2\\ (u\omega(u))=\omega(u-1), & u>2,\end{cases}$$

we can get

$$\omega(u)<\frac{1}{1{\cdot}763},\qquad u\geqslant 2.$$

From this and (22) we have

$$X<\frac{4}{1{\cdot}763}\left(3\log\tfrac{7}{5}-1\right)(1+o(1))\frac{N}{\log N}. \tag{23}$$

From (23), (20), (19), (18) and (15), we have

$$S(\mathcal{B};\mathcal{P},N^{\frac{1}{5}})<7{\cdot}928\mathcal{S}(N)\frac{N}{\log^2 N}; \tag{24}$$

and from this and (13), we obtain

$$D(N) < 7{\cdot}928\mathfrak{S}(N)\frac{N}{\log^2 N}$$

C. *A generalization of the Titchmarsh divisor problem.*

It is well known that, by use of Theorem 2, we can get the asymptotic formula

$$\sum_{p\leqslant X} d(p-1) \sim C_1 X$$

where $d(n)$ denotes the divisor function, and C_1 is a positive constant. Using the new mean value theorem, we can get even the following result:

Let $1 \leqslant y \leqslant X^{1-\varepsilon}$ $(o<\varepsilon<1)$, *and let* $f(a)$ *be a real function satisfying the condition* (Δ); *then we have*

$$\sum_{\substack{ap\leqslant x\\ a\leqslant y}} f(a)\, d(ap-1) \sim 2X \sum_{d\leqslant X^{1/2}} \frac{1}{\phi(d)} \sum_{a\leqslant y} \frac{f(a)}{a\log(X/a)}.$$

Putting

$$f(a) = \begin{cases} 1, & a = 1, \\ 0, & a > 1. \end{cases}$$

we obtain

$$\sum_{p\leqslant X} d(p-1) \sim C_1 X.$$

D. *The largest prime factor of* $p+a$.

Let P_X denote the largest prime factor of

$$\prod_{o<p+a<X} (p+a)$$

where a is a given non-zero integer.

In 1973, Hooley **[10]** proved $P_X > X^{\theta}$ when $\theta < \frac{5}{8}$. The key of his proof is the estimation of the sum

$$V(y) = \sum_{\substack{p+a=kq\\ p\leqslant X-a\\ y<q\leqslant ry}} \log q \tag{25}$$

where q denotes primes, and $X^{\frac{1}{2}} < y < X^{\frac{3}{4}}$, $1<r<2$.

Using the Selberg sieve method, we can turn the estimation of (25) into estimating the following sum:

$$\sum_{d\leqslant X^{1/2}\log^{-B}X} \ \sum_{k\leqslant X/y} \ \sum_{\substack{kq\leqslant X\\ kq\equiv a(\operatorname{mod} d)}} \log q.$$

It is clear that our theorem can be used here, too.

Now I am going to give a brief explanation of the relation between the sieve method and the new mean value theorem.

Let N be a large integer, $\mathscr{E}$ a set of positive integer satisfying the conditions

$$(e, N)=1, \quad o<e<x^{1-\eta_1}, \quad o<\eta_1<1, \quad e\in\mathscr{E},$$

and let

$$\mathscr{L}=\{l=N-ep, \quad e\in\mathscr{E}, \quad ep\leqslant N\}$$
$$\mathscr{P}=\{p: p\nmid N\}.$$

Evidently, when we estimate the sifting function

$$S(\mathscr{L};\mathscr{P},z)=\sum_{\substack{l\in\mathscr{L}\\(l,P(z))=1}}1, \quad z\leqslant N^{\frac{1}{4}-\varepsilon/2}, \quad o<\varepsilon<\tfrac{1}{2}. \tag{26}$$

By making use of Selberg's sieve method, the error term can be just estimated by the new value theorem provided

$$f(a)=\sum_{\substack{e=a\\e\in\mathscr{E}}}1,$$

satisfies the condition (Δ).

It is well known, that before Chen's work, we could not estimate the following sum of sifting functions,

$$\sum_{q\in\mathscr{Q}}S(\mathscr{B}_q;\mathscr{P}_q,z_q), \tag{27}$$

when $\max q\geqslant N^{\frac{1}{2}}$, where $\mathscr{Q}$ is a set of different positive integers, $\mathscr{B}=\{b=N-p, p<N\}$, $\mathscr{B}_q=\{b\in\mathscr{B}, q|b\}$, $\mathscr{P}_q$ is a subset of $\mathscr{P}$ depending on q, and z_q is a positive integer depending on q. Because when we used the Jurkat–Richert theorem to estimate every sifting function $S(\mathscr{B}_q;\mathscr{P}_q,z_q)$ the total error term caused by every $S(\mathscr{B}_q;\mathscr{P}_q,z_q)$ could not be estimated by Bombieri's theorem; of course, we can estimate the sum (27) under Halberstam's hypothesis.

Chen was the first to devise a method to estimate some kinds of sums (27), when $N^{\frac{1}{2}}\leqslant\max_{q\in\mathscr{Q}}q\leqslant N^{1-\eta_2}$, $0<\eta_2<1$. Briefly speaking, the idea of his method is to turn the estimating of the sum (27) into estimating (26); and we pointed out that the key to realizing Chen's method is just the new mean value theorem.

REFERENCES

[1] Bombieri, E.
On the large Sieve. *Mathematika.* **12** (1965), 201–225.

[2] Bombieri, E. and Davenport, H.
Small differences between prime number. *Proc. Roy. Soc. Ser. A* **293** (1966), 1–18.

[3] Chen Jing run.
On the representation of a large even integer as the sum of a prime and the product of at most two primes. *Sci. Sin.* **16** (1973), 157–176.

[4] Chen Jing run.
On the Goldbach's problem and the sieve method. *Sci. Sin.* **21** (1978), 701–739.

[5] Pan Cheng-Dong.
On the representation of large even integer as a sum of a prime and an almost prime. *Acta Math. Sin*, **12** (1962), 95–106.

[6] Cheng-Dong, Pan, Xiaxi, Ding, and Yuan Wahg.
On the representation of every large even integer as a sum of a prime and an almost prime. *Sci. Sin.* **18** (1975), 599–610.

[7] Cheng-Dong, Pan and Xiaxi, Ding.
A mean value theorem. *Acta Math. Sin.* **18** (1975), 254–262.

[8] Cheng Dong, Pan and Xiaxi, Ding.
A new mean value theorem (to appear).

[9] Wang, Yuan.
On the representation of large integer as a sum of a prime and almost prime. *Sci. Sin.* **11** (1962) 1033–1054.

[10] Hooley, C.
On the largest prime factor of $p+a$. *Mathematika* **40** (1973), 135–143.

[11] Halberstam, H. and Richert, H.-E.
"Sieve Methods," Academic Press, London, 1974.

[12] Barban, M. B.
New applications of the "great sieve" of Ju. V. Linnik. *Acad. Nauk Uzbek. SSR Trudy Inst. Mat.* **22**(1961), 1–20.

[13] Barban, M. B.
The "density" of the zeros of Dirichlet L-series and the problem of the sum of primes and "near primes". *Mat. Sb.(N.S.)* **61** (103) (1963), 418–425.

[14] Pan, Cheng-Dong.
On the representation of an even number as the sum of a prime and a product of not more than four primes. *Sci. Sinica* **12** (1963), 455–474.

[15] Pan, Cheng-Dong.
A new application of the Ju. V. Linnik large sieve method. *Acta Math. Sinica* **14** (1964), 597–606.

[16] Renyi, Alfréd.
On the representation of an even number as the sum of a single prime and a single almost-prime number. *Dokl. Akad. Nauk SSSR Ser. Mat.* **12** (1948), 57–78.

(See "Recent progress in analytic Number Theory, I, edited by H. Halberstam and C. Hooley, Acad. Press, 1981, 275-287).

References I

H. Davenport, *Multiplicative number theory*, Markham (1967); Springer Verlag (1980).

T. Estermann, *Introduction to modern prime number theory*, Cambridge tracts, 41 (1952).

A. O. Gelfond and Ju. V. Linnik, *Elementary method in analytic number theory*, Math. Phy. Liter. Pub. House, Moscow (1962).

H. Halberstam and H. E. Richert, *Sieve methods*, Acad. Press (1974).

Hua Loo Keng, *Additive theory of prime numbers*, Trud. Inst. Mat. Steklov, 22 (1947); Science Press, Beijing (1952); AMS (1965).

Hua Loo Keng, *Introduction to number theory*, Science Press, Beijing (1957); Springer Verlag (1982).

Hua Loo Keng, *Die Abschatzung von Exponentialsummen und ihre Anwendung in der Zahlentheorie*, Enz. der Math. Wiss; I, 2, Heft 13, Teil 1, Leipzig, Teubner (1959); Science Press, Beijing (1963).

M. N. Huxley, *The distribution of prime numbers*, Oxford, Clarendon Press (1972).

A. A. Karatsuba, *Basic analytic number theory*, Nauk, Moscow (1975).

E. Landau, *Uber einige neuere Fortschritte der additiven Zahlentheorie*, Cambridge tracts, 35 (1937).

Min Si He, *Methods in number theory*; (I): Science Press, Beijing (1958); (II): ibid (1981).

H. L. Montgomery, *Topics in multiplicative number theory*, Lec. Notes in Math., Springer Verlag, 227 (1971).

Pan Cheng Dong and Pan Cheng Biao, *Goldbach Conjecture*, Science Press, Beijing (1981).

K. Prachar, *Primzahlverteilung*, Springer Verlag (1957).

H. E. Richert, *Lectures on sieve methods*, Tata Inst., Bombay (1976).

N. G. Tchudakov, *Introduction to the theory of Dirichlet L-functions*, GITTL, Moscow (1947).

R. C. Vaughan, *The Hardy-Littlewood Method*, Cambridge tracts, 80 (1981).

I. M. Vinogradov, *The method of trigonometrical sums in the theory of numbers*, Trud. Inst. Math. Steklov, 23 (1947); Interscience, New York (1954); Nauk, Moscow, (1971).

I. M. Vinogradov, *Basic variant of the method of trigonometrical sums*, Nauk, Moscow (1976).

References II

N. C. Ankeny, H. Onishi

[1]. *The general sieve*, Acta Arith., 10 (1964-65) 31-62.

V. M. Arkhangelskaya

[1]. *Some calculations connected with Goldbach's conjecture*, Ukrain. Mat. Ź., 9 (1957) 20-29.

R. Ayoub

[1]. *On Rademacher's extension of the Goldbach-Vinogradoff theorem*, Tran. Amer. Math. Soc., 74 (1953) 482-491.

M. B. Barban

[1]. *New applications of the "great sieve" of Ju. V. Linnik*, Trudy Inst. Mat. Akad. Nauk UzSSR; 22 (1961) 1-20.

[2]. *The density of zeros of Dirichlet L-series and the problem of the addition of primes and almost primes*, Dokl. Akad. Nauk UzSSR; (1963) 9-10.

[3]. *The "density" of the zeros of Dirichlet L-series and the problem of the sum of primes and "near primes"*, Mat. Sbornik; 61 (1963) 418-425.

[4]. *Analogues of the divisor problem of Titchmarsh*, Vestnik Leningrad Univ., 4, 18 (1963) 5-13.

[5]. *The "large sieve" method and its applications to number theory*, Uspehi Mat. Nauk; 21 (1966) 51-102.

E. Bombieri

[1]. *On the large sieve*, Mathematika; 12 (1965) 201-225.

[2]. *On large sieve inequalities and their applications*, Trudy Mat. Inst. Steklov; 132 (1973) 251-256.

E. Bombieri, H. Davenport

[1]. *On the large sieve method*, see "Number Theory and Analysis" (papers in honor of Edmund Landau), New York (1969) 9-22.

[2]. *Small difference between prime numbers*, Proc. Roy. Soc., A, 293 (1966) 1-18.

K. G. Borozdkin

[1]. *On a problem of Vinogradov's constant*, Trudy Mat. Soc., SSSR, 1 (1956) 3.

N. G. de Bruijn

[1]. *The asymptotic behaviour of a function occurring in the theory of primes*, J. Indian Math. Soc., 15 (1951) 25-32.

[2]. *On the number of positive integers* $\leq x$ *and free of prime factors* $> y$, Indag. Math., 13 (1951) 2-12.

Viggo Brun

[1]. *Über das Goldbachshe Gesatz und die Anzahl der Primzahlpaare*, Archiv for Math. og Naturvid; B, 34, 8 (1915).

[2]. *Le crible d'Eratosthène et le théoreme de Goldbach*, C. R. Acad. Sci., Paris, 168 (1919) 544-546.

[3]. *Le crible d'Eratosthène et le théoreme de Goldbach*, Skr. Norske Vid. Akad, Kristiania, I; 3 (1920) 1-36.

A. A. Buchstab

[1]. *Asymptotic estimates of a general number theoretic function*, Mat. Sbornik; 44 (1937) 1239-1246.

[2]. *New improvements in the method of the sieve of Eratosthenes*, Mat. Sbornik; 46 (1938) 375-387.

[3]. *Sur la decomposition des nombres pairs en somme de deux composantes dont chacune est formée dún nombre borné de facteurs premiers*, Dokl. Akad. Nauk SSSR; 29 (1940) 544-548.

[4]. *On those numbers in an arithmetic progression all prime factors of which are small in order of magnitude*, Dokl. Akad. Nauk SSSR; 67 (1949) 5-8.

[5]. *On an asymptotic estimate of the number of numbers of an arithmetic progression which are not divisible by "relatively" small prime numbers*, Mat. Sbornik; 70 (1951) 165-184.

[6]. *On an additive representation of integers*, Moscow Gos. Ped. Inst. Uć. Zap; 71 (1953) 45-62.

[7]. *New results in the investigation of the Goldbach-Euler problem and the problem of prime pairs*, Dokl. Akad. Nauk SSSR; 162 (1965) 735-738.

[8]. *Combinatorial intensification of the sieve method of Eratosthenes*, Uspehi Mat. Nauk; 22 (1967) 199-226.

[9]. *A simplified modification of the combinatorial sieve*, Moscow Gos. Ped. Inst. Uć. Zap; 375 (1971) 187-194.

Chen Jing Run

[1]. *On large odd number as sum of three almost equal primes*, Sci. Sinica; 14 (1965) 1113-1117.

[2]. *On the representation of a large even integer as the sum of a prime and the product of at most two primes*, Kexue Tongbao; 17 (1966) 385-386.

[3]. *On the representation of a large even integer as the sum of a prime and the product of at most two primes*, Sci. Sinica; 16 (1973) 157-176; (II) ibid. 21 (1978) 421-430.

[4]. *On the Goldbach's problem and the sieve methods*, Sci. Sinica; 21 (1978) 701-739.

[5]. *On the exceptional set of Goldbach numbers*, (II); Sci. Sinica, A (1983) 327-342.

Cheng Jing Run and Pan Cheng Dong

[1]. *On the exceptional set of Goldbach numbers*, Sci. Sinica; 23 (1980) 219-232.

J. G. van der Corput

[1]. *Sur le théorème de Goldbach-Vinogradov*, C. R. Acad. Sci., Paris, 205 (1937) 479-481.

[2]. *Une nouvelle généralisation du théorème de Goldbach-Vinogradov*, C. R. Acad. Sci., Paris, 205 (1937) 591-592.

[3]. *Sur l'hypothèse de Goldbach pour presque tous les nombres pairs*, Acta Arith., 2 (1937) 266-290.

[4]. *Sur l'hypothèse de Goldbach*, Proc. Akad. Wet. Amerstdam; 41 (1938) 76-80.

H. Davenport, H. Halberstam

[1]. *The values of a trigonometric polynomials at well spaced points*, Mathematika; 13 (1966) 91-96; ibid, 14 (1967) 229-232.

J. M. Deshouillers

[1]. *Sur la constante de Śnirel'man*, Sém. DDP (1975-76), Théorie des nombres, Fasc. 2G16, sec. Math., Paris (1977).

L. E. Dickson

[1]. *History of the theory of numbers* (three volumes), Carnegie Inst., Washington, (1919, 1920, 1923).

Ding Ping, Zhang Ming Yao

[1]. *An improvement of Schnirelman constant*, Kexue Tongbao; 15 (1982) 897-900.

P. D. T. A. Elliott, H. Halberstam

[1]. *Some applications of Bombieri's theorem*, Mathematatika; 13 (1966) 196-203.

T. Estermann

[1]. *Eine neue Darstellung und neue Anwendungen der Viggo Brunschen Methode*, J. Reine Angew. Math., 168 (1932) 106-116.

[2]. *A new result in the additive prime number theory*, Quart. J. Math., Oxford, 8 (1937) 32-38.

[3]. *Proof that every large integer is the sum of two primes and a square*, Proc. London Math. Soc., 11 (1937) 501-516.

[4]. *Proof that almost all even positive integers are sums of two primes*, Proc. London Math. Soc., 44 (1938) 307-314.

R. F. Faiziev

[1]. *The number of integers, expressible in the form of a sum of two primes, and the number of k-twin pairs*, Dokl. Akad. Nauk Tadźik, SSSR; 2 (1969) 12-16.

E. Fogel

[1]. *On the zeros of L-function*, Acta Arith., 11 (1965) 67-96.

I. Földes

[1]. *On the Goldbach hypothesis concerning the prime numbers of an arithmetical progression*, C. R. lier Congrès Math. Hongrois (1950); Akad. Kiadó, Budapest (1952) 473-492.

E. Fouvry

[1]. *Un resultat nouveau en theórie additive des nombres premiers*, Sem. de Th. des Nom., Univ. Bordeaux I (1975-76).

A. Fujii

[1]. *Some remarks on Goldbach's problem*, Acta Arith., 32 (1977) 27-35.

P. X. Gallagher

[1]. *The large sieve*, Mathematika; 14 (1967) 14-20.

[2]. *Bombieri's mean value theorem*, Mathematika; 15 (1968) 1-6.

[3]. *A large sieve, density estimate near* $\sigma = 1$, Inv. Math., 11 (1970) 329-339.

[4]. *Primes and powers of 2*, Inv. Math., 29 (1975) 125-142.

[5]. *Local mean value and density estimate for Dirichlet L-function*, Indag. Math., 37 (1975) 259-264.

G. Halász, P. Turán

[1]. *On the distribution of the roots of Riemann zeta and allied functions, I*, J. Number Theory; 1 (1969) 121-237.

H. Halberstam

[1]. *A proof of Chen's theorem*, Asterisque; 24-25 (1975) 281-293.

H. Halberstam, W. Jurkat and H.-E. Richert

[1]. *Un nouveau résultat de la méthode du crible*, C. R. Acad. Sci., Paris, Ser. A-B (1967) 920-923.

G. H. Hardy

[1]. *Goldbach's theorem*, Math. Tid., B (1922) 1-16.

[2]. *Collected papers of G. H. Hardy, Vol. I*, Oxford, Clarendon Press (1966).

G. H. Hardy, J. E. Littlewood

[1]. *A new solution of Waring's problem*, Q. J. Math., 48 (1919) 272-293.

[2]. *Some problems of "Partitio Numerorum"; I: A new solution of Waring's problem*, Göt. Nach; (1920) 33-54; *II: Proof that every large number is the sum of at most 21 biquadrates*, Math. Z; 9 (1921) 14-27; *III: On the expression of a number as a sum of primes*, Acta Math.,

44 (1923) 1-70; *IV: The singular series in Waring's problem*, Math. Z; 12 (1922) 161-188; *V: A further contribution to the study of Goldbach's problem*, Proc. London Math. Soc., 22 (1923) 46-56; *VI: Further researches in Waring's problem*, Math. Z; 23 (1925) 1-37; *VIII: The number Γ(k) in Waring's problem*, Proc. London Math. Soc., 28 (1928) 518-542. (Number VII in this series is an unpublished manuscript on small differences between prime numbers).

[3]. Note on Messrs Shah and Wilson's paper entitled: 'On an empirical formula connected with Goldbach's theorem', Proc. Camb. Phil. Soc., 19 (1919) 245-254.

G. H. Hardy, S. Ramanujan

[1]. *Asymptotic formulae in combinatory analysis*, Proc. London Math. Soc., 17 (1918) 75-115.

C. B. Haselgrove

[1]. *Some theorems in the analytic theory of numbers*, J. London Math. Soc., 26 (1951) 273-277.

H. Heilbronn

[1]. Referat im Zbl. f. Math., 16 (1937) 291-292.

H. Heilbronn, E. Landau and P. Scherk

[1]. *Alle grossen ganzen Zahlen lassen sich als Summe von hochstens 71 Primzahlen darstellen*, Ćasopis Pést. Mat., 65 (1936) 117-141.

D. Hilbert

[1]. *Mathematische Probleme*, Archiv f. Math. u. Phys., 3, Bd. 1 (1901) 44-63; 213-237.

G. Hoheisel

[1]. *Primzahl Probleme in der Analysis*, Sitz. der Preutz. Akad. d. Wiss; Phys.-Math., Berlin (1930) 580-588.

C. Hooley

[1]. *On the representation of a number as the sum of two squares and a prime*, Acta Math., 97 (1957) 189-210.

Hsieh Sheng Kang

[1]. *On the representation of a large even number as a sum of a prime and a product of at most three primes*, Shuxue Jinzhan; 8 (1965) 209-216.

Hua Loo Keng

[1]. *Some results in the additive prime number theory*, Quart. J. Math. Oxford; 9 (1938) 68-80.

[2]. *Estimation of an integral*, Sci. Sinica; 2 (1951) 393-402.

[3]. Selected Papers, Springer Verlag, 1982.

M. N. Huxley

[1]. *On the difference between consecutive primes*, Inv. Math., 15 (1972) 164-170.

[2]. *Large values of Dirichlet polynomials*, Acta Arith., 24 (1973) 329-346; *II: ibid*; 27 (1975) 159-169; *III: ibid*; 27 (1975) 435-444.

M. N. Huxley, M. Jutila

[1]. *Large values of Dirichlet polynomials, IV:* Acta Arith., 32 (1977) 297-312; *V: ibid*, 33 (1977) 89-104.

A. E. Ingham

[1]. *On the difference between consecutive primes*, Quart. J. Math., Oxford, 8 (1937) 255-266.

K. Iseki

[1]. *A remark on the Goldbach-Vinogradov theorem*, Proc. Japan Acad., 25 (1949) 185-187.

H. Iwaniec

[1]. *Rosser's sieve-bilinear forms of the remainder terms-some applications*, see 'Recent progress in analytic number theory', I, Acad. Press, edited by H. Halberstam and C. Hooley, (1981) 203-230.

R. D. James

[1]. *On the sieve method of Viggo Brun*, Bull. Amer. Math. Soc., 49 (1943) 422-432.

[2]. *Recent progress in the Goldbach problem*, Bull. Amer. Math. Soc., 55 (1949) 246-260.

R. D. James, H. Wyel

[1]. *Elementary note on prime number problems of Vinogradov's type*, Amer. J. Math., 64 (1942) 539-552.

W. B. Jurkat, H.-E. Richert

[1]. *An improvement of Selberg's sieve method, I*, Acta Arith., 11 (1965) 217-240.

M. Jutila

[1]. *On the least Goldbach's number in an arithmetical progression with a prime difference*, Ann. Univ. Turku; Ser. A, I, 118 (1968).

[2]. *On Linnik's constant*, Math. Scand., 41 (1977) 45-62.

I. Katia

[1]. *A comment on a paper of Yu. V. Linnik*, Magyer Tud. Akad. Mat. Fiz. Oszt. Közl; 17 (1967) 99-100.

A. Khintchine

[1]. *Zur additiven Zahlentheorie*, Mat. Sbornik; (1932) 27-34.

N. I. Klimov

[1]. *The local density of certain sequences*, Nauk Tr. Kuíbyśev Gos. Ped. Inst., (1961) 11-15.

[2]. *Apropos the computations of Śnirel'man's constant*, Volź. Mat. Sb. Vyp., 7 (1969) 32-40.

[3]. *Improvement for the absolute constant in Goldbach-Schnirelman's problem*, Nauk. Tr. Kuibysev Gos. Ped. Inst., 158 (1975) 14-30.

N. I. Klimov, G. Z. Pil'tjai and T. A. Śeptiskaja

[1]. *The representation of natural numbers as sums of bounded number of prime numbers*, Nauk Tr. Kuíbyśev Gos. Ped. Inst., 1 (1971) 44-47.

S. Knopowski

[1]. *On Linnik's theorem concerning exceptional L-zeros*, Pub. Math. Debrecen; 9 (1962) 168-178.

L. F. Kondakova, N. I. Klimov

[1]. *Certain additive problems*, Volź. Mat. Sb. Vyp; 7 (1969) 41-44.

P. Kuhn

[1]. *Zur Viggo Brunschen Siebmethode, I*, Norske Vid. Selsk. Forh. Trondhjem; 14 (1941) 145-148.

[2]. *Neue Abschätzungen auf Grund der Viggo Brunschen Siebmethode*, 12 Skand. Mat. Kongr; Lund (1953) 160-168.

[3]. *Uber die Primteiler eines Polynoms*, Proc. Intern. Congr. Math., Amsterdam (1954) 35-37.

A. A. Kuzjaśev, E. F. Ćećuro

[1]. *The representation of large integers by sums of primes*, see 'Studies in number theory' 3, Izdat. Saratov Univ., (1969) 46-50.

E. Landau

[1]. *Uber die Zahlentheoretische Funktion $\phi(n)$ und ihre Beziehung zum Goldbachschen Satz*, Göt, Nachr; (1900) 177-186.

[2]. *Gelöste und ungelöste Probleme aus der Theorie der Primzahlverteilung und der Riemannschen Zatefunktion*, Proc. 5-th Intern. Congr. Math.; Camb., 1 (1912) 93-108.

[3]. *Die Goldbachsche Vermutung und der Schnirelmannsche Satz*, Nachr. Akad. Wiss. Math.-Phys. Kl.; (1930) 255-276.

A. F. Lavrik

[1]. *On the representation of numbers as the sum of primes by Snirel'man's method*, Izv. Akad. Nauk UzSSR, Ser. Fiz.-Mat., 3 (1962) 5-10.

B. V. Levin

[1]. *Distribution of "near primes" in polynomial sequences*, Dokl. Akad. Nauk UzSSR; 11 (1962) 7-9.

[2]. *Distribution of "near primes" in polynomial sequences*, Mat. Sbornik; 61 (1963) 389-407.

[3]. *Sieve method and its application*, Doctoral dissertation of the Moscow Univ., (1963).

[4]. *A one-dimensional sieve*, Acta Arith., 10 (1964-65) 387-397.

B. V. Levin, A. S. Faínleíb

[1]. *Application of certain integral equations to the questions of the theory of numbers*, Uspehi Mat. Nauk SSSR; 22 (1967) 119-197.

W. A. Light, T. J. Forres, N. Hammond and S. Roe

[1]. *A note on Goldbach's conjecture*, BIT; 20 (1980) 525.

Ju. V. Linnik

[1]. "The large sieve", Dokl. Akad. Nauk SSSR; 30 (1941) 292-294.

[2]. *On Dirichlet's L-series and prime number sums*, Mat. Sbornik; 15 (1944) 3-12.

[3]. *On the least prime in an arithmetic progression, I: The basic theorem*, Mat. Sbornik; 15 (1944) 139-178; *II: The Deuring-Heilbronn's phenomenon*, Mat. Sbornik; 15 (1944) 347-368.

[4]. *On the possibility of a unique method in certain problems of "additive" and "distributive" prime number theory*, Dokl. Akad. Nauk SSSR; 48 (1945) 3-7.

[5]. *On the density of zeros of L-series*, Izv. Akad. Nauk SSSR, Ser. Mat., 10 (1946) 35-46.

[6]. *A new proof of the Vinogradov-Goldbach theorem*, Mat. Sbornik; 19 (1946) 3-8.

[7]. *Some conditional theorems concerning binary problems with prime numbers*, Dokl. Akad. Nauk SSSR; 77 (1951) 15-18.

[8]. *Prime numbers and powers of two*, Trudy Mat. Inst. Steklov; 38 (1951) 152-169.

[9]. *Some conditional theorems concerning binary Goldbach problem*, Izv. Akad. Nauk SSSR, Ser. Mat., 16 (1952) 503-530.

[10]. *Addition of prime numbers with powers of one and the same number*, Mat. Sbornik; 32 (1953) 3-60.

[11]. *An asymptotic formula in an additive problem of Hardy-Littlewood*, Izv. Akad. Nauk SSSR, Ser. Mat., 24 (1960) 629-706.

[12]. *The dispersion method in binary additive problems*, Leningrad Univ. Press (1961); Providence R. I. (1963).

[13]. Collected papers, Nauk, Moscow, (1980).

J. E. Littlewood

[1]. *On the class number of the corpus $P(\sqrt{-k})$*, Proc. London Math. Soc., 27 (1927-28) 358-372.

Lu Ming Gao

[1]. *Some problems concerning the Goldbach number, I*, (to appear).

Lu Ming Gao, Chen Wen De

[1]. *On the solutions of system of linear equations with prime variables*, Acta Math. Sinica; 15 (1965) 731-748.

B. Lucke

[1]. *Zur Hardy-Littlewoodschen Behandlung des Goldbachschen Problems*, Diss. Math. Naturwiss. Göttingen (1962).

A. P. Lursmanashvili

[1]. *Representation of natural numbers by sums of prime numbers*, Thbilis Sàhelmc. Univ. Shrom. Mekh.-Math.-Mec. Ser., 117 (1966) 63-76.

B. Mann

[1]. *A proof of the fundamental theorem on the density of sums of sets of positive integers*, Ann. Math., 43 (1942) 27-34.

J. Merlin

[1]. *Sur quelques théorèmes d'Arithmetique et un enouce qui les contient*, C. R. Acad. Sci., Paris, 153 (1911) 516-518.

[2]. *Un travail sur les nombres premiers*, Bull. Sci. Math., 39 (1915) 121-136.

R. J. Miech

[1]. *Pseudo primes and the Goldbach problem*, J. Reine Angew. Math., 233 (1968) 1-27.

Min Si He

[1]. *Remark on a problem of limit*, Acta Math. Sinica; 4 (1954) 381-384.

H. L. Montgomery

[1]. *Zeros of L-functions*, Inv. Math., 8 (1969) 346-354.

H. L. Montgomery, R. C. Vaughan

[1]. *The exceptional set in Goldbach's problem*, Acta Arith., 27 (1975) 353-370.

Y. Motohashi

[1]. *A note on the large sieve; I:* Proc. Japan Acad., 53 (1971) 17-19; *II: ibid.* 122-124; *III: ibid.* 55 (1979) 92-94.

A. Page

[1]. *On the number of primes in an arithmetic progression*, Proc. London Math. Soc., 39 (1935) 116-141.

Pan Cheng Biao

[1]. *A new proof on three primes theorem*, Acta Math. Sinica; 20 (1977) 206-211.

Pan Cheng Dong

[1]. *Some new results on additive theory of prime numbers*, Acta Math. Sinica; 9 (1959) 315-329.

[2]. *On representation of even number as the sum of a prime and an almost prime*, Acta Math. Sinica; 12 (1962) 95-106; Sci. Sinica; 11 (1962) 873-888.

[3]. *On representation of large even integer as the sum of a prime and a product of at most 4 primes*, Sci. Sinica; 12 (1963) 455-473.

[4]. *A new application of Linnik's large sieve*, Acta Math. Sinica; 14 (1964) 597-608; Sci. Sinica; 13 (1964) 1045-1053.

[5]. *On Goldbach number*, Kexue Tongbao, The special series of Math. Phy. and Chem. (1980).

[6]. *The minor arcs of Goldbach problem*, Acta Sci. Natur. Shandong Univ., 3 (1980) 1-6.

[7]. *A new mean value theorem and its applications*, see "Recent progress in analytic number theory" I, edited by H. Halberstam and C. Hooley, Acad. Press (1981) 275-288.

[8]. *On the Goldbach problem*, Acta Sci. Natur. Shandong Univ., 1 (1981) 1-6.

Pan Cheng Dong, Ding Xia Qi

[1]. *A mean value theorem*, Acta Math. Sinica; 18 (1975) 254-262; ibid. 19 (1976) 217-218.

[2]. *A new mean value theorem*, Sci. Sinica, Special Issue (II); (1979) 149-161.

Pan Cheng Dong, Ding Xia Qi and Wang Yuan

[1]. *On the representation of every large even integer as a sum of a prime and an almost prime*, Sci. Sinica; 18 (1975) 599-610.

K. Prachar

[1]. *On integers having many representations as a sum of two primes*, J. London Math. Soc., 29 (1954) 347-350.

[2]. *Uber die Lösungszahl eines Systems von Gleichungen in Primzahlen*, Mon. Math., 59 (1955) 98-103.

[3]. *Uber die Anwendung einer Methode von Linnik*, Acta Arith., 29 (1976) 367-376.

H. Rademacher

[1]. *Beiträge zur Viggo Brunschen Methode in der Zahlentheorie*, Abh. Math. Sem. Univ. Hamburg; 3 (1924) 12-30.

K. Ramachandra

[1]. *On the number of Goldbach numbers in small intervals*, J. Indian Math. Soc., 37 (1973) 157-170.

[2]. *A simple proof of the mean fourth power estimate for* $\zeta(\frac{1}{2}+it)$ *and* $L(\frac{1}{2}+it, \chi)$, Ann. Scuola Norm. Sup. Pisa Cl. Sci., 4 (1974) 81-97.

[3]. *Application of a theorem of Montgomery and Vaughan to the zeta function*, J. London Math. Soc., 10 (1975) 482-486.

[4]. *Two remarks in prime number theory*, Bull. France Math. Soc., 105 (1977) 433-437.

A. Rényi

[1]. *On the representation of even number as the sum of a prime and an almost prime*, Dokl. Akad. Nauk SSSR; 56 (1947) 455-458.

[2]. *On the representation of an even number as the sum of a prime and an almost prime*, Izv. Akad. Nauk SSSR, Ser. Mat., 12 (1948) 57-78.

[3]. *Probabilistic methods in number theory*, Shuxue Jinzhan; 4 (1958) 465-510.

G. Ricci

[1]. *Su la congettura di Goldbach e la constante di Schnirelmann*, Boll. Un. Mat. Ital., 15 (1936) 183-187.

[2]. *Su la congettura di Goldbach e la constante di Schnirelmann; I:* Ann. Scuola Norm. Sup. Pisa (2), 6 (1937) 71-90; *II: ibid.* 6 (1937) 91-116.

H.-E. Richert

[1]. *Aus der additiven Primzahltheorie*, J. Reine Angew. Math., 191 (1953) 179-198.

[2]. *Selberg's sieve with weights*, Mathematika; 16 (1969) 1-22.

G. J. Rieger

[1]. *Uber die Folge der Zahlen der Gestalt* p_1+p_2, Arch. Math., 15 (1964) 33-41.

[2]. *Uber ein lineares Gleichungssystem von Prachar mit Primzahlen*, J. Reine Angew. Math., 213 (1963-64) 103-107.

B. Riemann

[1]. *Uber die Anzahl der Primzahlen unter einer gegebenen Grosse*, Ges. Math. Werke und Nach; 2 (1859) 145-155.

H. Riesel, R. C. Vaughan

[1]. *On sums of primes*, Arkiv für Math., 21 (1983) 45-74.

K. A. Rodoskij

[1]. *On least prime number in arithmetic progression*, Mat. Sbornik; 33 (1954) 331-356.

N. P. Romanov

[1]. *On Goldbach problem*, Izv. NEE Mat. and Tech. Univ. Tomsk; 1 (1935) 34-38.

P. M. Ross

[1]. *On Chen's theorem that each large even number has the form* p_1+p_2 *or* $p_1+p_2p_3$, J. London Math. Soc., 2 (1975) 500-506.

K. F. Roth

[1]. *On the large sieve of Linnik and Rényi*, Mathematika; 12 (1965) 1-9.

L. G. Schnirelmann

[1]. *Uber additive Eigenschaften von Zahlen*, Izv. Donck. Polytech. Inst., 14 (1930) 3-28.

[2]. *Uber additive Eigenschaften von Zahlen*, Math. Ann., 107 (1933) 649-690.

A. Selberg

[1]. *On the normal density of primes in small intervals, and the difference between consecutive primes*, Acta Math. Naturvid; 47 (1943) 87-105.

[2]. *On an elementary method in the theory of prime*, Norske Vid. Selsk. Forh. Trondhjem; 19 (1947) 64-67.

[3]. *On elementary methods in prime number theory and their limitations*, 11 Skand. Mat. Kongr; Trondhjem (1949) 13-22.

[4]. *The general sieve method and its place in prime number theory*, Proc. Intern. Math. Congr., Camb. Mass; 1 (1950) 286-292.

[5]. *Sieve methods*, Proc. Symp. Pure Math., AMS, 20 (1971) 311-351.

H. N. Shapiro, J. Warga

[1]. *On the representation of large integers as sum of primes, I*, Comm. Pure Appl. Math., 3 (1950) 153-176.

Shen Mok Kong

[1]. *On checking the Goldbach conjecture*, Nordisk Tidskr. Imfor. Behand; 4 (1964).

H. Siebert

[1]. *Darstellung als Summe von Primzahlen*, Diplomarbeit, Marburg (1968).

C. L. Siegel

[1]. *Uber die Classenzahl quadratischer Körper*, Acta Arith., 1 (1936) 83-86.

S. Srinivasan

[1]. *A remark on Goldbach's problem*, J. number theory; 12 (1980) 116-121.

P. Stäckel

[1]. *Uber Goldbach's empirisches Theorem: Jede grade Zahl kann als Summe von zwei Primzahlen darstellt werden*, Göt. Nachr; (1896) 292-299.

V. Statulevicius

[1]. *On the representation of odd numbers as the sum of three almost equal prime numbers*, Viliniaus Valst. Univ. Mokslu Darbai Mat. Fiz.-Chem., Molslu Ser. 3 (1955) 5-23.

J. J. Sylvester

[1]. *On the partition of an even number into two primes*, Proc. London Math. Soc., Ser. 1 (1871) 4-6.

V. A. Tartakovskij

[1]. *Sur quelques Sommes du type de Viggo Brun*, Dokl. Akad. Nauk SSSR; 23 (1939) 121-125.

[2]. *La méthode du crible approximatif "electif"*, Dokl. Akad. Nauk SSSR; 23 (1939) 126-129.

N. G. Tchudakov

[1]. *On the Goldbach problem*, Dokl. Akad. Nauk SSSR; 17 (1937) 331-334.

[2]. *On the density of the set of even integers which are not representable as a sum of two odd primes*, Izv. Akad. Nauk SSSR, Ser. Mat., 1 (1938) 25-40.

[3]. *On the Goldbach-Vinogradov's theorem*, Ann. Math., 48 (1947) 515-545.

N. G. Tchudakov, N. I. Klimov

[1]. *Concerning the Šnirel'mann constant*, Uspehi Mat. Nauk, SSSR; 22 (1967) 212-213.

E. C. Titchmarsh

[1]. *A divisor problem*, Rend. Circ. Mat. Palermo; 54 (1930) 414-429.

P. Turán

[1]. *Uber eine neue Methode in der Analysis und deren Anwendungen*, Akad. Kiadó, Budapest (1953).

[2]. *Certain function theoretic sieve methods in the theory of numbers*, Dokl. Akad. Nauk SSSR; 171 (1966) 1289-1292.

S. Uchiyama

[1]. *On the representation of large even integers as sums of two almost primes; I:* J. Fac. Sci. Hokkaido Univ. Ser. 1, 18 (1964) 60-68; *II: ibid*, 69-77.

[2]. *On the representation of large even integers as sums of a prime and an almost prime, II*, Proc. Japan Acad., 43 (1967) 567-571.

M. Uchiyama, S. Uchiyama

[1]. *On the representation of large even integers as sums of a prime and an almost prime*, Proc. Japan Acad., 40 (1964) 150-154.

R. C. Vaughan

[1]. *On Goldbach's problem*, Acta Arith., 22 (1972) 21-48.

[2]. *Mean value theorem in prime number theory*, J. London Math. Soc., 10 (1975) 153-162.

[3]. *A note on Śnirel'man's approach to Goldbach's problem*, Bull. London Math. Soc., 8 (1976) 245-250.

[4]. *On the estimation of Schnirelmann's constant*, J. Reine Angew. Math., 290 (1977) 93-108.

[5]. *Sommes trigonométriques sur les nombres premiers*, C. R. Acad. Sci., Paris, A, 285 (1977) 981-983.

[6]. *An elementary method in prime number theory*, see "Recent progress in analytic number theory", edited by H. Halberstam and C. Hooley, Acad. Press (1981) 241-248.

A. I. Vinogradov

[1]. *On an 'almost binary' problem*, Izv. Akad. Nauk SSSR, Ser. Mat., 20 (1956) 713-750.

[2]. *On the connections between the sieve of Eratosthenes and the Riemann ζ-function*, Vestnik Leningrad Univ., 11 (1956) 142-146.

[3]. *Application of ζ(s) to the sieve of Eratosthenes*, Mat. Sbornik; 41 (1957) 49-80; *Corrigendum: ibid.*, 415-416.

[4]. *The density hypothesis for Dirichlet L-series*, Izv. Akad. Nauk SSSR, Ser. Mat., 29 (1965) 903-934; *Corrigendum: ibid.*, 30 (1966) 719-720.

I. M. Vinogradov

[1]. *Sur le théoremè de Waring*, Izv. Akad. Nauk SSSR, Ser. Mat., (1928) 393-400.

[2]. *Some theorems in analytic theory of numbers*, Dokl. Akad. Nauk SSSR; 4 (1934) 185-187.

[3]. *Representation of an odd number as a sum of three primes*, Dokl. Akad. Nauk SSSR; 15 (1937) 291-294.

[4]. Selected papers, Akad. Nauk SSSR Press (1952).

A. Walfisz

[1]. *Zur additiven Zahlentheorie, II*, Math. Z; 40 (1936) 592-607.

Wang Yuan

[1]. *On the representation of large even integer as a sum of a product of at most three primes and a product of at most four primes*, Acta Math. Sinica; 6 (1956) 500-513.

[2]. *On the representation of large even integer as a sum of a prime and a product of at most 4 primes*, Acta Math. Sinica; 6 (1956) 565-582.

[3]. *On sieve methods and some of the related problems*, Sci. Record (N.S.); 1 (1957) 9-12.

[4]. *On the representation of large even number as a sum of two almost primes*, Sci. Record (N.S); 5 (1957) 15-19.

[5]. *On sieve methods and some of their applications, I*, Acta Math. Sinica; 8 (1958) 413-429; Sci. Sinica; 8 (1959) 357-381.

[6]. *On the representation of large integer as a sum of a prime and an almost prime*, Acta Math. Sinica; 10 (1960), 161-181; Sci. Sinica; 11 (1962) 1033-1054 (with a new Appendix).

[7]. *On Linnik's method concerning the Goldbach number*, Sci. Sinica; 20 (1977) 16-30.

Wang Yuan, Shan Zun

[1]. *A conditional result on Goldbach problem*, (to appear).

Wu Fang

[1]. *On the solutions of the system of linear equations with prime variables*, Acta Math. Sinica; 7 (1957) 102-121.

Yin Ding

[1]. *On checking the Goldbach conjecture to 3×10^8*, (to appear).

Yin Wen Lin

[1]. *Remarks on the representation of large integers as sums of primes*, Acta Sci. Nat. Univ. Pekinensis; 3 (1956) 323-326.

A. Zulauf

[1]. *Beweis einer Erweiterung des Satzes von Goldbach-Vinogradov*, J. Reine Angew. Math., 190 (1952) 169-198.

[2]. *Uber die Darstellung naturlicher Zahlen als Summen von Primzahlen aus gegebenen Restklassen und Quadraten mit gegebenen Koeffizienten; I: Resultate für genügend gross Zahlen*, J. Reine Angew. Math., 192 (1953) 210-229;

II: Die singular Reihe, ibid. 193 (1954) 39-53;
III: Resultate für "faste alle" Zahlen, ibid. 195 (1953) 54-64.

[3]. *On the number of representations of an integer as a sum of primes belonging to given arithmetical progressions*, Comp. Mat., 15 (1961) 64-69.